CONDITIONING TECHNIQUES IN CLINICAL PRACTICE AND RESEARCH

CONDITIONING TECHNIQUES in Clinical Practice and Research

Introduced and edited by

CYRIL M. FRANKS, Ph.D.,

Director, Psychology Service and Research Center, New Jersey Neuro-Psychiatric Institute

SPRINGER PUBLISHING COMPANY, INC.
NEW YORK

44 East 23rd Street New York, N.Y. 10010

Library of Congress Catalog Card Number: 64-22774

Printed in U.S.A.

CONTRIBUTORS

Leo Alexander, M.D.
Department of Psychiatry, Tufts University School of Medicine and Boston State Hospital, Boston, Massachusetts *(Chapters 2,5)*

Teodoro Ayllon, Ph.D.
Behavior Research Laboratory, Anna State Hospital, Anna, Illinois *(23)*

Thomas A. Ban, M.D.
Verdun Protestant Hospital, Verdun, Quebec, Canada *(3)*

Beatrice H. Barrett, Ph.D.
Behavior Prosthesis Laboratory, Psychological Research, Walter E. Fernald State School, Waverley, Massachusetts *(25)*

Herbert G. Birch, M.D., Ph.D.
Albert Einstein College of Medicine, Yeshiva University, New York, New York *(12)*

Isidore Bonstein, M.D.
Spécialiste F.M.H. Gynécologie et Obstétrique, Geneva, Switzerland *(19)*

John Paul Brady, M.D.
School of Medicine, Department of Psychiatry, Research Laboratories, University Hospital, Philadelphia, Pennsylvania *(24)*

Clinton C. Brown, Ph.D.
The Pavlovian Laboratory, The Johns Hopkins University School of Medicine, Baltimore, Maryland *(6,8)*

Dugal Campbell, Ph.D.
Departments of Psychology and Psychiatry, Queen's University, Kingston, Ontario, Canada *(14)*

Egbart Dekker, M.D.
Department of Cardiology and Clinical Physiology, University of Amsterdam, Wilhelmina Gasthuis, Amsterdam, The Netherlands *(10)*

Howard Demb, M.A.
Albert Einstein College of Medicine, Yeshiva University, New York, New York *(12)*

M. R. Dix, M.D., F.R.C.S.
Otological Research Unit, Medical Research Council, National Hospital, London, England *(4)*

B. Anthony Dvorak, M.D.
Department of Psychiatry, Tulane University School of Medicine, New Orleans, Louisiana *(13)*

Moneim A. El-Meligi, Ph.D.
Psychology Service and Research Center, New Jersey Neuro-Psychiatric Institute, Princeton, New Jersey *(20)*

Robert Efron, M.D.
Neurophysiology-Biophysics Research Unit, Veterans Administration Hospital, Boston, Massachusetts *(11)*

Charles B. Ferster, Ph.D.
Institute for Behavioral Research, Silver Spring, Maryland *(22)*

Cyril M. Franks, Ph.D.
Psychology Service and Research Center, New Jersey Neuro-Psychiatric Institute, Princeton, New Jersey *(Introduction)*

W. Horsley Gantt, M.D.
The Pavlovian Laboratory, The Johns Hopkins University School of Medicine, Baltimore, Maryland, and The Veterans Administration Hospital, Perry Point, Maryland *(1,8)*

Thomas V. Geppert, M.D.
Dean Clinic (Pediatrics), Madison, Wisconsin *(16)*

Juda J. Groen, M.D.
Department of Medicine, Hadassah University Hospital, Jerusalem, Israel *(10)*

C. S. Hallpike, F.R.C.S., F.R.C.P.F.R.S.
Otological Research Unit, Medical Research Council, National Hospital, London, England *(4)*

S. G. Laverty, M.R.C.P., B.Sc.
Departments of Psychology and Psychiatry, Queen's University, Kingston, Ontario, Canada *(14)*

Leonard Levy, M.D.
Department of Psychiatry, McGill University, Montreal, Quebec, Canada *(3)*

Detlev L. Lind, A.B.
Veterans Administration Hospital, Indianapolis, Indiana *(24)*

Ogden R. Lindsley, Ph.D.
Behavior Research Laboratory, Harvard Medical School, and Metropolitan State Hospital, Waltham, Massachusetts *(21)*

Ralph J. McGuire, M.A., B.Sc., Ed.B.
Department of Psychological Medicine, Southern General Hospital, Glasgow, Scotland *(18)*

Jack L. Michael, Ph.D.
Psychology Department, Arizona State University, Tempe, Arizona *(23)*

Ernest C. Miller, M.D.
Duval Medical Center, Jacksonville, Florida *(13)*

Henk E. Pelser, M.D.
Department of Internal Medicine, University of Amsterdam, Wilhelmina Gasthuis, Amsterdam, The Netherlands *(10)*

C. Quarti, M.D.
Médicine Psychosomatique, Hôpital Necker, Paris, France *(20)*

J. Renaud, M.D.
Médicine Psychosomatique, Hôpital Necker, Paris, France *(20)*

Charles Rubenstein, M.D.
Duarte, California *(10)*

R. E. Sanderson, Ph.D.
Department of Psychiatry, Queen's University, Kingston, Ontario, Canada *(14)*

Bertram C. Thorne, M.A.
Speech and Hearing Clinic, Kansas State University, Manhattan, Kansas *(See Introduction to Part I)*

Don W. Turner, B.S.
Department of Psychiatry, Tulane University School of Medicine, New Orleans, Louisiana *(13)*

Maelor Vallance, M.B., Ch.B., D.P.M.
Hawkhead Hospital, Glasgow, Scotland *(15)*

Muriel D. Vogel-Sprott, Ph.D.
Psychology Department, University of Waterloo, Waterloo, Ontario, Canada *(7)*

Charles E. Wells, M.D.
Division of Neurology, Vanderbilt University School of Medicine, Nashville, Tennessee *(9)*

John Graham White, Ed.M.
Department of Mental Health, Queen's University, Belfast, Northern Ireland *(17)*

James R. Whitman, Ph.D.
Research Service, Veterans Administration Hospital, American Lake, Washington *(8)*

PREFACE

For the past half century, discussion of etiology, diagnosis and treatment of psychiatric and allied disorders has been dominated by what has been termed the "psychodynamic" approach. But, despite five decades of endeavor and the unswerving confidence of many clinicians in the usefulness of psychodynamic concepts, there are at least two sources of disquiet. In the first place, despite the mass of psychodynamically oriented research data so far accumulated, the positive findings are few. There is no unequivocal evidence to show that psychodynamically oriented therapy is outstandingly effective or that psychodynamically oriented diagnostic techniques contribute any more to the description of behavioral abnormalities than do a combination of a good interview and actuarial data. In the second place, it is becoming increasingly apparent that, if the prognosis for many psychiatric patients is better now than it would have been at the turn of the century, this benefit stems but little from any appreciable advances within the realm of psychodynamic theory or technique. Credit for the extensive progress that has been made more appropriately goes to those whose concern has been with pharmacology, with physical methods of treatment, with nursing, with the welfare of the nation, and with the public conscience.

The postwar era has seen a burgeoning of available monies and community interest in the problems of mental health, but a dearth of skilled psychotherapists. Most psychodynamic techniques, especially those which follow conventional psychoanalytic procedures, require many hours of the therapist's time, often extending over years. Quite clearly, with the large number of people in need of psychiatric treatment and with the long time required to train an "orthodox" analyst, there is reason to seek new principles and new techniques.

Within the last decade a new trend has been emerging. In clinical psychology and psychiatry alike, the emphasis is beginning to be directed away from Freudian and other psychodynamic formulations towards a more explicitly behavioral orientation. This trend, which cuts across diagnosis, treatment and research, is reflected in the published literature, in the number of pertinent grant awards, in the emergence of new journals devoted exclusively to various aspects of behavioral practice, and in the programs of recent professional meetings. In the universities, students of clinical and abnormal psychology are being encouraged to familiarize themselves with behavioral approaches and, in psychiatric institutes and other centers of intern training, a similar concern is expressed.

The notion that study of the etiology, diagnosis and therapy of behavior disorders should focus not on hypothesized "psychodynamics" but upon observed behavior is so broad that it can encompass a vast number of techniques and teachings. Most schools of learning theory—and who knows how learning really takes place—see therapy as manipulating the circumstances which determine currently observable behavior rather than as uncovering those past experiences which are supposed to have instigated the present disorder.

Behavioral diagnosis, therapy and research are gaining prominence as psychologists and psychiatrists are developing diverse techniques, stemming from Pavlov, Hull and Watson (in contrast to Freud, Jung and Adler). In this respect, and in the English speaking world alone, the names Wolpe, Skinner, Lindsley, Gantt, Eysenck, Bandura, Brady, G. Jones, Rachman, Malmo, Ullmann, Shoben, L. Alexander, the Staats, Ellis, M. Shapiro, Mowrer, Lovibond, Bachrach, Spence, Krasner, Lacey, Masserman, Verplanck, Yates, V. Meyer and Bindra are some that come to mind. This list does not emphasize any one school of thought. Probably all that most of these individuals share is a belief in the intrinsic superiority of scientific methodology and some method of prediction and controlled modification over a combination of speculation, intuition and clinical "know how."

In selecting one particular area, conditioning, I had two reasons. First, while it would be naive to assume that all behavior can be satisfactorily described in terms of the conditioned response alone, it is equally naive to assume that conditioning is something to be carried out exclusively with the laboratory rat or as an academic exercise in the reflexology of the sophomore. Secondly, in spite of the surge of emphasis on practical methods of modifying behavior, the direct contributions of conditioning techniques themselves are in danger of being overlooked.

The subject of conditioning was once presented solely in terms of "the interesting things Pavlov has done with dogs." Ringing a bell to make an animal or person salivate was regarded as something quite remote from the complex problems of man in a modern society and irrelevant to the problems the clinician was likely to encounter. Although considerable developments have occurred since Pavlov, misconceptions remain. There is still a tendency to think that only organismically trite and relatively meaningless responses, such as the knee jerk or eyeblink, can be conditioned, and that, even if conditioning techniques work well in the "artificial" situation of the laboratory, they have little to do with the "more real" clinical situation. Two other misconceptions are frequently voiced. There is the feeling that the use of conditioning techniques unavoidably implies a simple-minded devotion to the notion that all man's higher processes can be accounted for in this manner. Coexisting with this feeling is an apprehension, mixed with indignation, that all sorts of remarkable and sinister conditioning techniques have been brought to an alarming degree of perfection in the countries of Eastern Europe, obviating the opportunities for free choice requisite to an open society.

The truth is, of course, that the effective control of behavior by conditioning is no longer confined to the animal laboratory, or even to the laboratory. The knowledge of conditioning and its applicability to human behavior has long outgrown the approach-avoidance stage of the rat experiment. At the same time, it must be recognized that conditioning techniques represent but one, albeit a most effective one, device in the behavioral scientist's armamentarium. It is also true that all forms of behavior modification, from behavior therapy to psychoanalysis, must eventually imply some control of one person by another and the necessity for one individual to make decisions about what is desirable for another. Soviet and other Eastern European scientists are not the custodians of unheard-of techniques that some Western pundits would have us believe. The danger, if any, lies not in research and clinical findings, but in the potentiality for misuse—but that is another matter.

One of the significant contributions of our Soviet colleagues is the manner in which scientists such as Bykov have been able to condition almost every organ in the human body, whereas we in the West until very recently have concentrated either upon animals or upon circumscribed reflex arcs in man. Certainly, it is in the Soviet Union that many of the striking advances in the clinical applications of conditioning are now taking place, whereas, in the United States, practicing clinicians are not as familiar with the theory and application of conditioning techniques as they should be or as some would like to be. It is unfortunate not only that comparatively little has been attempted in this country, but also that, by and large, the Soviet work remains unknown.

The present series of "conditioning" readings have been assembled as a sample of what is available in the English-speaking world. The one exception, translated from the French, provides an important example of the manner in which conditioning techniques may be used in general medicine. Neither animal studies nor primarily theoretical papers are included, and the application of conditioning techniques to the normal individual is completely excluded.

In assigning the various papers to sections of the book, I have been somewhat arbitrary. There is little agreement over such basic matters as what constitutes a classical conditioned response in contrast to the instrumental or operant variety, what constitutes an aversion conditioning paradigm and what does not, and how diagnosis differs from description. My final grouping is certainly not the only one that might be used. I have tried to choose papers which represent a variety of the many different ways in which conditioning techniques may be used in clinical practice and research. Because the majority of developments have taken place within the last ten years, almost all the papers selected are of comparatively recent vintage. It is to be hoped that the reader will be encouraged not only to discuss, teach and explore for himself the specific techniques herein described, but also, in true learning theory fashion, to generalize and extend these methods to a variety of new situations. To facilitate these processes a selective bibliography pertaining to the clinical applications of conditioning and closely allied procedures is appended.

I am indebted not only to those authors and publishers whose works are represented here but also to many writers whose papers do not appear in this volume. I am most grateful to Dr. A. Moneim El-Meligi for his skillful adaptation of the article in French written by Drs. Quarti and Renaud. Without the support of Dr. Bennett, the Medical Director of the New Jersey Neuro-psychiatric Institute, and other members of the professional staff, and Dr. Humphrey Osmond and his colleagues at the Bureau of Research in Neurology and Psychiatry, located at this Institute, it would not have been possible for me to carry out the necessary laboratory studies, clinical investigations and extensive reading which preceded the preparation of this volume. It should not, of course, be assumed that these individuals necessarily share the views herein expressed.

I am indebted to my colleagues in the Psychology Service and Research Center, to Dr. Leonard Blank, and, in particular, to the Assistant Director of the Center, Dr. A. Moneim El-Meligi, and his associates, Mrs. Bigelow, Mrs. Erdman and Dr. Temmer, who have encouraged, criticized, humored and accepted me as the need seemed appropriate. Finally, I wish to express my appreciation of the manner in which Mrs. Claire Harmon and Mr. Harry Franks patiently facilitated the preparation of this volume in addition to the many other demands made upon their services.

By way of conclusion let it be stressed again that, although the climate of psychiatric opinion in this country is such that conditioning is not generally regarded as an effective therapeutic technique, the state of our present ability to help those with behavioral disorders is also such that no possible avenues should remain unexplored merely because of theoretical bias. It is our professional and scientific responsibility to evaluate each new technique in its own right, rather than, on the one hand, rejecting it outright or, on the other hand, accepting it without systematic investigation.

Princeton, New Jersey
June, 1964

CYRIL M. FRANKS

CONTENTS

"How odd it is that anyone should not see that all observation must be for or against some view if it is to be of any service."

—CHARLES DARWIN

INTRODUCTION

by Cyril M. Franks, Ph.D.

Pavlovian Antecedents

Despite many advances in behavioral techniques and their growing impact on psychiatric practice, numerous misconceptions about both conditioning and Pavlovian psychiatry persist. Some clinicians are still inclined to dismiss conditioning techniques as mere laboratory exercises in animal reflexology and to regard Pavlov as a man who was naive enough to think that all behavior could be accounted for in terms of some form of simple conditioned response. The first belief is discredited by readily available evidence in both Western and Soviet psychiatric literature and requires no further consideration here; the second merits some discussion.

Pavlov was concerned with the principles governing the functioning of central or higher nervous activity and not with conditioning alone. Instead of examining these central processes directly, he had, of necessity, to *infer* their existence and properties from a study of a limited number of peripheral activities. Since these early days significant advances have taken place in the evolution of Pavlovian practice. These advances include: the development of techniques derived from histochemistry and electrophysiology for the more direct study of central processes; the gradual shift from rather circumscribed and organismically trivial responses, such as the eyeblink, to more complex and meaningful response patterns, involving modalities such as the second signal system (speech) and interoceptive conditioning; and the evolution of what the English-speaking world calls operant or instrumental techniques. Concurrent with this latter development is the emergence of a wide variety of behavioral procedures for diagnosis, descriptive analysis and therapy stemming from the concepts of Pavlov, Watson and Hull and the learning theorists who came after them.

Most of the classical conditioning techniques stem from the concepts of Pavlov, and it is therefore desirable to discuss briefly the more important aspects of Pavlovian theory before considering limitations and subsequent modifications. Pavlov's theory of higher nervous activity has three roots, two of a philosophical nature and one physiological. In terms of philosophy, Pavlovian psychology is materialistic and in line with the traditions of British empiricism and the writings of Priestley, Hobbes, Locke and Bacon. Out of such beginnings emerged the first systematic attempts to provide a physiological and non-mentalistic description of so-called mental phenomena.

In the nineteenth century, influenced by the writings of contemporary Russian philosophers such as Herzen, Pizarev and Chernyshevsky, and non-Russian thinkers such as Locke, Darwin and Bernard, the physiologist Sechenov initiated the physiology of higher nervous activity from the standpoint of the materialist and earned for himself the appellation of founder of scientific psychology in Russia. It was up to Pavlov, however, to discover the conditioned reflex (as contrasted with the innate or unconditioned reflex already known to physiology) and use it as a powerful instrument for studying the processes and principles governing higher nervous activity.

In his introduction to a series of papers on *Psychology in the Soviet Union,* Simon (20) summarizes the materialist viewpoint of Soviet psychology, as represented by Sechenov and Pavlov, as follows:

"1) Mental processes are the product of matter organized in a particular way; i.e., of the human brain. There are not two processes here—the material processes of the higher nervous system and the mental processes of consciousness; mental processes are simply one aspect of the functioning of the brain; there is only a single process.

2) Matter is primary, consciousness is secondary and derivative; i.e., sensations, perceptions and thought derive from an external material world that exists independently of consciousness. This means that nothing can come to birth in consciousness which is not a reflection of some aspect of the material world." (p. 2)

It is in the implication and application of these tenets that the dialectical materialism stemming from the writings of Marx and Engels parts company with traditional nineteenth century mechanistic materialism. Both are products of historical developments in the natural sciences. But, according to Marxist thinking, mechanistic materialism is unable to explain change in a satisfactory manner without introducing some crucial extra-scientific motivating force; even though the mechanistic materialist will permit a strict determinism to prevail *within* the system, he is quite willing to invoke external non-materialistic forces if necessary. Western behavioristic psychology is thus accused of attempting to reduce mentalistic phenomena to physiological terms while, at the same time, accepting the principle that there may be certain subjective processes of human awareness which can never be studied objectively.

However, as shall become evident shortly, the notions of purpose, historic inevitability and uncomprising monistic determinism, which are supposed to characterize Soviet psychology and differentiate it from its behavioristic counterpart as practiced in the West, appear increasingly spurious in practice. Dualism rears its ugly head, and the psyche begins to emerge as something not always synonymous with physical processes.

These philosophic roots underlying Pavlovian psychology are, perhaps, of more interest to the philosopher, the political historian, the sociologist and the research scientist than to the practicing clinician. Certainly, there is little need for the clinician to take note of such philosophic implications. Even a cursory examination of papers reporting clinical applications of conditioning, at least those printed in English, reveals no philosophic consistency whatsoever. The clinician should aim to use those techniques of Pavlov which he finds useful, modifying or rejecting the rest. It is probably this very freedom which will contribute most to the development of clinical psychology and psychiatry as exact sciences.

Pavlovian Theory

The physiological antecedents of Pavlov are of more immediate interest to the clinician. In the early part of the seventeenth century Descartes had already speculated about reflex activity. However, Descartes' thinking was confined within the dualistic framework of psychophysiological parallelism in which body and mind co-existed independently but harmoniously. Sechenov had first to divert himself of this unacceptable doctrine. He chose to base his thinking upon the physiology of the reflex, as developed by scientists such as Claud Bernard. The outcome, occurring at about the time Sherrington was engaged in his outstanding work on the spinal reflex, was a series of papers on brain physiology, reprinted in 1863 in the form of the now famous monograph, *Reflexes of the Brain.* This attempt to represent the subjective world of the mind from the standpoint of the physiologist was a remarkable achievement in an age singularly devoid of significant contributions in this area.

Of necessity Sechenov's work was essentially theoretical and it was left to Pavlov's genius to discover (in 1901) the conditioned reflex and show how the physiology of the cerebral hemispheres could be investigated experimentally in the intact animal by methods that were objective and scientific. To recognize the historical significance of this event, one must realize not only that, with a few outstanding exceptions, research in brain physiology was undeveloped and largely confined to the mutilated animal, but also that the psychology of behavior, under the leadership of men like William James and Sigmund Freud, was emerging in the form of various speculative systems founded upon foundations of subjective experience, instincts and psychical forces. (This point is made only to underscore the meaning of Pavlov's work within the context of his era.)

Thereafter progress was rapid. In 1904 Pavlov was awarded the Nobel Prize for his researches on the activity of the digestive glands. In 1907 his associate Krasnogorski, closely followed by Ivanov-Smolensky, commenced his studies of the conditioned reflex in children. During the next half century, thousands of important papers appeared.

Physiologically, the concept of inhibition is crucial to a comprehension of Pavlovian psychiatry. First demonstrated in 1840 by Weber and shortly afterwards by Pflüger, it was left to Sherrington to show conclusively that inhibition was much more than a negative phase of excitation. Sherrington first confirmed the remarkable work of Hughlings Jackson and then showed that inhibition and excitation are of equal importance physiologically.

For Pavlov, conditioning is essentially a matter of association by contiguity, in which a neutral stimulus is paired or associated with a stimulus which usually elicits an innate or unlearned response. At this stage the neutral stimulus does not elicit any such response. But after an appropriate number of such pairings, the neutral stimulus on its own will elicit the response which originally would be given only to the other stimulus. The neutral stimulus is then said to have become the conditioned stimulus (CS) and the acquired response the conditioned response (CR). The other stimulus and its innate response are known as the unconditioned stimulus (UCS) and the unconditioned response (UCR), respectively. Once a CR has been established, second order conditioning can be set up by treating the conditioned reflex arc as if it were an unconditioned arc and linking the original CS with a new CS.

For example, salivation to food is a UCR, normally present from birth and not dependent on previous experience. The sound of a bell is a neutral stimulus as far as salivation is concerned in that it is not usual for people to have the innate ability of salivating to such a sound. If food is given to a dog and this is *preceded* slightly by the sounding of the bell, then, after a number of repetitions of this procedure, the dog will salivate to the sound of the bell even though the food is omitted. A conditioned alimentary response has thus been established to a neutral auditory stimulus.

This kind of conditioning, in which the CS precedes but overlaps with the UCS is known as forward conditioning. Backward conditioning, in which the onset of the CS *follows* the onset of the UCS, is not as effective as forward conditioning. There are various other kinds of forward or backward conditioning in which there is no overlap between the CS and the UCS, or in which the CS and the UCS overlap but the second stimulus begins long after the onset of the first.

The relative positions of the onsets of the CS and UCS, their absolute and relative intensities and durations, together with the number of pairings (or reinforcements) given, are all determinants of the quality of the conditioned bond set up. There are many other pertinent variables which must be strictly controlled, and it is essential that the clinician be familiar with these principles if conditioning techniques are to be successfully applied. Many clinicians attempting to apply these techniques have met with little or no success because they have neglected to take into consideration not only the established principles of classical conditioning but also the developments in learning theory which have taken place since these early days.

The result of overlooking these precautions may be seen in the treatment of alcoholism. Backward conditioning has been clearly shown to be a weak procedure; yet it is advocated and practiced in the form of conditioned aversion therapy for alcoholics. When this tenuous method fails, conditioning therapy is called ineffective.

Conditioning can occur to all kinds and combinations of stimuli, including time itself. Conditioned responses can be positive or negative, depending on which of Pavlov's two central processes of *excitation* and *inhibition* is primarily involved. According to Pavlovian physiology, positive CR are determined primarily by the central process of *excitation* whereas negative CR pertain to the process of *inhibition*.

When Pavlov first worked with these two concepts it was not possible to say much about their neurophysiological natures except to regard them both as positive processes with similar properties and each as the outcome of real and active events taking place within the higher nervous system. Pavlov, recognizing that physiological elucidation of their natures had to await future scientific developments, was given to comparing the central nervous system to an illuminated mosaic, consisting of ever-changing points and configurations of excitation. With the methods of investigation now available for direct electrophysiological study of these processes, it has been shown that the Pavlovian brain model is neurologically inaccurate in many respects; for example, Pavlov assumed a point-to-point, but not topological, cortical representation of the peripheral receptors. Nevertheless, the Pavlovian model served its purpose and is amenable to modification in the light of subsequent knowledge.

Both excitatory and inhibitory impulses are said to spread over the cortex by a process of *irradiation,* the impulses ordinarily becoming weaker as they spread outwards. At first there may be *generalization* of both CS and CR. But, after a sufficient number of reinforcements, increasing specificity of both stimulus and response begins to emerge. For example, the aim may be to condition a dog to move the lower portion of only one limb to a metronome beat of 100 per minute. At first, though in decreasing amounts, frequencies above and below 100 will produce a CR which may initially extend to all positions of all four limbs. Eventually, if only the one frequency is reinforced, the conditioning process will become specific. By such a process of *discrimination* the organism learns to discriminate among the various stimuli in its environment.

The manner in which these processes influence the pattern of conditioning, and hence of behavior, are dependent upon many factors. These factors include the physical parameters of the stimuli involved and also the constitutional endowment of the organism. The assumption that there are different types of nervous systems might account for individual differences in conditioning among organisms exposed to similar stimuli and reinforcement procedures, and it is to this topic that attention must now be directed.

Despite great interest in the United Kingdom and in the United States in individual differences in conditioning as related to personality variables, no one has yet satisfactorily developed and demonstrated a working Pavlovian-style typology. One difficulty in attempting to unravel and apply Pavlov's typological system systematically has been —until 1963—the absence of a clear treatment of the subject in English. In remedying this deficiency MacMillan (15) points out that it is an equal disservice to neglect the Pavlovian concept of typology or to oversimplify and reduce the entire framework to the excitation-inhibition dimension.

Pavlov, like any man of inquiring mind, was by no means consistent or static in his formulations. His typology, originally based only upon the *balance* of his two central processes, later came to include two other aspects of their interrelationships, namely *strength* and *mobility*. Balance refers to the predominance of one process over the other; strength to the manner in which each of the processes modifies the outcomes of various conditioning procedures; mobility to the speed with which these two processes replace one another.

On the criterion of *strength,* Pavlov divided his animals into two types, the strong and the weak, the latter corresponding to the melancholic temperament in Hippocrates' ancient classification. The strong animals were further divided into balanced and unbalanced, the latter corresponding to Hippocrates' choleric temperament. Finally, the strong balanced type was subdivided, on the basis of *mobility* or *lability,* into the strong inert and "phlegmatic" type on the one hand, and the strong labile and "sanguine" type on the other. It should be noted that this accounts for but four of the 24 combinations which are mathematically possible with this classification.

This system is further complicated in man by the presence (in addition to the primary or concrete signal system) of a second signal system in which words stand for direct stimuli. The two systems may be balanced harmoniously or, according to classical Pavlovian theory, one may predominate over the other. In the *artistic type,* the first signal system is said to predominate over the second; in the *thinking type* the second predominates over the first, and in the *intermediate type* the systems are balanced.

In the artistic type, transmission of either excitatory or inhibitory stimuli from the first to the second signal system is difficult, imprecise and inadequate. In the thinking type, transmission from the second to the first signal system is slow and imprecise. In the intermediate type, in which transmission occurs with equal ease in both directions, two variants are found; in one the transmission is easy, in the other it is difficult.

As MacMillan points out, and as an examination of Soviet research confirms, the relationships between the specifically human types and the more general animal types have been largely overlooked. There is good reason for regarding these typologies as the weakest parts of the Pavlovian system. Nevertheless the following personality types can be delineated and would appear to be worthy of more exploration than most of them have been given: the weak intermediate type, or neurasthenic personality, producing neurasthenia under certain stress circumstances; the weak artistic type, or hysteroid personality, producing frank symptoms of hysteria under stress; and the weak thinking type, or psychasthenic personality, producing psychasthenic symptoms under conditions of stress.

Disturbances within or across these two signal systems can be brought about by one or more of the many factors complicating man's complex biosocial adjustment. Circumstances which set up conflict or collision between the excitatory and the inhibitory conditioned reflexes are especially likely to cause such disturbances. Wars, natural calamities, emigration, family conflicts, work stress, physical fatigue, drugs, disease, accident, old age, and constitutional factors may all interfere with these complex relationships and bring about disharmony. To divide these factors into organic and functional categories is misleading since, in the Pavlovian view of things, no such dualistic dichotomy is possible.

There is a widespread belief that the results of conditioning are invariably evanescent. While it is true that CR can decay with time, they can be readily regenerated with comparatively few reinforcements. In one recent study (5) it was shown that U.S. veterans retained autonomic CR pertaining to their war time "battle stations" signals for as long as 20 years without any known reinforcement. If it is true that cardiorespiratory and other autonomic responses can persist long after skeletal and other responses have been extinguished, this would help account for the fact that autonomic components are often the only discernible symptoms in neurotics. The implications for treatment by behavior therapy are challenging.

If CR are elicited repeatedly without any reinforcement they will weaken. This process of extinction is facilitated if the repetitions of the CR follow each other in quick succession. Sometimes the temporarily extinguished CR reappears or recovers without further reinforcement; spontaneous recovery or re-emergence is then said to occur (the learning theorist would term this phenomenon *reminiscence*).

A positive CR may be inhibited in a variety of ways other than excessive elicitation: by lack of use, by lengthening the interval between the CS and the UCS, by linking the positively conditioned stimulus to a negative response producing CS (*conditioned inhibition*), by the interjection of an external stimulus (*external inhibition*) and so forth.

Not only positive CR can be inhibited by an extraneous signal; such a signal can also inhibit an inhibitory process in which the subject has learned not to respond. This can result in the temporary resumption of a positive response pattern (known as *disinhibition,* or *inhibition of inhibition*). For example, this would occur if a sudden outside noise, such as the sound of an automobile horn, temporarily brought back a CR which had been apparently eliminated. This is why Pavlov insisted on conducting his experiments within his "tower of silence," a requirement which modern workers are learning to circumvent.

To describe the intricacies of Pavlovian psychology is beyond the purpose of this brief overview; it would require exploration of both original concepts and their subsequent developments. Even this background would be insufficient without a comprehensive knowledge of contemporary learning theory. Of the additional concepts central to Pavlovian psychiatry one may mention the following: positive and negative induction; the paradoxical and ultraparadoxical phases; protective inhibition.

As the present tendency among learning theorists is to emphasize *modern* learning theory, it is quite possible that insufficient attention is being given to older concepts which might have therapeutic applicability. For example, the concept of protective inhibition has been largely neglected in the United States. Yet Pavlov's whole theory of schizophrenia is based upon the notion of *excessive* protective inhibition in the cerebral cortex, and there is considerable research emanating from the Soviet Union purporting to demonstrate that excessive protective inhibition is *one* cause of schizophrenia. On the other hand, protective inhibition in adequate amounts is regarded as an effective method of avoiding injury to the nervous system and has been used extensively in the East (and occasionally in the West) as a therapeutic device. Sleep therapy is based upon this principle, in that it strengthens protective inhibition and allows the cortical cells to recover from their exhausted state.

Contemporary Soviet Developments

The contemporary developments in Pavlovian psychology and psychiatry rest upon long established principles such as those outlined. The innovations lie more in the areas of application, in the charting of new territories and in the integration of diverse phases of Pavlovian theory than in the emergence of new concepts or drastic reformulations.

Since the days of Pavlov's original studies, the whole phylogenetic and ontogenetic ranges have been studied, in almost every conceivable modality, under almost all possible circumstances, and employing both classical and "instrumental" techniques. Much is now known about the formation and patterning of conditioned responses. For example, it is established that stimulant drugs facilitate conditioning and make it more difficult to bring about extinction, whereas depressants, along with certain forms of brain damage, have the opposite effect. It is known that there are wide individual differences in conditioning, probably constitutional in origin, and that many psychopathological phenomena can be induced and modified by various conditioning techniques.

Out of such beginnings arose the attempts in the West to establish diagnostic techniques based on the methods of the CR, culminating in the application of these methods to the description of abnormal human behavior and to the modification of such behavior in the therapeutic situation. In the Soviet Union the emphasis, until recently, has been upon the long-term experimental study of the mechanisms involved in conditioning used as an analytic rather than a clinical or therapeutic tool. It is therefore not surprising that most of the more impressive Soviet innovations have taken place within the past ten or fifteen years. It is from these recent developments that clinical advances are beginning to emerge. The post-1950 studies stand out, by comparison with earlier researches, in their increasing dependence upon experimental design and adequate statistical procedures. They are of especial significance in that they shed light on the problem of unconscious-conscious interactions and that, in general, they are not yet being duplicated in other countries. Indeed, they would probably be totally unknown in the United States were it not for the outstanding efforts of individual psychologists such as Razran and the few translations made available by organizations such as the Foreign Languages Publishing House in Moscow and the United States Public Health Service in this country.

In describing Soviet experiments aimed at making "the Unconscious observable instead of inferable and the Conscious inferable whether it is or is not observable," Razran classifies these studies in three separate but mutually supplementary groups: interoceptive conditioning, semantic conditioning, and studies of the orienting reflex.

Interoceptive conditioning refers to situations in which either the CS or the UCS or both are delivered directly to the mucosa of some specific viscus, as contrasted with conventional classical conditioning which is wholly exteroceptive. Razran (19) presents the knowledge derived from the Soviet studies of conditioning in the form of six propositions, of which he regards the following three as definitively established:

"1. Unlike the continuum of exteroceptive stimulation which is the body-material of all our conscious experience, the continuum of interoceptive stimulation leads largely to unconscious reactions.

2. Interoceptive conditioning, whether involving conditioned or unconditioned interoceptive stimuli, is readily obtainable and is by its very nature largely unconscious in character.

3. While interoceptive conditioning is by its nature more limited than is exteroceptive conditioning with respect to total kinds of variety of stimulations, the interoceptive kinds of stimulations are, on the other hand, by their very nature much more recurrent, periodic, and organism-bound, making interoceptive conditioning an almost built-in function that is constantly generated and regenerated in the very process of living and acting."

There has been an erroneous impression, fostered to a large extent by early Soviet political tradition but now happily corrected, that physiology died with Pavlov and that the investigation of biological laws was permitted to advance no further. Perhaps the most striking progress, and certainly the best known since it is available in English, is represented by the writings of Bykov (4). Working with a variety of visceral responses Bykov has shown that these responses obey the same laws as does the CR secretion of saliva. Especially important is his work with the kidney, in which the mechanism of the urinary CR was shown to involve both the pituitary gland and the nervous system. In a similar manner, Bykov and his associates have been able to establish and manipulate CR of bile, heat regulation of the body, blood sugar and so forth. Working in this country Gantt and his associates have extended these studies to other autonomic functions, including the vestibular function of equilibration and even to intraneural cerebellar conditioning.

Soviet investigators have devoted considerable attention to the study of schizophrenia (see 14). In the process of developing a "theory of schizophrenia," one item of knowledge has emerged that is especially pertinent here, namely that conditioning is poor in schizophrenic subjects. This possibility, largely unexplored in the West, may lead to new methods of assessing the effects of drugs and other methods of treating schizophrenia and, more directly, to methods of speeding up the CR patterns of such patients. Such exploration opens up new horizons to American and British psychiatrists, psychologists and physiologists. It takes conditioning out of the realm of the artificial and the contrived into the world of man, and provides a potential avenue for a scientific and non-mentalistic explanation of phenomena that were hitherto the province of the psychodynamic schools of thought.

Pavlov regarded words, speech, and the ability to make abstractions as part of a second set of conditioning signals, in contrast to the primary conditioning facilities and their more concrete impressions of the environment. This distinction is of importance in understanding the methods whereby Pavlovian clinicians explore psychiatric pathology. They view such pathology, in both its subjective and behavioral aspects, as a disturbance within or between these two signal systems. This disturbance may be the outcome of temporary circumstances such as fatigue, drugs, transient toxic states, or external stimulation. It may be the consequence of more permanent impairment arising from brain damage of known or unknown origin, or it may be a product of constitutional individual differences in the functioning of nervous tissue.

The fact that man alone has this second signal system serves as a basis for a whole Pavlovian system of psychodiagnostics and psychotherapy (e.g., *see* 18). The *word,* by virtue of its dual physiological and social significance, is capable of replacing, reflecting and generalizing the meaning of the concrete stimuli emanating from the external and internal environment. In this way a complex system of abstract ideas is set up, a system which can be sustained not only through the life of the individual but also throughout the centuries.

As in the first signal system, so in the second, the principles of association, extinction, differentiation and the like apply. By relating the two systems experimentally, a theory of speech function may be constructed and tested. In this way it is possible to account for many of the phenomena of *subliminal conditioning* in which the stimulus is too weak to permit a transference to the second signal system, and so the subject is unable to verbalize his experiences.

Under certain circumstances verbal stimuli can bring about or modify a wide variety of physiological reactions, some simple, others complex, some at the level of awareness, others of which the subject is normally quite unaware. It is claimed that in this way it is possible to influence metabolism, the secretions in the gastrointestional tract, vasomotor activity, trophic processes, endocrine and vegetative changes and so forth. It is even believed possible to modify immunization processes (although Western attempts to replicate this have so far been unsuccessful) and to influence activities hitherto regarded as "instinctive."

A related concept is that of semantic conditioning, or conditioning to meaning, regardless of the particular word components, letters or sounds used to express the meaning. Until about 1950 this area was studied only sporadically in the Soviet Union or the United States. It is now the subject of considerable attention in both countries. Again, the implications are enormous, embracing the symbolism of Freud and others, cultural anthropology, linguistics, studies of speech and reading patterns, psychotherapy, and the theoretical and practical aspects of communication and attitude formation, including advertising and other forms of propaganda.

The "orienting" reflex (also variously known as the "what-is-it" or the "investigating" or the "attitudinal" reflex) originally referred to the overt and normal reactions of Pavlov's dogs to relatively novel CS, prior to the disappearance of the CS as the conditioning process proceeded. It is now known that this reflex pattern, which should be regarded not as a single entity but rather as a centrally organized holistic system of a variety of complex biological reactions, is difficult to arouse in certain pathological groups of schizophrenics and in brain-damaged and feeble-minded children. Studies of the effects of drugs and of brain extirpation are beginning to localize the central basis of this reflex, and there are some recent Soviet attempts to demonstrate an additional relationship with the activity of the reticular formation.

This brief survey of certain developments in Pavlovian psychology is sufficient to indicate the tremendous advances that have been made since the days of "Pavlov and his dogs." Many important topics have been omitted because their relevance to the clinical applications of conditioning techniques is only tangential. Lyublinskaya, to cite but one example, has written a typical text on child development in which language, memory, emotions, thinking and volition are all convincingly treated in terms of Pavlovian theory.

Western Developments

Probably the most outstanding accomplishment in the West is the development of learning theory into practical modes of behavior therapy. In this respect it should be noted that behavior therapists utilize many techniques and do not necessarily limit themselves to classical Pavlovian conditioning or even to any form of conditioning. Furthermore, when behavior therapists do make direct use of various conditioning procedures, their antecedents are those of American learning theory rather than Pavlovian type conditioning. The notion of food as a *reinforcer* instead of as a stimulus to salivation was the unique contribution of American behavioristic psychology. It was the Americans who developed the various drive and reinforcement schools of avoidance and reward conditioning and it is within this setting that the present day behavior therapies have arisen.

Behavior therapy may be defined as the systematic application of principles derived from behavior or learning theory and the experimental work in these areas to the rational modification of abnormal or undesirable behavior. The definition extends to the prevention of such behavior, the building up of positive or desirable characteristics and the improvement of learning efficacy. Behavior therapy thus reflects not any special technique but an attitude of mind and training which amounts virtually to a "professional way of life." The two basic requirements of this way of life are a profound awareness of learning theory and a belief in the supremacy of logic and scientific methodology in any attempt to understand and control the complex bio-social environment in which we live.

Since behavior therapy is a generic term and not a specific technique there can be no one comprehensive and universally applicable set of postulates. All behavior therapies have in common the general tenets noted above; certain behavior therapists may, or may not, share common postulates. Nevertheless, all behavior therapists would probably be in agreement about an additional broad principle, namely that, even if the ultimate determinants of behavior are largely constitutional in origin, environmental manipulation is also effective in bringing about modifications in behavior and even in structure. Apart from the obvious structural changes brought about by drugs, disease, accident or surgery it is becoming increasingly apparent that such physical changes can also modify both already learned behavior and the ability to learn new behavior. Conversely, it is becoming recognized that apparently simple and innocuous external or internal stimuli can, under the right circumstances, produce changes in structure within the various body systems.

Such relationships between imposed stimuli and physical structure are explained by psychodynamically oriented psychiatrists and psychologists in terms of various analytic hypotheses in which the explanations or laws are deduced from the clinical relationships themselves. The behavior therapist prefers to reverse this procedure and conform to the more customary methodology of science, namely to begin with a limited observation, to bring this observation under experimental control and, from the data so accumulated, to establish a law or more general relationship between these accumulated observations. In this manner, a general theory is established from which more and more testable deductions can be made and investigated and the theory gradually modified or extended to new situations as the evidence dictates.

It is by such processes that techniques are being devised for the possible modification of those defects or deficiencies in the learning pattern which contribute in part to the development of abnormal behavior or the failure to learn desirable behavior patterns. It is not the purpose of the present survey to review such techniques in any detail or provide a practical guide to their application. An increasing number of articles describing the practical details and the theoretical implications of various techniques of behavior therapy in a variety of situations are appearing in the literature. Thirty-six of these articles, with appropriate commentaries, have been collected into one volume (6), and other such volumes are to appear.

Despite the impressive published reports of the therapeutic value of these behavioral techniques there is, as yet, little rigorous evidence with respect to their permanent value or their superiority over the more conventional forms of therapy, including psychotherapy.* There is undeniable need for systematic investigation of the efficacy of these

* On the other hand, the claim that behavior therapies are *not* effective in removing or ameliorating the presenting symptoms is even less warranted. Another criticism stems from the tendency of the behavior therapist to concentrate upon symptom removal. The traditional therapist maintains that the behavior therapist concentrates on a presenting symptom, which may be of symbolic or only minor significance, at the expense of the "underlying" disorder. It is alleged—but the allegation has never been validly substantiated—that removal of the symptom often is followed by recrudescence of the symptom or appearance of a different one, and that, even if the symptom is effectively removed without adverse effects, a "cure" does not usually occur unless the behavior therapy is followed up by or combined wih psychotherapy. In other words, Freudian theory appears to predict that the removal of

techniques and for meticulous investigation of failures, with a view to refining existing procedures and developing new ones. The advantage of these procedures lies at present in the inherent possibilities of an orientation which permits principles to be deduced from formally stated theories and subjected to test within and outside the laboratory. Procedures and theories may then be modified as experience and accumulated evidence dictates.

In this, rather than in present claims of clinical success, lies the potential superiority of behavior therapy. It is this difference between the behavior or learning theory approach to clinical problems and that of the psychoanalyst which makes the possibility of a rapprochement between the two remote; the difference is *not* one of semantics. The other advantage of behavior therapy (and its necessary consort, behavior diagnosis) is that eventually a disciplined body of knowledge will arise through it which can be taught in a systematic manner. In this way, hopefully, training in therapy will take on the aspects of a clinical science rather than an art.

The customary division into classical or Pavlovian conditioning, on the one hand, and operant or instrumental conditioning, on the other, is far from clear-cut. In classical conditioning the subject is usually a passive participant who has little control over events which are to follow; in operant conditioning the subject is active and has to work to modify the situation, in order to obtain positive reward or to avoid punishment. However, in many actual conditioning situations it is sometimes difficult to differentiate between the two. For example, the

---

one symptom frequently is followed by the emergence of another. No such prediction follows from any known theory of learning.

It is reputed that Pavlov, in such situations, was accustomed to pointing out that man is a complex biological system who utilizes countless numbers of reflexes of all kinds, conditioned and unconditioned, beneficial and harmful. The original cause may once have been a relevant, even traumatic, factor but, in many instances, the original cause no longer has any relevance or direct concern for the subject; it may even no longer exist. There is thus justification for concentrating on what is of concern, namely the symptom. Quite often, it is not the original trauma which still is causing the symptom, but it is the symptom itself which is bringing about emotional disturbance. For example, an emotional trauma may have contributed towards the origins of (say) enuresis in the past, but *in the present* it is the enuresis that is the source of distress, anxiety, embarrassment and other emotional disturbance to the child. So perhaps, rather than expecting the removal of this "symptom" to result in the appearance of other symptoms, one might expect the removal of the bed wetting to bring about the disappearance of other symptoms.

It is sometimes conceded that conditioning or behavior therapies may be effective in the treatment of "monosymptomatic" or simple cases such as specific phobias, but not in the treatment of the more complex neurotic states. Conditioning therapies are supposed to leave unmodified the "deep" causes of neuroses. Apart from the futility of speculating about the effects of such therapies on hidden processes whose causal relationship to manifest neurosis remains to be demonstrated, there is good reason to believe that conditioning therapies are equally effective in the treatment of neuroses regardless of their complexity (25).

difference between aversive and non-aversive conditioning is not always unequivocal. If the subject is conditioned to blink his eyes to a tone stimulus which has been repeatedly paired with a noxious air puff, it can be argued that this is or is not an example of avoidance conditioning, depending upon the success of the blink in avoiding the puff of air. It has even been argued that Pavlov's original experiments are not perfect examples of classical conditioning. For Pavlov's dogs have not only to make the correct response of reaching for the food, they also have to make the correct response of secreting saliva for the food to become moist and palatable and hence positively reinforcing.

Although operant conditioning techniques—under other names—have been in use in the Soviet Union for many decades (Ivanov Smolensky's method of investigating learned behavior in children by means of a bulb pressing device has been in use since 1927), their development has occurred almost exclusively in the United States. Today, operant conditioning procedures represent some of the more sophisticated tools available to the behavioral scientist interested in problems of clinical research and treatment.

Free-operant conditioning techniques, as they are called, offer several advantages over the more classical varieties. When the subject *operates* a lever or some such device he is *reinforced* by the presence of a rewarding event or the withdrawal or avoidance of an aversive event. The subject is not bound by the rigid and more artificial presentation of the CS as in classical conditioning; he is physically unrestricted and *free* to respond or not to respond at any time during the experimental session. If Pavlov was the first to substitute the chronic for the acute experiment, thereby showing how the animal could be studied under nearly normal conditions, Skinner, Lindsley and their associates are among the first to liberate the conditioning experiment from almost all bondage. It is claimed, with good reason, that the free-operant method of conditioning approximates closely the unrestricted behavior of individuals in their natural environments. In comparing this technique with those of classical conditioning or learning theorists other than Skinner, it is important to note that, although Skinner's concept of reinforcement is based upon no formal construct system and requires no theorizing about central processes, it shares with other schools of behavior therapy a reliance upon precise observation and objective techniques of investigation and control.

Originally developed for the study of animal behavior, operant conditioning procedures are now being usefully applied in almost every branch of pure and applied psychology: in diagnosis, in therapy, in psychopharmacology, in industry, in advertising and even in the exploration of space. The major limitation of operant methods seems to pertain not to their effective application in the control and strengthening of *existing* responses but to the difficulties encountered in using these techniques to *initiate* new responses. It is perhaps for such reasons that attempts are being made to precede the operant conditioning *per se* by a method wherein the desired new behavior may be readily initiated.

One such method consists of a modeling technique in which the subject is induced to imitate the behavior of a real-life model. This newly adopted pattern can then be maintained and strengthened by conventional operant conditioning techniques. These modeling techniques are sometimes objected to on the grounds that they short-circuit the more painstaking and slow but somehow necessary processes which are intrinsic to the Skinnerian conception of behavior. Despite these objections it may well be that modeling, an old concept, has a new future, and that learning theory will have to outgrow the traditional S-R jackets of the nineteen-fifties. Another possibility is that some form of imprint learning model, so far largely consigned to lowly creatures such as the mallard duck, will provide the necessary clue to the manner in which new responses are initiated in the developing personality.

Some Crucial Issues

Although conditioning techniques have come of age, it must not be assumed that this implies either their maturity or the absence of problems of development. Quite apart from the more general theoretical and technical problems pertaining to the applications of all forms of behavior therapy (3, 10), a vast number of unresolved issues and unknown variables still remain to be isolated (9). As yet no generally accepted theory of conditioning, or even agreement as to what constitutes a CR, has emerged. It is still not known with certainty to what inborn responses CR can be formed, and what responses can be conditioned. Although we may assume that it is possible, under appropriate circumstances, to condition any part of the autonomic system (a possibility that Western medicine is loath to recognize), it is probably unwarranted to assume, as certain Soviet scientists do, that any function whatsoever can be conditioned. According to Gantt (12), effects which have a central (usually cortical) representation through afferent fibers (even though enteroceptive) as well as an efferent control can be conditioned, while those without such adequate representation or those having no efferent connection with the central nervous system can not. It is also necessary to remember that, for reasons too complex to be detailed here, a particular reaction may be conditionable at one time and not at another.

The relationships between age, sex, intelligence, constitutional factors, learning and human conditioning still remain unclear. It is far from certain that all learning is a matter of some form of conditioning or S-R linkage; learning could conceivably also take place by the process of trial and error, by modeling behavior or by insight. The possibility of developing forms of behavior or learning therapy based on such principles remains virtually unexplored.

The advantages of a conditioning theory in accounting for either observed facts or experimentally obtained data are not always clear. For example, in one study (7) it was the poorly reimbursed subjects who indicated that they had generated more positive affect towards a very dull experimental situation. Such a finding is extremely difficult to explain in terms of reinforcement theory and is, indeed, a striking example of the possible advantage of cognitive dissonance theory as an explanatory concept.

Even more basic is the question of the validity of the assumption that "conditionability" represents a general trait and whether it would be preferable to confine one's observations to a discussion of how well a subject forms and retains specific CR within the contexts of specific conditioning situations. If conditioning is dependent upon Pavlov's central processes of excitation and inhibition, and if these processes are generalized properties of the nervous system, then a general factor of conditioning should also exist and it should be meaningful to speak of a person's conditionability rather than to restrict one's observation to how well he conditions in a specific conditioning situation. Such a generality should pervade all types of conditioning situations, irrespective of the nature of the reflex arc and the sensory modalities concerned. It should extend, if in varying amounts, to the rather circumscribed and usually organismically trivial reflex arcs of the laboratory such as the knee jerk and the eyeblink, to complex social conditioning situations, to totally exteroceptive conditioning arcs and even to interoceptive viscus conditioning of which the individual is not even aware. To put such a wide range of tests into one battery, to be sure that all sensory modalities are included and then to factor analyze the ensuing data to see if a general factor of conditionability emerges is a truly gigantic task for both experimenter and subject alike, and it is hardly surprising that this has not been adequately attempted. However, the trend towards the use of high speed electronic computers and automated data processing is beginning to make such a project quite feasible. The outcome of such a project is difficult to predict but it is possible to present strong and plausible arguments against the existence of any such factor.

The problem of a general factor of conditioning is really a specific case of a more general problem. Many investigators have argued that human behavior must be mediated by the nervous system and that some generalized central process or processes must partially determine all aspects of behavior. Depending on their own interests, research workers have sought to establish unifying concepts to explain particular areas of behavior such as perception, intelligence, personality and learning. Others have sought to integrate all of these areas within an overall concept. Others have sought to develop a general concept to account for individual differences in the efficiency or mode of functioning of the nervous system (especially those components relating to higher nervous activity) while giving it special prominence in the explanation of behavior in one particular area. Thus, to mention but a few, the name of Köhler is associated with neural satiation; Wertheimer with metabolic efficiency; Klein and Krech with cortical conductivity; Lashley with cerebral efficiency; and Pavlov, Hull, Eysenck and others with the concept of inhibition in its many forms. However, theorizing about such concepts and even adducing some supporting evidence is a very different matter from establishing their existence as general factors.

These are some of the problems besetting those concerned with the question of generality in the psychophysiological manifestations of central processes, and it is clear that they have many implications, both theoretical and practical. Most pertinent in practice would be the question of how much of the total variance in any given situation may be accounted for by the general factor under consideration. For example, even if the existence of a general factor of conditioning were established, this would be of little value in predicting an individual's conditionability from one occasion or from one reflex arc to another if it should also be true that this general factor accounted for only a small amount of the variance present in any one situation.

On the more positive side, it should be noted that the absence or inconsequentiality of such general factors need not preclude the use of empirically developed specific conditioning techniques for specific predictive purposes. For example, if it were ascertained that a specific laboratory test of eyelid conditioning could be used to predict which patients would respond, and how well, to conditioned aversion therapy for the treatment of alcoholism, this would be of practical value regardless of theoretical implications and of the generality of conditioning. The only practical limitation would be that the predictions would have to be confined to situations employing that particular technique of eyelid conditioning and could not be extended to apply to any other laboratory reflex. It is precisely because such a state of affairs is unsatisfying theoretically and limiting in practice that the questions and issues raised here concerning the nature and extent of general factors need eventually to be resolved.

Despite all that is known about conditioning techniques there is much resistance to their acceptance in the English-speaking world. This resistance goes back in part to the same source as the widespread reluctance to utilize Pavlovian concepts either in psychiatry or in general medicine, that is, to a tenacious adherence to a Cartesian dualism of body and mind. Adherents to this dualism, having differentiated in their thinking the so-called functional and organic components and having excluded the organic, customarily consider the remaining "psychopathology" in terms of vague and subjective concepts such as motivation, free will and the mind.

As far as therapy is concerned, conditioning techniques are frequently regarded as soulless and mechanistic forms of brain washing which somehow deny the individual his right to free choice. The explicit goal of the conditioning or behavior therapist is the modification of behavior in a direction selected and approved by the therapist or some other individual; this goal may not be elected by the patient. Juxtaposed, in seeming contrast, are the goals of traditional psychotherapy where the development of insight and the disentangling of psychic encumbrances enables the patient to deal with this insight as he pleases.

An examination of these two apparently opposed goals suggests that the divergence is not as wide as at first might appear. The goals and directing role of the conditioning or behavior therapist are explicit, obvious and specific, but they are limited by constitutional factors in the patient and his social and cultural milieu. The less directive role of the psychotherapist is often more directive than it seems. In practice, as two experimentally minded psychiatrists, Stewart and Winokur, have pointed out (21), it has long been tacitly acknowledged that no matter how non-directive the therapist strives to be, the patient tends to imitate the attitudes, values and habits of the therapist. It is also true that in many specific ways, such as the prescription of drugs, the psychodynamic therapist is forced to become quite directive. Furthermore, these authors say, in practice much of psychotherapy, like conditioning and behavior therapies, concerns itself not so much with remolding personality as with helping the patient resolve a specific problem area. Just as a patient who goes to a surgeon places himself completely in the surgeon's hands, so the patient seeing a psychotherapist puts himself in the therapist's hands. In both instances, the therapist is making decisions about goals, value systems and what is good for his patient. As the surgeon accepts responsibility in his field, so must the therapist in his. He must decide what is probably best for his patient, what is desirable in terms of human behavior, and how to induce the desired changes. In many ways, the behavior therapist is in a better position than the psychotherapist to avoid the accusation of acting omnipotently because he is usually able to debate directly with his patient and anyone else concerned the pros and cons of the specific treatment goals, the specific symptoms, precisely how he intends to change them, and why, in his opinion, this is desirable.

Conclusions

There is little doubt that conditioning has outgrown the stage of the demonstration maze and the salivating dog. Nevertheless, in the Soviet Union and the West alike, the clinical applications of conditioning and learning theory have, until recently, been somewhat neglected. There are compelling but different reasons why this relative disregard occurred. In the Soviet Union, traditionally conditioning was used by the disciples of Pavlov mainly as an experimental, analytic tool for the long-term study of physiological mechanisms in the individual case. In the United States, psychiatry and clinical psychology alike have been dominated by the psychodynamic schools of thought, and an implicit dualism still pervades medical and psychiatric thinking. Compounding this state of affairs is the justified resistance of Western physicians to the indiscriminate and sometimes questionable application of "Pavlovianism" to every branch of medicine. All too often the result has been to ignore or regard as suspect *any* application of Pavlovian principles. At the same time Pavlovian techniques are regarded as somehow omnipotent, sinister and immoral. The danger, of course, lies not in the research findings but in their possible misuse.

On the more positive side, the English speaking world has witnessed a demonstration of continued successes in the application of free operant conditioning techniques to an ever-widening range of problems, clinical and otherwise. Also on the positive side, although the amount of systematic validation is still small, is the recent emergence of diverse techniques for behavior modification based upon a revived interest in the application of modern learning theory to the clinical situation. While these latter developments are desirable and laudable, it is to be hoped that they will not take place at the expense of what conditioning theory itself has to offer the clinician. The following papers are offered to the reader with this thought in mind—not only to make him more aware of what has been accomplished in the West but also to encourage him to apply conditioning techniques in his own practice and carry out further research. In reading this book the clinician should bear in mind that each one of the papers may be adapted to problems and circumstances other than those discussed by its author. To accomplish this the clinician need neither be an uncompromising materialist nor an acknowledged expert in conditioning and learning theory. What is necessary is that he familiarize himself with the principles involved and be prepared, upon occasion, to seek counsel from experts in these matters before embarking upon a new application.

References and Suggested Background Reading

1. Alexander, L. *Objective approaches to treatment in psychiatry.* Springfield, Illinois: C. C Thomas, 1958.
2. Ban, T. *Conditioning and psychiatry.* Chicago: Aldine Pub. Co., 1964.
3. Beech, H. R. Some theoretical and technical difficulties in the application of behaviour therapy. *Bull. Brit. Psychol. Soc.,* 1963, 16, 25-33.
4. Bykov, K. *The cerebral cortex and the internal organs.* (transl. R. Hodes). Moscow: Foreign Languages Publ. House, 1959.
5. Edwards, A. E., and Acker, L. E. A demonstration of the long-term retention of a conditioned GSR. *Psychosom. Med.,* 1962, 24, 459-463.
6. Eysenck, H. J. (ed.) *Behaviour therapy and the neuroses.* London: Pergamon Press, 1960.
7. Festinger, L., and Carlsmith, J. M. Cognitive consequences of forced compliance. *J. abnorm. soc. Psychol.,* 1959, 58, 203-210.
8. Foggitt, C. H. Pavlov's theory in medicine. *Medical World, London,* 1956, 84, 201-209.

9. Franks, C. M. Some fundamental problems in conditioning. *Acta Psychol.,* 1958, 14, 223-246.
10. Franks, C. M. Behavior therapy, the principles of conditioning and the treatment of the alcoholic. *Quart. J. Stud. Alcohol,* 1963, 24, 511-529.
11. Frolov, Y. P. *Pavlov and his school.* (transl. C. P. Dutt) London: Kegan Paul, 1938.
12. Gantt, W. H. The physiological basis of psychiatry: The conditional reflex. In *Basic problems in psychiatry* (ed. J. Wortis). pp. 52-89. New York: Grune & Stratton, 1953.
13. Gray, J. A. (ed.) *Pavlov's typology: recent theoretical and experimental developments from the laboratory of B. M. Teplov.* Oxford: Pergamon Press, 1964.
14. Lynn, R. Russian theory and research on schizophrenia. *Psychol. Bull.,* 1963, 60, 486-498.
15. MacMillan, M. Pavlov's typology. *J. nerv. ment. Dis.,* 1963, 137, 447-454.
16. Pavlov, I. P. *Conditioned reflexes and psychiatry.* (transl. W. H. Gantt) New York: International Publ., 1941.
17. Pavlov, I. P. *Psychopathology and psychiatry: Selected works.* (transl. D. A. Myshne and S. Belksy). Moscow: Foreign Languages Publ. House, circa 1960.
18. Platonov, K. *The word as a physiological and therapeutic factor: the theory and practice of psychotherapy according to I. P. Pavlov.* (transl. D. A. Myshne). Moscow: Foreign Languages Publ. House, 1959.
19. Razran, G. The observable unconscious and the inferable conscious in current Soviet psychophysiology: Interoceptive conditioning, semantic conditioning, and the orienting reflex. *Psychol. Rev.,* 1961, 68, 81-147.
20. Simon, B. (ed.) *Psychology in the USSR.* London: Routledge and Kegan Paul, 1957.
21. Stewart, M. A., and Winokur, G. Ethical issues in learning theory psychotherapy. Paper delivered at the 70th Annual Convention of the American Psychological Association, St. Louis, September, 1962.
22. Skinner, B. F. *Science and human behavior.* New York: Macmillan, 1953.
23. Wells, H. K. *Pavlov and Freud,* 1. *Ivan P. Pavlov.* New York: Internat. Publ. Co., 1956.
24. Wolpe, J. *Psychotherapy by reciprocal inhibition.* Stanford: Stanford Univ. Press, 1958.
25. Wolpe, J. Behaviour therapy in complex neurotic states. *Brit. J. Psychiat.,* 1964, 110, 28-34.

Also recommended is the new quarterly journal *Behaviour Research and Therapy,* published by the Pergamon Press. Vol. 1, No. 1, appeared in May, 1963.

PART I

CONDITIONING PROCEDURES AS DIAGNOSTIC AIDS

Despite half a century of laboratory accomplishment the development of the principles of conditioning into clinically useful diagnostic tools is of comparatively recent origin. Gantt, the director of the Pavlovian Laboratory at the Johns Hopkins University, is one of the few in this country who has been concerned with this problem since before World War II. The article reproduced here describes in detail the relatively simple procedures worked out by Gantt for the use of motor-conditioned reflexes as an aid to the diagnostic differentiation of various organic and psychogenic disturbances.

In the next two papers, Alexander shows how the psychogalvanic skin response may be used to assist the clinician in the often difficult differential diagnosis between physical and psychogenic pain states, and Ban explores the use of the conditioned eyeblink response in the exploration of the "functional activity" of the central nervous system.

Dix and Hallpike discuss an improved and simplified version of their well known method of peep-show audiometry for the assessment of hearing loss in very young children. One advantage of their method is that the need for explanation of the nature of listening and hearing is completely avoided. There are many ways in which the basic procedure may be modified to suit specific needs. For example, Thorne found that some of his children were unable to focus their attention on the pure tone stimulus in the required manner. He therefore developed a technique whereby bone conduction sound vibration is used to reinforce the pure tones with a composite of tactile and visual cues. His procedure is described as follows:

"During conditioning the child is given a pegboard or spool and spindle and shown how to play with it. The bone vibrator is taken off the headband and shown to the child. Activated by a 500-cycle tone at 50 db to 65 db, the vibrator is placed where the child can benefit from the vibration and sound at the same time. This may mean that the vibrator is placed on the top or the side of the peg that the child is playing with, on the table near him, or on his chair.

"Generally the child reacts with surprise or curiosity. Some children do not notice the combination of cues at all. In cases where reaction is obtained, the child is encouraged to put the pegs or spools in their proper position on signal. If the child does not react to this situation, the vibrator is placed on hard portions of his body and gradually moved toward the head. In both cases, conditioning with the bone vibrator proceeds toward the head with the vibrator eventually being placed on the child's forehead or mastoid process. By such a procedure the child becomes conditioned to the sound through tactile cues, to the tester through body rapport, and to the eventual use of headphones by having the sound vibrator near the head.

"On occasion it is best that the child hold the vibrator between his fingers or on his palm so that he can more readily identify the stimulus. This enables the child to understand where the sound is actually coming from.

"Quite soon we introduce the earphones by first showing the phones to the child while an intense (100-db) 500-cycle air-conduction tone is introduced. To allay further fears, the phones are first placed on the tester's head and then matter-of-factly transferred to the child's head and the test game continues. If the child still objects to the earphones, one of the phones is removed and placed within the shell of a toy plastic telephone and brought to the test ear.

"Conditioning and testing may be completed in one sitting or broken up into tests of one frequency at each sitting. The 500-cycle tone is the preferred test tone because of its range of intensity and its marked oscillations. While the 250-cycle tone produces larger oscillations, it does not have the intensity range of the former on the standard audiometer. The conditioning process is more complete when the examiner praises the child overtly for each success at the task."*

One of the difficulties associated with such diagnostic sensory techniques is that conditioning may be difficult to establish for reasons other than poor hearing. Brain damage, depressant drugs and certain constitutional deficiencies in the nervous system could all produce an impairment in ability to form and retain conditioned responses. There is a consequent danger that conditioned response audiometry can give rise to misleading conclusions in those very cases where current techniques are inadequate. On the other hand, a knowledge of this hazard may be helpful in confirming a clinical diagnosis of communication disorder other than peripheral deafness. For example, Goldstein, Ludwig and Naunton** advocate the use of the psychogalvanic skin response to confirm the clinical diagnosis of *aphasia* in children.

* Thorne, B. Conditioning children for pure-tone testing. *J. Sp. hear. Dis.*, 1962, *27*, 84-85. Quoted by permission of the author and the Journal of Speech and Hearing Disorders.

** Goldstein, R., Ludwig, H., and Naunton, R. F. Difficulty in conditioning galvanic skin responses: its possible significance in clinical audiometry. *Acta Oto-Laryngologica*, 1954, *44*, 67-77.

1

THE CONDITIONAL REFLEX FUNCTION AS AN AID IN THE STUDY OF THE PSYCHIATRIC PATIENT

by W. Horsley Gantt, M.D.

History

Soon after the establishment of the Pavlovian Laboratory at the Phipps Psychiatric Clinic in 1931, I began to apply the conditional reflex (cr) methodology to the study of the psychiatric patient. The present method, though derived from my experience with the methods of Krasnogorsky and of Ivanov-Smolensky, both of whom I worked with in Russia in 1925-29, is chiefly a new adaptation based on the requirements of the psychiatric clinic.

Krasnogrosky (6) employed the salivary cr mainly in infants and in retarded children. While this is a useful method for the study of infants and very young children, it is of little value in this country with older subjects because of the fact that unless American children are starved they do not show the interest in food that the average Russian child did. In adults, owing to the excessive amount of inhibition of the food reflex in the experimental setting, the salivary method is usually unsatisfactory, even in Russia. The average adult does not give a clear-cut reflex to the experimental amounts of food used to evoke salivation.

Ivanov-Smolensky, whose method was derived mainly from Bekhterev, studied the motor component of the food reflex, or of the orienting reflex (OR) of the child to a picture (17). Neither of these methods is applicable to the psychotic patient because of his suppressed interest and reactivity to most stimulations.

Various studies have been made in this country with the cr method in human subjects. Among the early experiments have been those of Watson (24) in 1915 with the motor components, and of Mateer (19) and Lashley (18) with the salivary secretion. Recently, Sutherland and Finesinger (3) investigated the salivary crs in psychotics, and

---

Reprinted by permission from P. H. Hoch and J. Zubin (eds.), *Relation of Psychological Tests to Psychiatry*. Grune & Stratton, New York, 1950.

Welch, the psychogalvanic reflex (PGR) in anxiety patients (25). My early work at the Phipps Clinic showed that even though there was a great apparent impairment in some cataleptic patients, a marked difference was seen between the character of the impairment in the psychogenic and in the organic psychoses (8, 9, 10, 11, 12, 21). Thus, I demonstrated that severe catatonics, including cateleptics, could form conditional reflexes, whereas my collaborators and I have demonstrated that many severe organics cannot form conditional reflexes; Gantt and Muncie have demonstrated failure for the Korsakov's (12); Fleck and Gantt (5) found impairment after electroshock; Reese, Doss, and Gantt noted parallel impairment in the psychogalvanic and respiratory components of the cr in organics (21).*

There are, of course, other objective methods for the study of behavior and intelligence. Halstead in his recent book, *Brain and Intelligence,* (16) has stated emphatically both the great need for, as well as the lack of, such objective methods in psychiatry, and he has developed a series of objective tests, the results of which he interprets by a rather complex system of psychological analysis. No attempt is made in the present article, however, to review or evaluate methods other than the one here described.

Method

The patient is separated from the experimenter by a partition—a glass window about 30″ x 30″ fitted for one-way vision. On the patient's side is a table on which are two plate electrodes, on a platform suspended by a spring. At a convenient point are placed a series of colored lights (white, green, red, blue). Auditory signals are given from an audiometer. In front of the patient is a rubber bulb for use of the free hand. This bulb is so connected that it serves for short-circuiting the current to the restricted hand and also for recording the movements of the free hand. Movements of the restricted hand are recorded by a pneumograph. A ground glass screen above the table serves for projection of pictures, and written word signals as needed.

For children a food box is provided so adjusted that it can be opened by the experimenter at will, but by the child only with the appropriate signal.

On the other side of the partition there is a switchboard controlling 1) the conditional stimulus (cs), visual or auditory; 2) the unconditional stimulus (US), shock, through a time device which is designed to give in regular sequence, usually every two minutes, the cs for 5″, immediately followed by the US. The intensity of the latter is governed through a Variacs producing a voltage of 0-125 AC. A

* During 1950 Reese and Gantt established a laboratory at the Veterans Hospital at Perry Point, Md. for the study of motor, circulatory, and other automatic responses in patients (22).

continuous-feed Phipps and Bird kymograph records 1) respiration, 2) conditional signal, 3) movements of the free hand (bulb), 4) movements of the restricted hand (on electrodes). (See Fig. 1.)

Preparation of Patient

This should be designed to put the patient at his ease, to relieve his apprehension concerning the procedure, avoiding conversation of a suggestive nature. The subject is allowed a few minutes to become quiet in the room; some casual conversation may help to do this. Reliable results cannot be obtained in a patient fearful of the procedure. If any explanation is required, the patient should be told that the examination is to determine his progress or to test his coordination in terms with which he is familiar and which do not excite him unduly. It may, however, be necessary for disturbed patients to come back for a second test; a repeat test is essential on every patient who makes a low score on the initial examination.

The order of procedure is as follows:

1. Perception: Have the patient name all signals—visual, auditory.
2. Sensitivity: Hands on electrodes. Test each hand three times for lower threshold (perception of current) and higher threshold (pain).
3. Five repetitions of one pair of signals, beginning with the negative. No instructions are to be given here except for the patient to place one hand on the electrodes, the other on the bulb, and to observe what happens. Look for evidence of the primitive cr formation.
4. Integrated cr: "Now, from what you have seen and heard here, from your experience, I want you to press this bulb just before you think the shock would come. Press once now so that I can see that you press it hard enough. Hold it a couple of seconds before releasing it. Don't ask questions, but do the best you can from your experience. When you press the bulb at the right time, you won't get the shock. If you get the shock, you are not using the bulb in the right way."
5. After the appearance of the integrated cr with differentiation (failing to press with the unreenforced signal), use auditory signals to see if spontaneous transfer of learning occurs. If it does not, observe in the patient's formulation his subjective feeling about these signals and why he did not react. Grade A – if he fails on transfer.
6. If patient does not learn from the first series of five repetitions or fails to differentiate, repeat training five more times or use electrodes on wrist with constant reenforcement so that he cannot avoid the shock. Grade A –.

Grade as high as B if the patient is capable of reacting correctly by increasing the number of repetitions, however, without the use of pointed directions. Grade B – and not C if integrated crs occur irregularly to signal but do not occur in the intervals between stimuli. If differentiation is poor, grade separately for differentiation.

7. If patient cannot elaborate integrated crs, (a) repeat or, if necessary, (b) have him repeat "shock" and "no shock" with positive and negative lights, and then, if necessary, (c) "white light–no shock," "red light–shock." Grade C after this if he can perform correctly even for three times.

8. Grade D if he fails on above but can execute three times: "Press with red and not with white." D – if irregular or presses to both.

Use kinesthetic reenforcement when necessary and grade as above.

9. Grade E if he fails on D.

With the appearance of the primitive cr, grade the same as for integrated cr except with small letters. Primitive crs occurring with the integrated may be expressed by using, e.g., Aa.

10. Verbal Grading.

Deduct 25 for evidence of failure to note difference between positive and negative signals. If the patient does not mention spontaneously the significance of the two signals, deduct 5 and ask, "Any difference between the meaning of the different lights (or sounds)?"

Failure to *enumerate* negative signals, deduct 5 and ask, "Any difference between meaning of the different lights or sounds?" Failure to note difference between positive and negative signals, deduct 20.

The verbal formulation by the patient is of interest in throwing light on his thinking, or for its contrast with the performance, as seen in many psychogenic patients. Under the conditions of this test, a low verbal grade is not necessarily significant of impairment of cortical function.

Our conventional report sheet of an impairment from a brain tumor appears in Table 1.

Results

Normal Variations. All intact healthy subjects from infancy to senescence can form crs, but the pattern of the cr, especially the voluntary, motor component, varies considerably, sometimes in the same individual as a result of disease, but especially from one individual to the other.

Types. The patterns of reactivity show marked variation. An extended study would probably reveal definite functional types related to the personality. Without attempting a complete classification, but to give a few examples, one may distinguish among normals 1) the childish type, 2) the artistic type, and 3) the scientific type. The first type resembles the subhuman (dog) reaction in that the spontaneous crs predominate. (See Figs. 1, 2 and 3.)

The second type is characterized by a hyperreactivity with considerable irregularity and disturbance in the respiration. See, for example, the chart of a prominent author (Fig. 2).

The third or scientific type is marked by a regularity of response seen in both the respiration and in the movements (Fig. 3).

Fluctuations in the Same Hand. The cr is subject to variation not only on the basis of physical and toxic influences, e.g., alcohol, but also it varies with a large number of *conceptual factors.* As an extreme degree of this, let us take the variation that can be brought about in a susceptible person by *hypnotic* suggestion. The following twenty-three-year old soldier was a patient of Dr. Herbert X. Spiegel. Dr. Spiegel could get this patient to regress to any age level by suggesting under hypnosis that he would act as if he were the suggested age. The mental age measured by the Binet corresponded to the suggested age. The cr record was also comparable to the hypnotic age; the movements were seen to be more intense, as they are in younger children, and to be absent in the baby. (Although babies can form crs they would not be revealed in this type of test used for adults.) (See Figs. 4, 5, 6 and 7.)

Pathological Disturbances. Deviations from the normal in general can be arranged in a hierarchy from slight to grave. The slightest deviations are marked by an irregularity of latent period—the more intelligent subjects tend to make the latent period nearly equal to the duration of the cs, although this varies with individuals and with the apprehension. Next in order come a failure of generalization, a failure of differentiation, a slowness in forming crs, a complete inability to form the specific motor cr but with some emotional components of a general nature (respiratory, circulatory) and finally, in the idiot, intoxicated or poisoned individual there is a suppression of the orienting reflex (OR), as well as of the URs, including the response to pain, etc. (See Fig. 8.)

Toxic Conditions. Acute intoxications show only a temporary impairment, e.g., acute alcoholic intoxication. Figs. 9 and 10 are records of a normal medical student before and during alcoholic intoxication. Note the appearance of primitive crs in the restricted hand, the irregularity of cr amplitudes, the failure to differentiate between the positive and negative signals. The chronic toxic psychoses, e.g., Korsakov's, alcoholic dementia, post-insulin shock, give the most marked picture—the complete inability to form the motor cr.

Organic conditions, e.g., hydrocephalus, senility, brain tumors, show all grades of impairment according to the damage. In general, those which are severe enough to produce psychotic symptoms usually have a loss of ability to form the motor crs.

In acute disorders the impairment of the cr function is more marked than in the chronic. One may see this in the following two patients. The first (10) was a patient with a brain tumor who showed a marked failure to form crs until the operation, but recovery thereafter; the second patient (JDP) who had a congenital absence of one frontal lobe and a cyst of the other, showed only a slight loss of cr function (failure of differentiation). If the injury in this patient had been re-

The Johns Hopkins Hospital
Phipps Clinic

Summary of Conditional Reflex Test for Cortical Function

Name ___R. L.___ Ward ______ Age _37_ Date __________

I. UR: defense to shock

II. Reaction to unconditional stimulus: +++
(perception)

a. threshold of sensitivity (rt.hd.): 20-21-20
(perception) (lt.hd.): 10-11-12

b. threshold of pain (rt.hd.): 70-65-60
(lt.hd.): 40-30-30

c. amplitude of reaction: 1) barely perceptible, 2) diminished, 3) average, 4) increased, 5) greatly exaggerated:
CR: + UR: +++

III. CR (motor) function (adaptation):

	Spontaneous (primitive CR)	Integrated CR
Ability to:		
a. form (synthesis):	−	+
b. differentiate (analysis):	−	−
c. extinguish:	−	−
Speed: (no. repetitions necessary):		
a. for elaboration:		>5
b. for differentiation:		
c. for extinction:		

Retention:
a. motor: +
b. verbal: +

$\frac{\text{Latent period}}{\text{Duration CR}} : \frac{1.5}{2.0}$

IV. Reaction to conflicting stimuli:

V. Reaction to reality (suggestibility or accuracy of perception determined by estimation of presence and intensity of current):
a. localized; b. referred; c. *fabrication;*

VI. Emotional reaction: *overt* (muscular); autonomic (*respiratory*)
(speech) (cardiac)

a. intensity (1–5 as under IIc.) +

b. type of response (aggressive, uncooperative, *indifferent*, *cooperative*, interested, intellectual):

VII. Verbal responses: a. *meager;* b. average; c. profuse; d. spontaneous; e. relevant or *irrelevant.*

VIII. Attention during test (concentration): good, average, *poor.*

IX. Other memory tests:
a. orientat. t. p. per. x
b. 100–7: ___3 minutes___ time (sec.): ___ errors: _10_
c. digit frwd _4_ bkwd _2_

X. Formulation (verbal) score: 25
Tell me briefly in your own words the important parts of this examination—what you have done and what you have learned from your experience here—only the significant items (important things).

Comprehension

Active (spontaneous) = 100	Passive = 50
Items: sensitivity (5)	1) How did you know when the shock was coming (50)
Enumeration of signals (5)	
1 2 3 4 5 6	If failure ask:
Meaning of signals: positive (45)	2) What did you see or
negative (20)	hear? (5)
Use of bulb (15)	3) What happened? (5)
Time under 2 min. (10)	4) What did you do? (5)
under 3 min. (5)	5) Repeat 1). (25)
(allow 5 min.)	(allow 5 min.)

Permissible: You needn't give details.
Don't try to explain it.
Deduct 5 each repetition: "Anything else"?
Score on cr:

Key: A = no impairment of formation or differentiation of motor conditional reflex (forms in less than 5 trials) formulation, retention, perception normal.
B = slight impairment of 1 or more above elements.
C = marked impairment of 1 or more above elements; cannot form conditional reflexes without help in pointing out signals and involving speech center.
D = complete inability to elaborate conditional reflexes; no insight into problem, but can execute order, "Press with R, not with W."
E = same as for D plus inability to carry out orders.
a, b, c, d, e = used instead of capitals to indicate performance as above but in terms of primitive crs.
If pt. gets above C it means he can elaborate crs without help.

Table 1. Sample report sheet.

cently acquired, as in a patient examined with bilateral frontal lobe extirpation, he would have shown a much greater deficit. Evidently the patients with the congenital lesions have a special advantage over the patients with the acquired lesion in the ability to make new adaptations, though perhaps not in the function of retention.

In dogs even with large cortical extirpations, there is relatively good retention of the ability to form new crs. Thus two dogs, "Crazy" and "Checkers," having extirpations of the whole of one cortex and the gyrus cingulus of the other, could form and differentiate motor and cardiac crs to two tones (T256+ and T512−) an octave apart, and also form, though with some difficulty, the time cr to a regularly recurring sequence of two stimuli every two minutes.

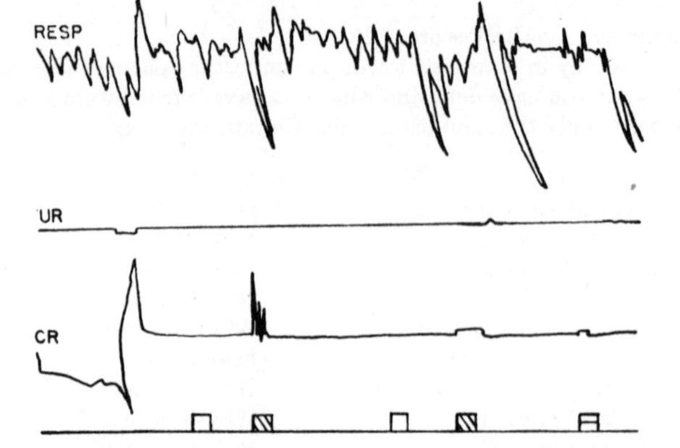

Fig. 1. CR in adolescent (A.G.), age 11. (November 22, 1947.)

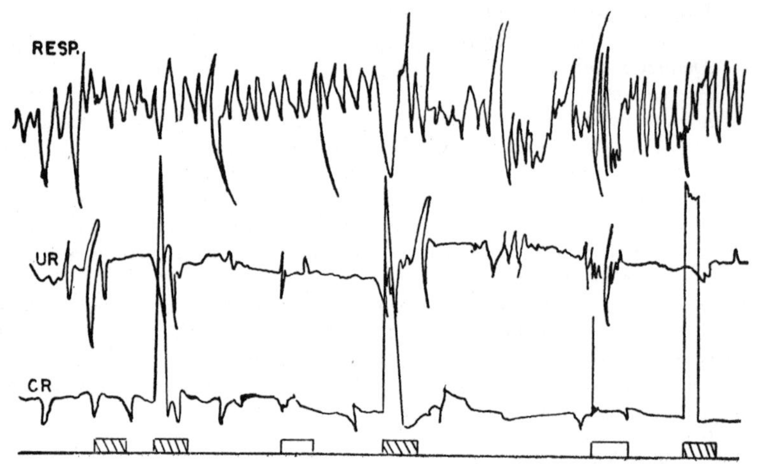

Fig. 2. CR in artistic type (J.D.P.), author. (March 29, 1939.)

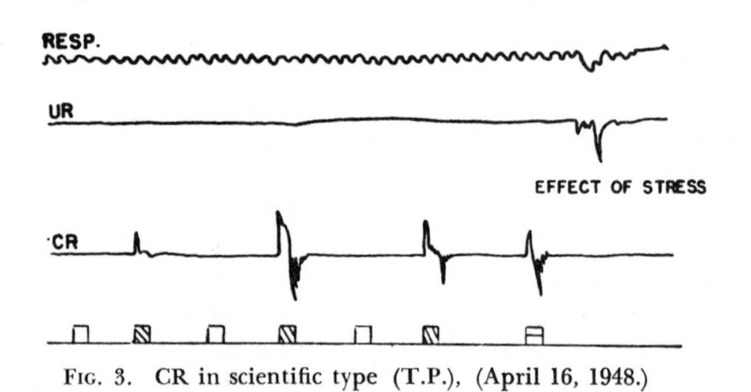

Fig. 3. CR in scientific type (T.P.), (April 16, 1948.)

□ — CR and — CS ▨ + CR and + CS ⊟ (+ CR, — CR) ■ Un CS

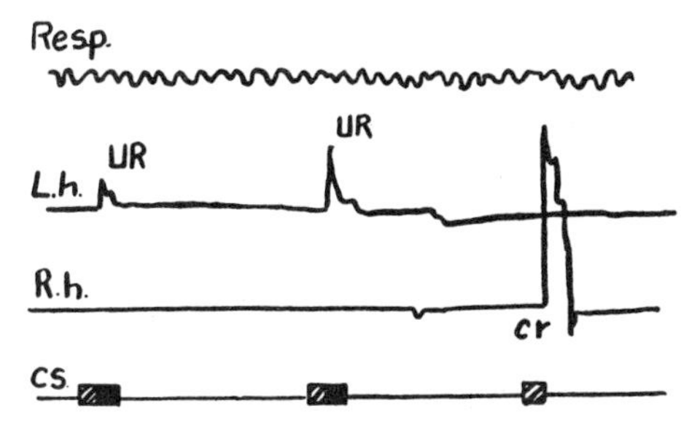

Fig. 4. (Hypnosis I.) Normal CR record, twenty-three-year old soldier (K.H.), (October 11, 1943.)

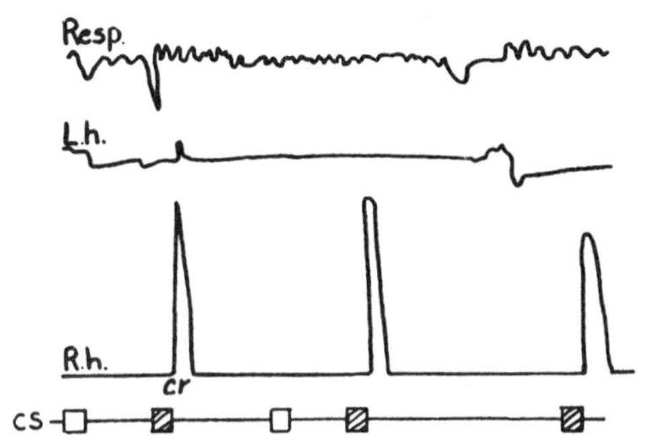

Fig. 5 (Hypnosis II.) CR record in K.H. under hypnotic suggestion "age 11." Same as normal except for irregular respiration. (October 11, 1943.)

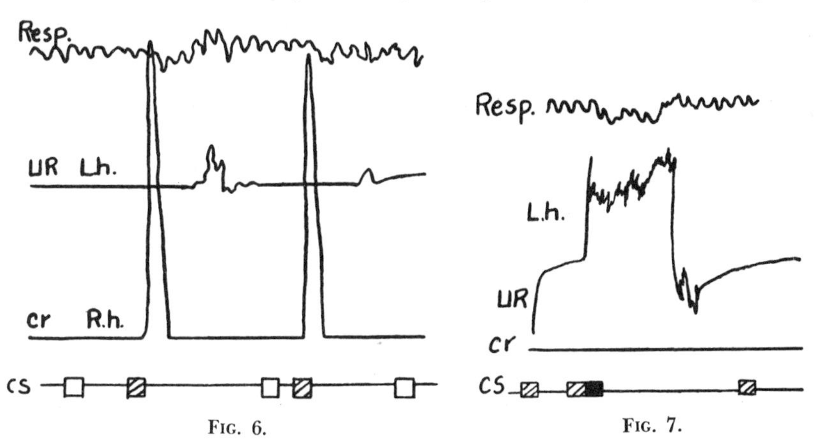

Fig. 6. Fig. 7.

Fig. 6. (Hypnosis III.) CR record in K.H. under hypnosis "age 5." Note increased amplitude CRS, irregular respiration, hyperreactivity L.H. characteristics of five-year old. (October 27, 1943.)

Fig. 7. CR record in K.H. under hypnosis "age 6 months." Note absence CRS, UR activity partly characteristic of baby. (October 11, 1943.) Binet Simon M.A. roughly corresponded to hypnotic ages. *(Experiments of Dr. Herbert Spiegel.)*

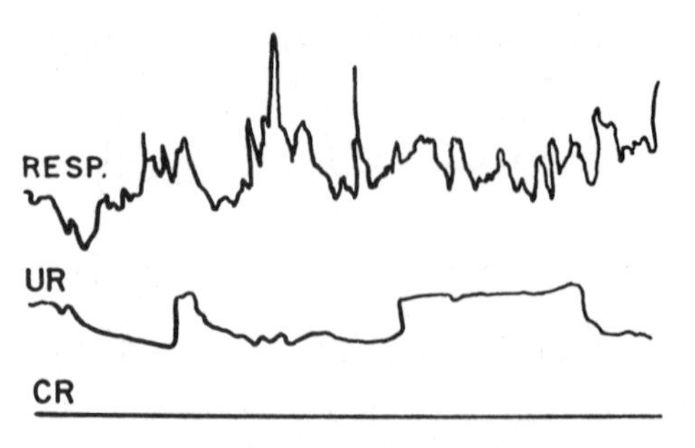

FIG. 8. Imbecile (J.C.), age four.

A variety of procedures in the dog have been shown to impair the cr function—metrazol convulsions (23), exposure to high altitudes (13), alcohol (4, 7), vitamin B group deficiency (14), etc. Judging from those cases where a comparison has been made between human and subhuman species, the equivalent damage will produce a much greater loss of function in the human than in lower animals, and therefore the impairment caused by the same agents (convulsions, anoxia, drugs, vitamin deficiency) would be reflected by a much greater loss of cr function in the human than those we have demonstrated in the dog. (See Figs. 11, 12 and 13.)

Fleck and Gantt (5) found in ten patients tested before, during, and after electroshock therapy that there was a decline in performance in six of the ten, lasting from 24 hours to more than 9 weeks. These results are roughly parallel with what Rosen and Gantt (23) found in dogs after metrazol convulsions.

Sensory Disturbance (Deafness, Blindness, Anesthesias). This test may be employed to detect hysterical blindness, deafness, anesthesias. The hysterical patient will at first inhibit the cr involving sensations concerned in the illness; however, a distinction can be seen between the organic and the psychogenic sensory disturbance; the latter patient will form the cr but will inhibit the movements, but this movement can be elicited in a variety of ways, the simplest of which is to combine, e.g., an auditory and a visual stimulus (in hysterical deafness); after forming the cr to the compound stimulus the patient will give a reaction to either component used singly.

The test can also be used in those patients, especially children who are unable to talk, to determine whether there is true deafness. I have been using this examination with Dr. W. M. Phelps for a number of years to detect the hearing ability in children. For the last few years, Dr. John Bordley has developed the cr test for deafness using the *psychogalvanic reflex* to shock as the US (2). The psychogalvanic reflex has especial advantages over the motor cr in certain diseases, which will be discussed in a subsequent article (21).

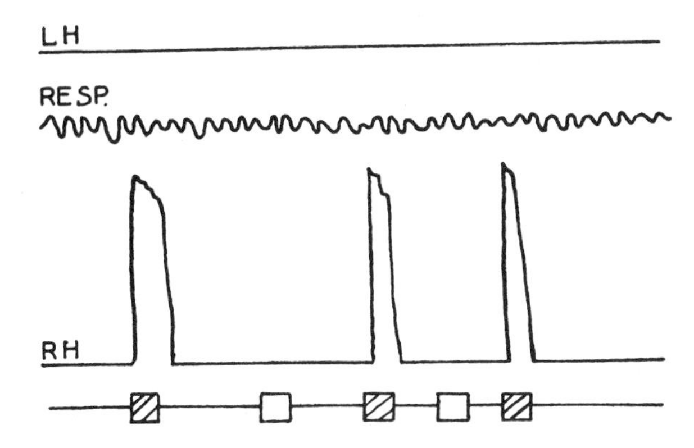

FIG. 9. Normal CR record, medical student.

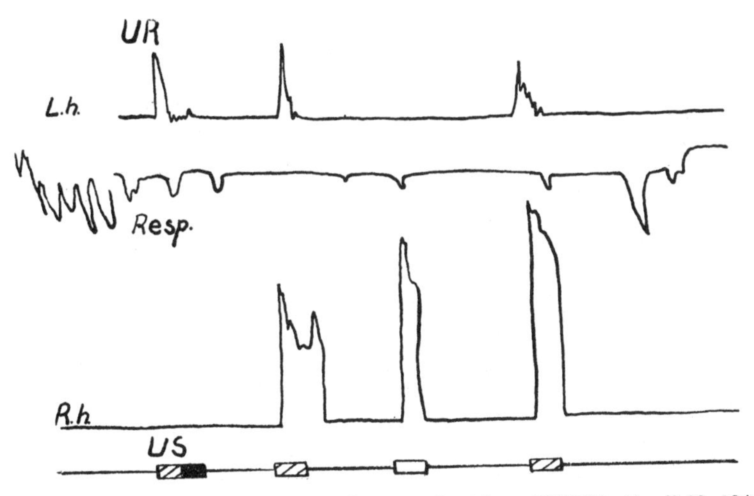

FIG. 10. Alcohol (2 cc. per kg.) on CR in normal subject (JWTR). (April 29, 1944.)

Besides the psychogenic patient, this examination is of value in the study of cerebral palsies, athetoses, and aphasias to determine the ability for making adaptation as well as to compare the right and left sides. So far, there has been no difference discernible in ease of learning between the right and left hands in right and left handed people, nor even in some organic partial hemiplegias, provided the patient can express the learned response. It would also demonstrate the general rather than the specific nature of learning and adaptation (cf. Kellogg).

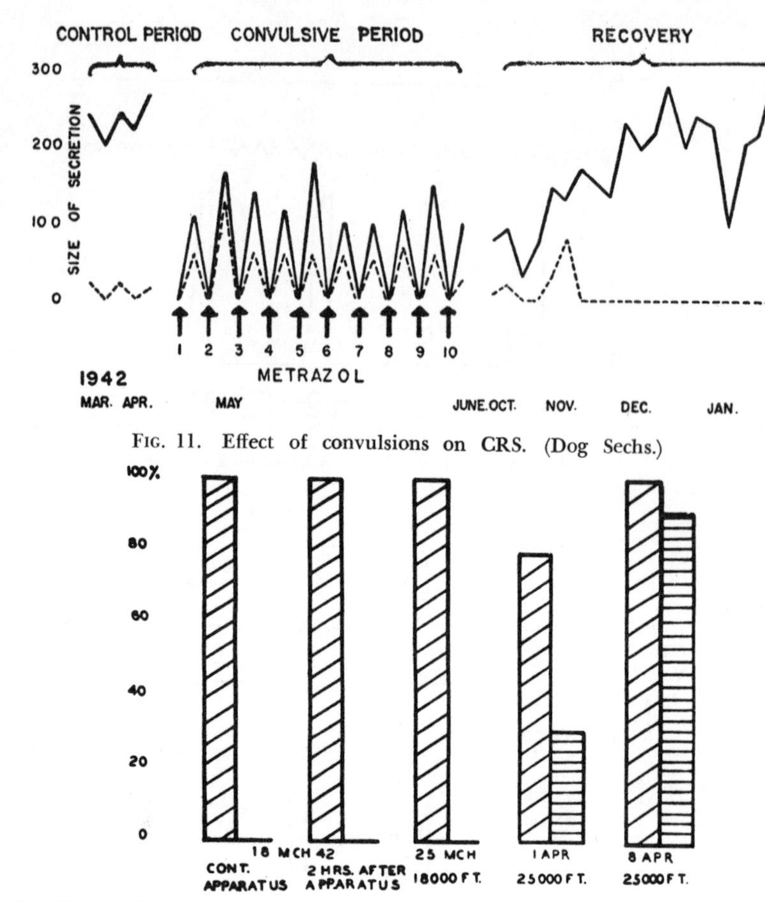

FIG. 11. Effect of convulsions on CRS. (Dog Sechs.)

FIG. 12. Effect of anoxia on motor CRS—Pain # 1. (Dog Connie, age four.)

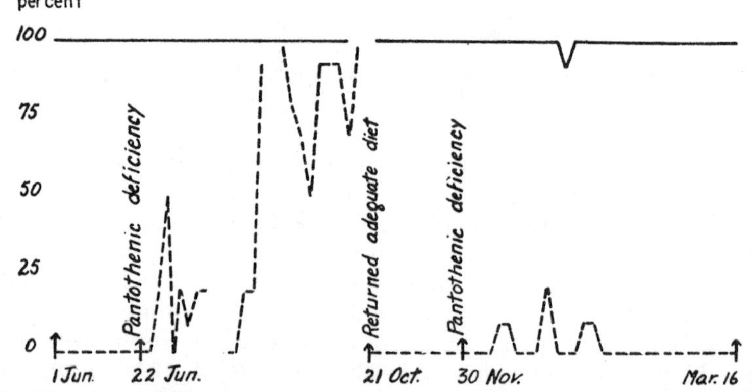

FIG. 13. Vitamin deficiency on CRS. Note impairment of differentiation and return of differentiation with adequate diet. (Dog Neptune II.)

Discussion

Of the several measurable components of the cr (*general,* e.g., respiratory, cardiac, PGR, and *specific,* e.g., salivation with food or voluntary motor to pain), the respiratory and motor have been used in these tests. The motor more than the others has the advantage of revealing special characteristics of the individual; it has the disadvantage of having manifold nervous connections and of being more subject to conscious inhibition—therefore "voluntary." An ideal study should include both autonomic and motor components; such an investigation is now underway at the Veterans Administration Hospital, Perry Point, Md. (Gantt, Reese, Doss, Harris.) The response in this test is on two levels—first, the spontaneous, primitive, dog-like withdrawal response in the restricted hand on the electrodes, and the more complex, integrated response of the free hand on the bulb to avoid the shock by squeezing the bulb. The integrated cr, as we record it, is theoretically more complex than the simple spontaneous one; there are some differences—e.g., in anxious patients, in children, and in some psychotics, the spontaneous cr predominates—but the primitive and the integrated crs are roughly parallel. In most organic patients there is a loss of the ability to form the primitive as well as the integrated cr, with retention of old crs. Retention is a much more stable, less delicate function than is the ability to make new connections.*

Much of the work with patients is in the inductive stage, where we are studying well-defined organic and toxic conditions such as brain tumors, alcoholic and Korsakov psychoses, and contrasting them with the unequivocal psychogenic cases. In spite of the newness of the study and the general lack of laboratories, both theoretical and practical conclusions seem warranted. Although this test has been developed chiefly as an empirical method, it has both a theoretical basis and a relation to previous experimental work.

The function which is tested for is the ability to make adaptations to a new environment. This is a characteristic of every intact living organism, whether simple or complex, high or low. It may be effected through either some sort of conducting system (the nerves) or through chemical substances (endocrines, hormones); frequently, both methods of transmission are present. As we ascend in the evolutionary scale the learned adaptations become more dependent on the most specialized, highest development of the crs, viz., the cortex.

Conditional reflexes may be formed on the basis of simple inborn reflexes, i.e., tendencies to react in the presence of an adequate stimu-

* "Learning" would seem the simple word to denote "new connections," but as this word has been used in a broader sense not always equivalent to new cr formation, it is desirable to employ the phrase—in spite of its awkwardness—which best describes the results of the experiments on which my conclusions are based, viz., the "ability to form new crs," or "cr function."

lus—e.g., sex, food, pain. The organism not only combines with the signals for these inborn reflexes, but during its life it must adapt to the signals as they change in value—when the signal no longer signalizes the inborn event, a perfect adaptation requires a newly learned response (differentiation or inhibition). The organism is thus constantly forming combinations and decompositions with its environment.

The inborn reflex used chiefly in this examination is the reaction to the nervous stimulus (pain). Lacking this function (to react to the signals for nocuous stimuli) the individual will rapidly succumb unless he is continually protected.

In the mammals, and especially in the primates, it is known that this cr function—the individually acquired responses—is dependent upon an intact cortex for its existence; a damage to the cortex seriously impairs learning. Although in the rat and in the dog a large part of the cortex can be removed without completely abolishing the cr function, almost any damage to the cortex is reflected by some impairment of the cr function. Pavlov (20) has shown in the dog that although not only the area striata but the whole occipital lobe can be extirpated without eliminating crs to visual signals, nevertheless, the finer discriminations are lost; and I have demonstrated in dogs in whom there has been extirpated the cortex of one side and the gyrus cingulus of the other that both motor and cardiac crs to pain can be formed but that the time cr, as well as the ability for good differentiation, is impaired (15). (Experiments with Dr. Woolsey.)

Furthermore, numerous toxic and circulatory disturbances impair cr functions in dogs, e.g., vitamin deficiency (14), metrazol convulsions (23), certain forms of electroshock (5), alcohol (4, 12), anoxia—four hours exposure at 25,000 feet impaired crs for six months (13), six minute anoxia by pressure of the arteries (Gantt and Kabat unpublished data).

Partly on the basis of the work with dogs and partly on the tests with patients, there appears to be a hierarchy of the aspects of the adaptive cr function. These, when arranged in order from the least to the most serious, are:

(1) Disturbance in the latent period of the cr.
(2) Speed of formation of the cr.
(3) Ability to form differentiated crs, i.e., to positive and negative signals.
(4) Disturbance of the function of generalization.
(5) Ability to form spontaneous but not integrated crs.
(6) Failure to retain previously formed crs.
(7) Inability to form any experimental cr.
(8) Lack of retention of very old crs, including those to word signals and failure of the ability to carry out orders.
(9) Failure of some of the URs, e.g., the OR—seen only in idiots and in severe organic cases.

Retention of old crs is a very stable function and one that is not easily lost. There is a marked difference between the ability to execute an order based on old responses and the ability to make a new connection in the nervous system. Thus, a patient with a hopeless Korsakov's psychosis can readily carry out an order but he cannot form a new cr. There is a tremendous gap between the ability to "press the bulb with the red light but not with the white," and "press the bulb when you expect the shock"; the Korsakov patient can do the first task immediately, but he fails miserably on the second, i.e., to form a *new* nervous connection, even after hours of seeing the red light precede the shock every two minutes. This would mean that a Korsakov patient could never learn to cross the street on the green light and stop on the red, although he could perhaps retain the habit previously formed or cross with the proper light when told each time what to do.

Comparison of this method with our laboratory studies of crs in dogs reveals some important differences. First, language function is ordinarily involved with the patient—although it is possible to arrange the test without the use of language, as we do in children, certain aphasias, etc. In such cases, we look for evidence of learned adaptations in the autonomic responses—respiratory, circulatory, psychogalvanic. Secondly, in the human, we study both the spontaneous, primary, direct cr of the restricted hand as well as the integrated, secondary, indirect, substituted cr of the free hand, while in the animal we ordinarily observe only the equivalent of the primary cr, viz., the withdrawal of the foot.*

There are important differences between the primary, primitive, direct cr and the secondary, indirect cr. The former is observed in young children before the integrated can be formed. The primitive cr—viz., the movement of the restricted hand on the electrode, either a sudden, brief jerking or a complete removal—though usually suppressed by intelligent adults and replaced by the secondary cr, may reappear in the normal subject if the US is very intense or in certain types of patients, e.g., in malingerers, hysterics, catatonics, states characterized by anxiety, or even in some hyperreactive normals.

But in spite of the apparent greater complexity of the indirect cr, when the organic patient cannot form this cr, it is found that he has also lost the ability to form the primitive cr; thus, the Korsakov patient finds it just as impossible to withdraw the hand to the cs as he does to perform the more complex movement of an integrated response in the other hand. The great difficulty seems to be in making the nervous connection at the basis of the cr—it is this function that is lost in organic brain disease, although there is usually more or less

* Some laboratory methods with animals, such as the opening of problem boxes, as well as animal training, do involve the equivalent of our indirect cr in the human, but the classical Pavlovian methodology employs only the spontaneous, direct cr.

preservation of the function of retention except in injuries involving a few specific centers, e.g., some of the speech centers where the old crs to word signals are lost.

Although the organic patients usually show a marked difference from the psychogenic in the cr function—in the direction of absolute failure (organic) versus intensity of formation (psychogenic), Leo Alexander has pointed out (1) that the "organic" damage is not always irreversible. Thus, in the impairment of function after electroshock (5), after metrazol convulsions (23), after anoxia (13), and after vitamin deficiency (14), with the removal of the cause there is a gradual return of the cr function. This finds a parallel in the change of cr function postoperatively. Pavlov has shown in dogs (20) and I have shown in patients that even after removal of considerable portions of the cortex, the lost function gradually partly returns.

In the psychogenic psychoses, on the other hand, there is no absolute loss of the function of cr formation, although this function may be suppressed or altered. In some patients, e.g., catatonics and hysterics, due to inhibition the new cr may not be seen, but it can be brought out by using a stronger US. However, the old, deteriorated schizophrenic is difficult to evaluate and I have not determined whether they behave more like the psychogenic or the organic, i.e., they lack absolutely the ability to form new crs.

In brief, the marked organic and toxic psychotic shows an absolute loss of ability to form new crs, while the psychogenic patient with disturbances apparently as severe as the organic, may show an almost normal cr function in this test, or if he has deviations they are aberrations related to the concepts and emotions involved in his psychosis, or they are covered up by a more or less deep inhibition.

Comparison With Other Tests

In the test for cr function it is possible to study separately the ability to form crs in the present and the preservation of old previously formed crs. Many psychological tests such as the Binet either depend chiefly on the function of retention or else they do not make a clear distinction between retention and new cr formation. Thus, in the Binet, although there are several items requiring present ability as distinct from retention, e.g., the lost ball in a field, the tasks do not usually allow a clear-cut distinction. Also, the question of motivation is not controlled in the usual test; the Rorschach and most I.Q. tests reflect the emotional interest and are therefore often difficult to evaluate in those patients who do not show a spontaneous interest. Emotional interest, though also a considerable factor in the cr test, can be adapted to the threshold of the individual by increasing the faradic shock to the point of obtaining a good unconditional reflex; the unconditional stimulus in this test is not of a standard fixed intensity but it is adapted to the particular person so that he gives an adequate response.

The change in cr function may be parallel with certain metabolic factors (blood cholesterol and M) while the I.Q. does not alter, as seen in the hypothyroid patient after thyroid therapy (Fig. 14).

The disadvantage of the cr examination is that it requires more apparatus and a better trained person to administer the test and interpret the results than do some of the simpler psychological tests.

The EEG has the advantage of objectivity, and it is independent of language even more than is the cr test. It also possesses advantages for localization of tumors and in the diagnosis of epilepsy. On the other hand, the EEG depends more upon certain basic metabolic factors and less upon higher nervous activity than does the cr function.

The study of the cr function in the normal human subject, as well as in the patient, should be of even greater importance for psychiatry than is the examination of the tendon and skin reflexes for neurology. Although a well-equipped laboratory for investigation of the autonomic crs (HR, PGR, etc.) would be as costly as the EEG laboratory, simple motor crs can be studied with apparatus costing about $100, as I have described elsewhere (9), and the time involved is about that of an EEG examination or of a Binet.

Unfortunately, the investigation by the method of the cr has become associated in the minds of some people with the restricted views of behaviorism and "reflexology." The conceptual errors of these schools, however, should not blind one to the positive value of the method and the data. One is not committed to any particular theory of electronic constitution of matter when he uses the telephone or even the radio. A lack of complete understanding of the mechanism of the cr should not inhibit our use of the known laws any more than a lack of insight into the nature of gravity should prevent a recognition of Newton's law of falling bodies.

A major deterrent in such a study as this is the lack of instruction in the medical curricula, both the theoretical and practical aspects of the cr function. In spite of the usefulness in many branches of medicine and psychiatry of the cr methodology, the medical schools where such systematic instruction is given in either theory or methodology can be counted on the fingers of one hand. In turn, the lack of such instruction is partly dependent upon the recognition of the validity and value of the concepts.

Summary

This article describes in detail the method of studying the motor conditional reflexes in normal subjects, in psychogenic and organic psychoses, in children, with both sensory and motor dyscrasias.

(1) The motor conditional reflex is characteristic of the type of individual (e.g., adolescent, artistic, scientific).

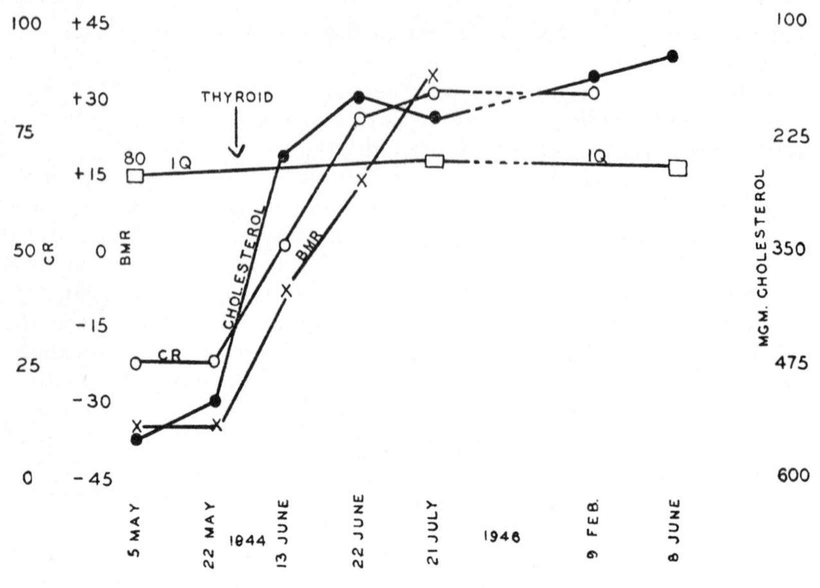

FIG. 14. Effect of thyroid on CR, BMR, cholesterol and I.Q.

(2) Impairment of the conditional reflex function is revealed in latent period, speed of formation, failure to differentiate, failure of retention of previously formed conditional reflexes, absolute failure to form the conditional reflex, diminution or absence of the unconditional reflex.

(3) Psychogenic and organic psychoses can be distinguished on the basis of the formation of the motor conditional reflex. The former patient may inhibit the expression of the elaborated conditional reflex but the inhibition can be revealed, while the organic psychotic has an absolute failure of the function to form new adaptive responses which function can hardly be improved by practice.

References

1. Alexander, Leo: Non-convulsive electric stimulation therapy. *Amer. J. Psychiat., 107,* 241-250, 1950.
2. Bordley, J. E., Hardy, W. G., and Richter, C. P.: Audiometry with the use of galvanic skin resistance response. *Bull. Johns Hopkins Hosp., 82,* 569, 1948.
3. Finesinger, J. E., Sutherland, G. F., and McGuire, F. F.: The positive conditional salivary reflex in psychoneurotic patients. *Amer. J. Psychiat., 99,* 1942.
4. Finkelstein, N., Alpern, E. B. and Gantt, W. H.: Amphetamine (Benzedrine) Sulfate upon higher nervous activity compared with Alcohol. II. Human experiments. *Bull. Johns Hopkins Hosp., 2,* 61-74, 1945.

5. Fleck, Stephen and Gantt, W. H.: Conditional responses in patients receiving electric shock treatment. *Amer. J. Psychiat., 108,* 280-288, 1951.
6. Gantt, W. H.: *Medical Review of Soviet Russia.* London: Brit. Med. Assoc., p. 100, 1928.
7. ———: Effect of alcohol on cortical and subcortical activity measured by the conditioned reflex. *Bull. Johns Hopkins Hosp., 2,* 1935.
8. ———: *Application of Conditioned Reflex Methods to Psychiatry.* Contributions Dedicated to Dr. Adolf Meyer, Johns Hopkins Press, 78-80, 1937.
9. ———: A method of testing cortical function and sensitivity of the skin. *Arch. Neur. and Psychiat., 40,* 1938.
10. ———: Impairment of the function of adaptability as measured by a simple conditioned reflex test in certain psychogenic contrasted with organic diseases. *Sou. Med. J., 12,* 1938.
11. ———, and Fleischmann, Walter: Effect of thyroid therapy on the conditional reflex function in hypothyroidism. *Amer. J. Psychiat., 11,* 1948.
12. ———, and Muncie, Wendell: Analysis of the mental defect in chronic Korsakov's psychosis by means of the conditioned reflex method. *Bull. Johns Hopkins Hosp., 6,* 1942.
13. ———, Thorn G., and Dorrance, C.: Anoxia on conditional reflexes in dogs. *Fed. Proc., 1,* 1949.
14. ———, and Wintrobe, M.: Effect of vitamin B. complex on higher nervous activity *Fed. Proc., 1,* 1945.
15. ———, and Woolsey: Cardiac reactions in partially decorticated dogs. *Trans. Amer. Neur. Assoc.,* 1948.
16. Halstead, W. S.: *Brain and Intelligence.* Chicago, 1947.
17. Ivanov-Smolensky, A. G.: *The Investigation of the Higher Forms of Neurodynamics of the Child.* Moscow, 1944. (Russian.)
18. Lashley, K. S.: The human salivary reflex and its use in psychology. *Psychol. Rev., 23,* 446-464, 1916.
19. Mateer, F.: Child behavior, a critical and experimental study of young children by the method of conditioned reflexes. Boston, *Badger,* Vol. 239, 1918.
20. Pavlov, I. P.: *Lectures on Conditioned Reflex.* (Tr. and Ed. Gantt.) New York: Internat. Publ., 1941.
21. Reese, W. G., Doss, Richard, and Gantt, W. H.: *Autonomic Responses in the Differential Diagnosis of Organic and Psychogenic Psychoses.* Psychosom. Med., in press.
22. ———, Gantt, W. H., and Strahan, Charles: Technique for study of autonomic (cardiac, respiratory, PGR) and motor adaptive responses (CRS) in the human. *Amer. J. Physiol., 3,* 1950.
23. Rosen, Victor H. and Gantt, W. H.: Effect of metrazol convulsions on conditioned reflexes in dogs. *Arch. Neur. and Psychiat. 50,* 1943.
24. Watson, John B.: The place of the conditioned reflex in psychology. *Psychol. Rev. 23,* 1916.
25. Welch, Livingston: See Chapter 15 in P. H. Hoch and J. Zubin (eds.), *Relation of Psychological Tests to Psychiatry.* New York: Grune & Stratton, 1950.

2

DIFFERENTIAL DIAGNOSIS BETWEEN PSYCHOGENIC AND PHYSICAL PAIN

The Conditional Psychogalvanic Reflex as an Aid

by Leo Alexander, M.D.

The differential diagnosis between physical and psychogenic pain states is often difficult. This difficulty is essentially due to the fact that these conditions may not be encountered or remain for long in their pure and pristine states. Thus, certain patients actually suffering from physical pain of unidentified causation may in the course of prolonged and inconclusive diagnostic studies develop an overlay of dejection, concern, and preoccupation that may make these patients clinically resemble those suffering from psychogenic pain.

Severe and excruciating physical pain inevitably becomes associated with emotional suffering, which in predisposed individuals may evoke regressive emotional disturbances sufficiently severe to mask the entire clinical picture and to simulate mental disturbance. Psychogenic pain, on the other hand, often evokes peripheral, reflex-like reverberations in the target area, which may be so prominent as to suggest that these peripheral effects actually summon the pain or are evidence of psychosomatically induced or primarily physical disease.

The erroneous impression of physical illness is especially convincing when the successful displacement and projection of conflict or anguish in the form of pain prevents the overt eruption of anxiety or depression for a long time, thus masking the entire clinical picture as one of physical disease. This is particularly true for somatization reactions in the form of one specific localized pain (psychalgia), which occur not uncommonly as somatic equivalents of depression that often and for long periods may be mistaken for states of physical pain. Thus, we are frequently faced with a clinically vexing picture, and often an actual admixture of mental suffering to physical pain, and of physical reverberation to psychogenic pain.

Reprinted from *The Journal of the American Medical Association,* September 8, 1962, Vol. 181, pp. 855-861.

Nevertheless, the clinical diagnostician (and the consulting psychiatrist from whom he requests assistance) is continually faced with the necessity of making a differential diagnosis for cogent reasons, regardless of an overlay of emotional and mental anguish or disturbance. He must find the severe life-threatening illness of which the pain may be the first signal, before it is too late to alter the course of the disease; and he must recognize the psychogenic nature of a pain in spite of a contracted neck or a twisted pelvis, in order to be able to rehabilitate the patient.

A test that may be useful as an objective measure or marker in this often difficult task should be able to reflect both the qualitative and quantitative aspects of pain as well as of mental disturbance. Such a test should faithfully record the response of the nervous system to pain signals arising from physical noxious stimulation of peripheral tissues, unobscured by superimposed emotional or mental disturbance, and should reveal the presence of mental disorder, unobscured by the peripheral muscular or circulatory effects of psychogenic pain. The psychogalvanic reflex appears to be adaptable to this task.

The psychogalvanic reflex consists of a sharply defined fall in skin resistance in response to painful stimuli, startling noises, mental challenges (such as mathematical tasks), or acutely disturbing thoughts. This reflex occurs after a latency of 1½ to 2½ seconds in response to such unconditional stimuli, while the latency of the reflex in response to conditional stimuli is longer (2 to 3 seconds) (1, 2).

In a study of the conditional and unconditional psychogalvanic reflex in patients suffering from a variety of nervous and mental disorders, carried out with the aim of establishing an objective parameter of psychiatric diagnosis, prognosis, and evaluation of treatment effects (1-4), a number of patients were encountered whose chief complaint was pain. It soon became apparent from our polygraphic recordings that the galvanic skin responses in patients suffering from physical pain were strikingly different from those suffering from psychogenic pain when the spontaneous fluctuations of the skin resistance were compared with the evoked responses, especially the conditional ones (4, 5).

Case Material

The present study is based on 20 consecutive patients whose chief complaint was pain, in whom it has so far been possible to ascertain its nature unequivocally, as either physical or psychogenic (Tables 1 and 2). For the purposes of this study, the 2 pain states are defined as physical pain—pain that originates in the body of the patient from noxious stimulation of peripheral tissues by disease or injury, with demonstrable pathology, and that is perceived and reacted to by the mind in varying degrees; and psychogenic pain—pain that originates in the mind of the patient from tension or anguish, and that is projected upon a bodily target area, with or without physiologic effects upon the target area.

Table 1. Psychogenic pain states.

Case No.	Sex	Age	Diagnosis	SP	CR—	CR+	Ratio	UR	GTR
1	F	53	Psychalgic reaction (abdominal) with agitated involutional psychotic depression (issue: loss)	550	767	350	0.40	5,500	0
2	F	38	Psychalgic reaction (atypical right facial neuralgia) with psychotic manic-depressive hypochondriac depression	150	17	50	2.94	1,567	50
3	F	75	Psychalgic reaction (cephalgia with bilateral facial pain), with neurotic reactive depression of psychasthenic-anhedonic type (issue: loss)	100	17	808	47.53	9,227	317
4	M	48	Psychalgic reaction (abdominal, left-sided) with neurotic psychasthenic-anhedonic depression (issue: power)	293	242	742	3.07	1,825	25
5	F	55	Psychalgic reaction (atypical facial neuralgia) with neurotic hypochondriac depressive reaction (issue: loss)	1,606	5,000	9,042	1.81	5,729	333
6	F	36	Psychalgic reaction (pseudoanginal chest pain) with neurotic hypochondriac depression (issue: loss and guilt)	128	317	1,262	3.90	2,395	0
7	F	62	Psychalgic reaction (headaches, occipital, radiating down left side of body and extremities), with depressive reaction, involutional, psychotic borderline, of psychasthenic-anhedonic type (issue: loss)	0	562	2,568	4.57	12,500	41
8	M	34	Psychalgic reaction (facial and occipital myalgia, right) with paranoid schizophrenia	0	2,333	6,495	2.80	6,272	812
9	F	62	Psychalgic reaction (cephalgia with aural and facial neuralgia, bilateral), with anxiety tension reaction, involutional, neurotic	1,944	4,364	13,167	3.02	10,813	182
10	F	50	Psychalgic reaction (back pain at cervico-dorsal junction, radiating into left extremities), with anxiety-hysteric reaction, neurotic	1,944	5,729	8,562	1.49	4,817	427
11	M	43	Psychalgic reaction (cephalgia, right-sided), with anxiety tension reaction, chronic, neurotic	8,500	12,955	15,636	1.21	3,500	1,125
12	M	43	Psychalgic reaction (right upper chest pain), with anxiety reaction with depressive features (issue: loss)	500	1,145	1,750	1.50	9,062	62

Table 2. Physical pain states.

Case No.	Sex	Age	Diagnosis	SP	CR—	CR+	Ratio	UR	GTR
13	F	53	Adenocarcinoma of pancreas	11,097	4,150	3,500	0.84	6,200	100
14	F	39	Endometriosis	10,300	1,042	2,000	1.92	7,625	667
15	F	64	Cervical arthritis with root sleeve fibrosis, C7—T1, left	8,500	2,809	4,500	1.60	2,340	1,827
16	F	20	Salpingitis, acute, left	8,600	1,550	5,900	3.81	4,300	700
17	F	46	Vasculitis, left leg	4,027	283	741	2.60	4,108	158
18	M	54	Hygroma, subdural, left frontal	1,333	45	641	14.20	3,899	16
19	F	52	Volvulus	5,222	1,687	2,458	1.40	5,520	291
20	F	81	Angina pectoris	1,572	336	177	0.52	631	381

Abbreviations used in tables and figures:
SP=Average spontaneous fluctuations of skin resistance per minute, in ohms.
CR=Average psychogalvanic reflex response to inhibitory (nonreinforced) tone, in ohms
+=Average psychogalvanic reflex response to excitatory (reinforced) tone, in ohms.
Ratio=Average response to CR+ divided by average response to CR— differential ratio between psychogalvanic responses to excitatory and inhibitory signals.
UR=Average response to unconditional stimulus (electric shock to finger), in ohms.
GTR=Average generalized time reflex to 5th second of inhibitory tone, in ohms.

The physical cause (8 cases, Table 2), was demonstrated in Cases 13 through 19, by operation or biopsy, and by cardiologic study in Case 20. The diagnosis of psychogenic pain (12 cases, Table 1), was regarded as validated when no organic cause was found after appropriate search and sustained relief was afforded by means of psychiatric treatment (Cases 1 to 7 and 9 to 12; Table 1). In one case of paranoid schizophrenia, the patient's pain was identified as a somatic delusion by prolonged psychiatric observation (Case 8).

For purposes of control, a group of 15 consecutive patients free from pain who showed spontaneous fluctuation of skin resistance were compared with the 2 pain groups, the psychogenic and the physical.

The entire group of 20 patients had been referred either as depressive or anxiety reactions with somatization in the form of pain, or for the purpose of differential diagnosis between such reactions and a physical illness. It is of interest that in approximately one-half of the group (8 of 20), a definite physical cause of the pain was found by careful diagnostic search. This is consistent with the general proportion found by others (6) among such diagnostic problems which are a distinct and often difficult diagnostic task of the clinical psychiatrist.

Method

The method of the test is the Pavlovian conditional reflex technique used in Dr. W. Horsley Gantt's laboratory (7, 8) with his method of spacing and alternation of differential stimuli. The stimuli and the responses, as well as any responses occurring during the intervals between stimuli, were recorded continuously on a 5-channel polygraph (1). For the purposes of quantitative study, only the psychogalvanic responses were utilized because they could be easily and accurately measured, and hence, readily be subjected to quantitative analysis.

After the orienting responses were abolished, a conditional reflex was established according to the classical Pavlovian method by pairing 1 of 2 tones with an electric shock to the tip of a finger during the fifth second the tone was sounded, while another tone, which was never so reinforced, was presented in regular alternation with the reinforced tone at 1-minute intervals. The reinforced (excitatory) tone was one of 512 cps, while the non-reinforced (inhibitory) tone was one of 256 cps. The reinforcing electric shock was selected by the patient according to his tolerance limit, varying from 0.7 to 2.5 ma., average, 1.5 ma.

Whenever an evoked psychogalvanic reflex response occurred, it was sharply defined and came within about 1.5 to 2.5 seconds after the beginning of the unconditional stimuli and within 2 to 3 seconds after the onset of the conditional stimuli. It consisted of an easily distinguishable drop in skin resistance, measured in ohms. Thus, the reaction to the excitatory tone and its overlapping shock stimulus consisted usually of 2 deflections: the first to the tone, classified as the excitatory or positive conditional response (CR+); the other to the shock, classified as the unconditional response (UR). The response to the never-reinforced, that is, the inhibitory tone, was called the inhibitory conditional response (CR–). In cases of perfect differentiation, such a response was absent and counted as zero. When response to the inhibitory tone occurred, this was usually a response to the on effect, that is, to the first second of the sounding of the tone, appearing about 2 seconds after the start of the sounding of the tone, classified as CR–. This was sometimes followed by an additional response to the fifth second of the inhibitory tone which occurred about 1 second after termination of the tone, and was classified as a generalized time reflex (GTR), since it was obviously a generalization effect by means of a time reflex, patterned after the excitatory tone and its overlapping unconditional stimulus (1-4).

These 4 psychogalvanic reflex responses (CR–, CR+, UR, GTR) were measured as ohms drop in skin resistance for each pair of presentations of the stimuli in all patients. Averages for the responses in each of the 4 categories were calculated in ohms for each conditioning session, which uniformly consisted of 12 pairs of presentations. Conditionability, that is, the capacity to differentiate between the excitatory and the inhibitory signals, was calculated by dividing the average response to the excitatory tone (CR+) by the average response to the inhibitory tone (CR–), and termed differentiation ratio. All spontaneous fluctuations of the skin resistance were measured in ohms during the intervals between the stimuli, beginning 5 seconds after and ending 5 seconds before each stimulus. Thus, any confusion of spontaneous responses with time reflexes was avoided. The spontaneous fluctuations were calculated in ohms per minute for the entire period of observation, comprising usually 18 minutes of interval time between stimuli which, as defined above, consisted of the presentation of 24 signals (12 pairs of presentations) for each conditioning session.

Results

Of the 12 patients suffering from psychogenic pain states, 7 were psychalgic states incidental to depressive illnesses. Six of them achieved complete or social recovery, either after electroconvulsive treatment (Case 1), or after drug therapy and psychotherapy (Cases 3 to 7). One achieved marked improvement close to social recovery (Case 2) by means of the latter form of treatment. Case 8, the schizophrenic patient in the group, did not recover after a brief period of drug therapy. Four patients suffered from psychalgic states incidental to anxiety reactions. Cases 9, 10, and 12 achieved complete or social recovery by means of psychotherapy aided by drug therapy, while Case 11 achieved improvement close to social recovery in the course of such therapy.

In 5 of the 7 patients with depressive psychalgic states, the conditional response pattern was inhibitory, in that the positive conditional psychogalvanic reflex (CR+) measured less than 2,000 ohms (Table 1), such as is characteristic of depressive states in general (1, 4, 5, 9). In patients who showed such profound inhibition as in Case 2, for example, the excitatory signal often evoked no response (Fig. 1). This finding was representative of the responses to 7 of the 12 excitatory signals administered, while only a small response of 100 ohms each was obtained to 4 of the 12 signals, and one of 200 ohms to 1 signal. The spontaneous fluctuations were of a similar low order in these cases (Table 1 and Fig. 2). In 1 patient (Case 7), the positive conditional psychogalvanic reflex fell into the average range; in Case 5, into the excitatory range; the spontaneous fluctuations in Case 5 were comparatively low (Table 1), in Case 7, they were absent (Table 1).

Of the 4 psychalgic states secondary to anxiety reactions, including anxiety hysteria, 3 were characterized by markedly enhanced conditional PGR responses (Table 1, Cases 9 to 11), and one of them (in whom depressive features were quite prominent) by inhibitory responses (Case 12). In all of them the conditional PGR responses greatly exceeded the spontaneous fluctuations of skin resistance (Table 1 and Fig. 3), as in anxiety states without pain.

In psychogenic pain states, the spontaneous fluctuations of the skin resistance fell into a category similar to or below the amplitude of the conditional responses and were generally very much below the level of the unconditional responses. The sole exception in this latter respect is Case 11, in which the unconditional responses (averaging 3,500 ohms) have not been accurately measurable because of the shift in the base line engendered by the preceding high positive conditional responses that averaged 15,636 ohms.

Patients who suffered from physical pain showed marked spontaneous fluctuations of skin resistance that corresponded to the waxing and waning of the physical pain (Fig. 4), while the responses to the positive conditional stimuli remained uninhibited (Fig. 5). A particularly severe wave of pain was occasionally accompanied and followed by temporary inhibition of the next 2 or 3 pairs of conditional responses, after which conditional responses were resumed. In fact, the pain seemed, at times, to improve responses to the conditional signals, probably because it produced an excitatory state that irradiated and thus facilitated conditional responsiveness. This may account for the fact that of the 8 cases in this group (Table 2), 5 fell into the average or excitatory response groups, with the positive conditional reflex averaging 2,000 to 4,000 ohms or more respectively, while only 3 showed inhibitory response patterns, with the CR+ averaging less than 2,000 ohms (3).

In spite of the fact that in the majority of the patients in this group the positive conditional psychogalvanic responses fell into the average or excitatory group, in all of the patients suffering from physical pain states, the average spontaneous fluctuations per minute greatly exceeded the conditional responses, being of an order similar to or greater than the unconditional responses (Table 2, and Fig. 6).

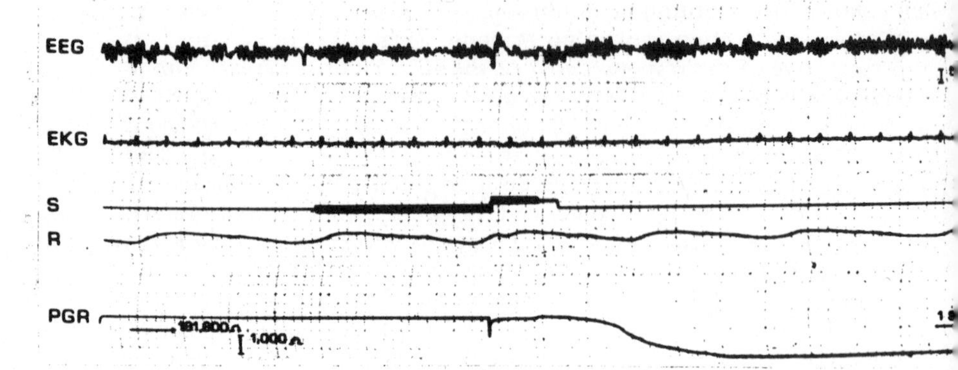

FIG. 1. Polygraph recording in manic-depressive patient with psychalgia (Case 2) Channels are EEG, EKG, S (signals); R (respiration); and PGR (psychogalvani reflex). Reading for skin resistance is shown lower left. Thick line on signal channe marks sounding of tone, elevated thick line, reinforcing shock. Note absence c conditional psychogalvanic reflex to tone and adequate but delayed unconditiona response of patient to shock stimulus.

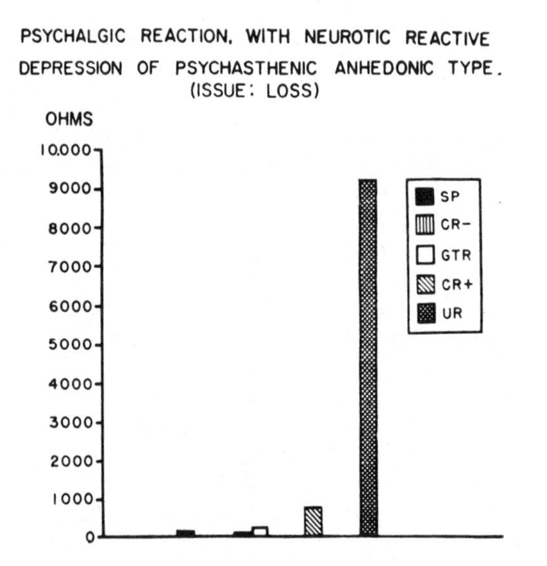

FIG. 2. Galvanic skin responses measured during pretreatment conditioning session (Case 3.) Note low spontaneous and conditional responses, but with CR+ greater than SP, CR−, and GTR; and adequate unconditional response (UR).

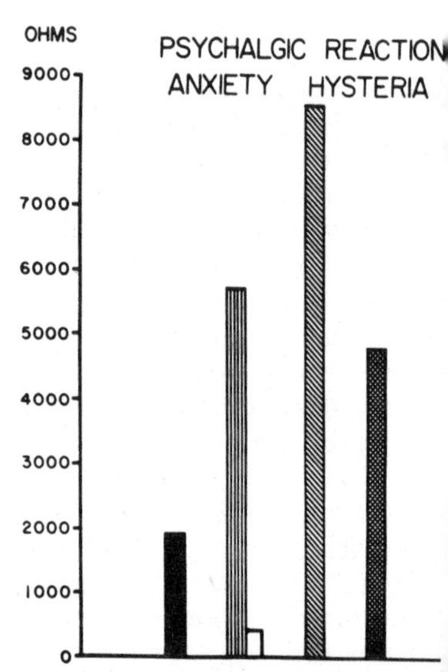

FIG. 3. Bar graph that illustrates galvani skin responses measured during pretreatment conditioning session (Case 10). Al evoked responses, especially CR+, greatl exceed spontaneous fluctuations pe minute.

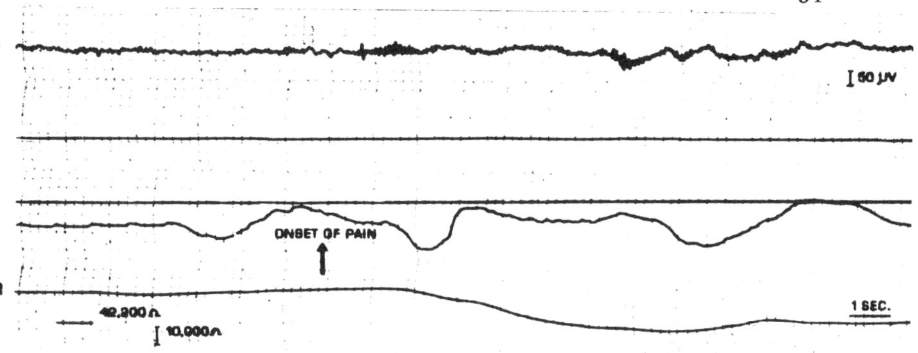

FIG. 4. Adenocarcinoma of the pancreas, with abdominal pain (Case 13). Note spontaneous fluctuation of skin resistance (PGR) that correspond to the waxing and waning of patient's physical pain.

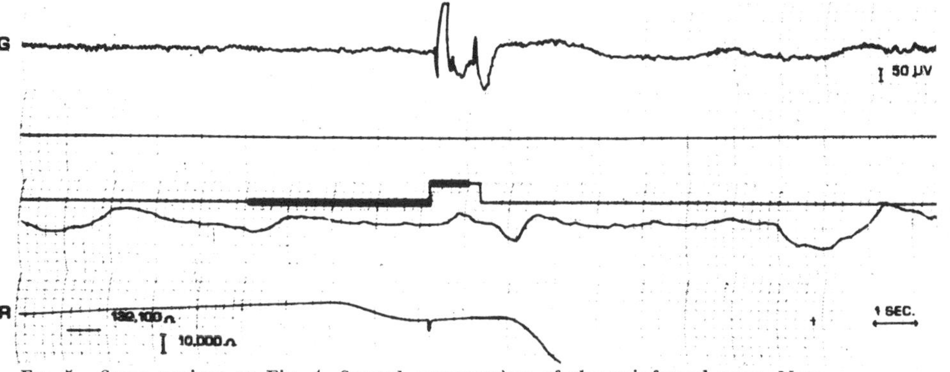

FIG. 5. Same patient as Fig. 4. Second presentation of the reinforced tone. Note good conditional PGR response (9,000 ohms) to tone 2 seconds after onset of tone and prompt and marked unconditional PGR response (in excess of 25,000 ohms) to shock beginning 1.8 seconds after onset. Note responses to conditional stimuli.

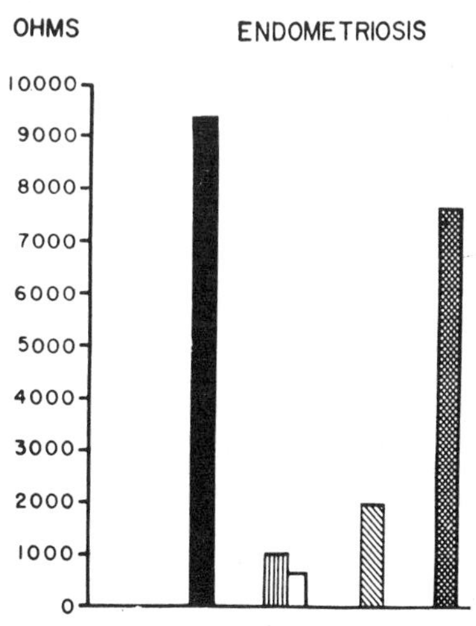

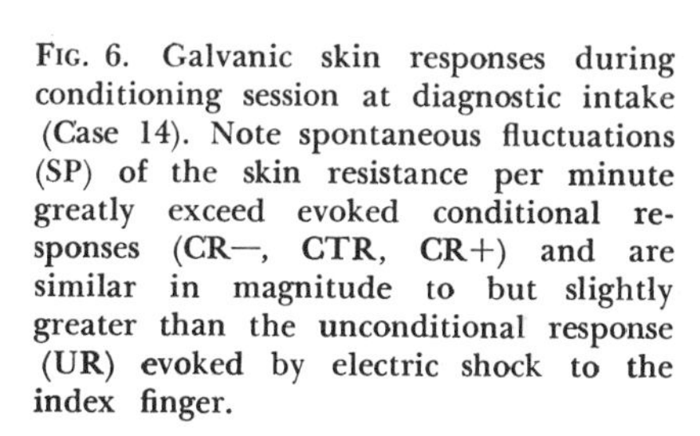

FIG. 6. Galvanic skin responses during conditioning session at diagnostic intake (Case 14). Note spontaneous fluctuations (SP) of the skin resistance per minute greatly exceed evoked conditional responses (CR—, CTR, CR+) and are similar in magnitude to but slightly greater than the unconditional response (UR) evoked by electric shock to the index finger.

Statistical Comparison of Psychogalvanic Responses

In the psychogenic pain group, the average unconditional response exceeded the spontaneous fluctuations per minute in 11 of the 12 cases (Table 3), and the average positive conditional reflex exceeded the spontaneous fluctuations in 10 of the 12 cases (Table 4). By contrast, in the patients suffering from physical pain, the spontaneous fluctuations per minute exceeded the average positive conditional reflex in all 8 cases (Table 4), and exceeded the average unconditional response in 5 of the 8 cases (Table 3).

Comparison of the spontaneous fluctuations per minute with the unconditional response differentiated between the physical and the psychogenic pain group at better than the 0.05 level of significance (Table 3), while comparison of the spontaneous fluctuations per minute with the positive conditional reflex differentiated between the physical and psychogenic pain groups at better than the 0.01 level of significance (Table 4).

Another differentiation between the 2 groups may be noted by comparing the amount of spontaneous fluctuations per minute in the 2 groups. The median for the psychogenic group (Table 1) is between 500 and 550 ohms, while that for the organic pain group is between 5,200 and 8,500 ohms (Table 2). This difference is significant at better than the .01 level by Mann-Whitney U test ($U=10.5$).

For comparison with the 2 pain groups, 14 consecutive patients who did not complain of pain, but who showed spontaneous fluctuations of the skin resistance, were selected at random (Table 5). In some of these cases, the patients related these fluctuations to disturbing thoughts, for example, an obsessive patient who had a buying compulsion (Case 21) became disturbed by the thought that the store might be closed, while the patient suffering from a schizo-affective reaction wanted to ruin the test to prove the doctor wrong, by thinking of incidents of humiliation (Case 22). The median for spontaneous fluctuations per minute in this group (Table 5) was between 900 and 1,200 ohms. This measure did not differ from the psychogenic pain group ($U=55.5$; $P=>0.05$), but was significantly different from the organic pain group ($U=10$; $P=<0.01$).

Comment

In states of physical pain, the spontaneous fluctuations of the skin resistance per minute exceeded the evoked conditional responses and were of an order similar to or greater than the unconditional responses. This suggests that physical pain impinges upon the nervous system in a manner comparable to that of any other external or unconditional stimulus.

In states of psychogenic pain, the spontaneous fluctuations of the skin resistance per minute were almost always much smaller than the

Table 3. Comparison in physical and psychogenic pain of spontaneous fluctuations of skin resistance per minute (SP) with average unconditional evoked responses (UR).

Types	SP>UR	SP<UR	Total
Physical Pain	5	3	8
Psychogenic Pain	1	11	12
X^2 (with Yates' correction) = 4.37	P = <0.05		

Table 4. Comparison in physical and psychogenic pain of spontaneous fluctuations of skin resistance per minute (SP) with average psychogalvanic reflex responses to excitatory tone (CR+).

Types	SP>CR+	SP<CR+	Total
Physical Pain	8	0	8
Psychogenic Pain	2	10	12
X^2 (with Yates' correction) = 10.2	P = <0.01		

Table 5. Spontaneous fluctuations of skin resistance in patients not complaining of pain.

Case No.	Sex	Age	Diagnosis	SP	CR−	CR+	Ratio	UR	GTR
21	F	36	Psychoneurosis, obsessive-compulsive reaction, chronic, severe	763	1,937	1,416	0.70	8,812	1,437
22	M	21	Schizo-affective reaction with depressive features	2,222	770	541	0.70	5,354	479
23	F	49	Schizophrenia, paranoid, with depressive features	2,222	308	541	1.75	2,133	100
24	M	25	Schizophrenic reaction, catatonic	1,233	283	112	0.30	1,983	291
25	M	29	Undiagnosed neurological syndrome with cerebral dysrhythmia and superimposed anxiety reaction	761	137	208	1.50	737	179
26	M	47	Depressive reaction, psychotic, involutional, with reactive triggering (issue: guilt)	194	50	50	1.00	754	0
27	M	36	Depressive reaction, with anxiety, neurotic (issue: loss, uprooting)	500	629	545	0.80	2,220	125
28	M	62	Depressive reaction, neurotic (issue: loss)	1,433	1,000	1,083	1.08	1,383	445
29	F	31	Depressive reaction with anxiety, neurotic, chronic, psychasthenic-anhedonic (issue: power, envy)	833	3,458	4,666	1.30	4,479	645
30	M	33	Depressive reaction, neurotic, psychasthenic-anhedonic (issue: power)	1,666	1,750	1,937	1.10	4,604	791
31	F	18	Schizo-affective reaction with depressive and hysterical features	916	2,375	8,333	3.51	12,607	125
32	M	21	Schizo-affective reaction with depressive features	367	1,300	1,171	0.90	3,538	75
33	F	60	Malignant melanoma, metastatic to liver. Symptomatic depressive reaction	1,431	1,855	1,745	0.94	5,545	109
34	F	26	Schizophrenic reaction, paranoid. History of spastic colitis, and of right ovarian cystectomy.	2,500	2,900	3,400	1.17	4,900	1,000

evoked unconditional responses and were of an order smaller than or similar to that of the conditional responses. Furthermore, in psychogenic pain, the spontaneous fluctuations of the skin resistance per minute resembled the responses to the inhibitory signals more than those to the excitatory signals. This suggests that psychogenic pain may represent a conditional state of the nervous system, and that, like depression itself, it may represent an inhibitory state. The low rate of spontaneous fluctuations in these cases, as well as the low level of the evoked conditional responses, also suggest a provocative relationship between depressive psychalgic states and Yoga trance states. In the latter, the spontaneous and evoked psychogalvanic responses have also been found to be greatly reduced (10).

An alternative explanation may be that physical pain states tend to be intermittent and varying, hence evoking apparently spontaneous psychogalvanic responses, while psychogenic pain states tend to be continuous and unvarying (11), hence evoking less frequent and less marked psychogalvanic responses.

A surprising finding was that headaches with occipital myalgia (Cases 7 and 8), or atypical facial neuralgia (Case 9), in which peripheral physiologic effects in the form of muscle contractions are not only associated with, but also have been thought to cause the pain, did not differ from purely psychogenic pain by our test procedure. Both purely psychogenic pain and psychogenic pain with peripheral effects gave distinctly different test findings from physical pain with demonstrated pathology. This may be due to one of several reasons:

1. That the muscular contractions of the neck and scalp muscles do not actually cause the pain.

2. That since these muscular contractions are initiated by the nervous system, they lack the startling and alerting quality necessary to elicit a psychogalvanic reflex response, in contrast to pain arising from noxious stimulation of peripheral tissues, which, impinging upon the nervous system de novo, exerts such a startling and alerting effect.

3. That physical pain, tending to be intermittent and varying, evokes frequent and distinct psychogalvanic reflex responses with each crescendo, while psychogenic pain, tending to be constant and unvarying, lacks the capacity of evoking comparable psychogalvanic reflex responses. This explanation is in line with the views of White and Sweet (11).

Summary

The comparison of the spontaneous fluctuations of the skin resistance per minute with the conditional and unconditional evoked responses, especially with the positive conditional psychogalvanic reflex, offers a helpful test for the often difficult differential diagnosis between physical and psychogenic pain states. This test, like any other test, is not intended to replace a thorough clinical examination and good clinical judgment, but merely to supplement them and to be useful as a helpful marker on the road to diagnosis. It is hoped that the test described will be useful to clinicians in pointing the diagnostic search in the right direction.

We wish to thank Professor Austin W. Berkeley, Department of Psychology, Boston University, for his advice and assistance with the statistical treatment of the material.

References

1. Alexander, L.: Apparatus and Method for Study of Conditional Reflexes in Man. Preliminary Results in Normal Control Subjects, in Mental Disorders and as Result of Drug Action. *Arch. Neurol. 80:*629-649 (Nov.) 1958.
2. Alexander, L.: Objective Approach to Psychiatric Diagnosis and Evaluation of Drug Effects by Means of Conditional Reflex Technic, In: Masserman, J. G. (Ed.) *Biological Psychiatry.* New York: Grune & Stratton, 1959, pp. 154-181.
3. Alexander, L., and Horner, S. R.: Effect of drugs on conditional psychogalvanic reflex in man. *J. Neuropsychiat. 2:*246-261 (June) 1961.
4. Alexander, L.: Effects of Psychotropic Drugs on Conditional Responses in Man, *Neuro-Psychopharmacology,* vol. 2. Amsterdam: Elsevier, 1961, pp. 93-122.
5. Alexander, L.: New Diagnostic and Therapeutic Aspects of Depression, In: Rogers, D. M. (Ed.): *Depression and Antidepressant Drugs.* Waltham, Mass.: Metropolitan State Hospital, Division of Massachusetts Department of Mental Health, 1960, pp. 23-33.
6. Wretmark, G.: Personal communication to the author, 1961.
7. Gantt, W. H.: Conditional Reflex Function as Aid in Study of Psychiatric Patient, In: Hoch, P. H. and Zubin, J. (Eds.): *Relation of Psychological Tests to Psychiatry.* New York: Grune and Stratton, 1952, pp. 165-188.
8. Gantt, W. H. (Ed.): *Physiological Bases of Psychiatry.* Springfield, Ill. Charles C Thomas, 1958, pp. 1-344.
9. Alexander, L.: Objective evaluation of anti-depressant therapy by conditional reflex technique. *Dis. Nerv. Syst. 22:* (Sec. 2, Suppl.) 14-22 (May) 1961.
10. Bagchi, B. K., and Wenger, M. A.: Electro-Physiological Correlates of Some Yogi Exercises, First International Congress of Neurological Sciences, Brussels, July 21-28, 1957. London: Pergamon Press, vol. 3, pp. 132-149.
11. White, J. C., and Sweet, W. H.: *Pain: Its Mechanisms and Neurosurgical Control.* Springfield, Ill.: Charles C Thomas.

3

PHYSIOLOGICAL PATTERNS: A DIAGNOSTIC TEST PROCEDURE BASED ON THE CONDITIONED REFLEX METHOD

by Thomas A. Ban, M.D., and Leonard Levy, M.D.

Since Pavlov's original behavioral observations on animals, there has been considerable growth in the knowledge of the electrophysiological correlates of conditioning. Workers in the field, such as Gastaut, Eccles, Jasper, Magoun, Moruzzi, and others, have greatly enlarged our understanding of the working of the central nervous system. These latter experimenters have increased the original Pavlovian hypothesis and have provided comprehensive data for the setting up of a further operational hypothesis.

The problem of assessment and validation of clinical change in psychiatric patients has been in the forefront of research activity in research centers throughout the world. There is general dissatisfaction with currently available methods of evaluation of clinical change. Psychological tests such as Q-sorts, projective techniques, rating scales and simple observation have not provided sufficient scientifically measurable data for validation of clinical change.

During the last several years, work has been directed at the Allan Memorial Institute towards investigation of other parameters for measurement of these changes in psychiatric patients. Previous publications (1, 2) have dealt with the use of movie analysis, electronic voice analysis and GSR recordings. The purpose of this paper is to describe a diagnostic test based on current knowledge of conditioned reflex theory to provide measurable evidence of change in patients exposed to any treatment regime. In this first report, we are describing part of the total design of a test battery for diagnostic and evaluation purposes.

In this procedure, applying the eyelid closure conditioned reflex technique, eight parameters are investigated as follows:

1. the extinction of the orienting reflex
2. formation of the primary conditioned reflex

Reprinted with permission from the *Journal of Neuropsychiatry*, 1961, *2*, 228-231.

3. the extinction of the primary conditioned reflex
4. conditioned stimulus generalization
5. differentiation of positive and negative conditioned stimuli
6. the formation of retarded conditioned reflex
7. the secondary conditioned reflex formation
8. the mobility of the conditioned reflexes.

The experiment was conducted in the Conditioning Laboratory of the Allan Memorial Institute. The subject was seated comfortably in an armchair separated from the experimenter by a one-way screen. An Offner 8-channel standardized EEG machine was used for simultaneous recording of the unconditional stimulus (a puff of air), conditioned stimuli (tones), and of the subject's response (eye blinks). The subject had two Grass electrodes fixed by bentonite, one immediately above and one immediately below his right eye. An air pipe was placed ½″ away from the cornea of the left eye. All controls were regulated from the experimenter's observational chamber on the other side of the one-way screen.

The unconditional stimulus consisted of an air puff, 1.5 litres per square inch pressure. The conditional stimuli were 400 CPS and 1000 CPS tones produced by an audio-oscillator transmitted through earphones fixed to the subject's head. Stimuli were transmitted at random ranging from 20 to 40 seconds. Both conditioned stimuli and unconditional stimulus were presented on five consecutive occasions. On the sixth trial, only the conditioned stimulus was presented. The test trial was occasionally administered on the fifth or seventh occasion to provide variation. Testing was carried out on five consecutive days over periods lasting from 35 to 45 minutes. The programming was as follows:

First day: Measurement of the extinction of the orienting reflex, primary conditioned reflex formation, and extinction of the primary conditioned reflex.

Second day: Generalization of conditional stimuli together with differentiation of positive and negative conditional stimuli.

Third day: The formation of retarded (delayed) conditioned reflex.

Fourth day: Secondary conditioned reflex formation.

Fifth day: Mobility of the conditioned reflexes recorded.

The criterion for the establishment of any of these reflex phenomena was the appearance of the appropriate response on at least three consecutive occasions during the test trial. To avoid exhaustion of the organism, test administrations were restricted to 100 stimulations at each session.

Results are demonstrated in the plates presented here.

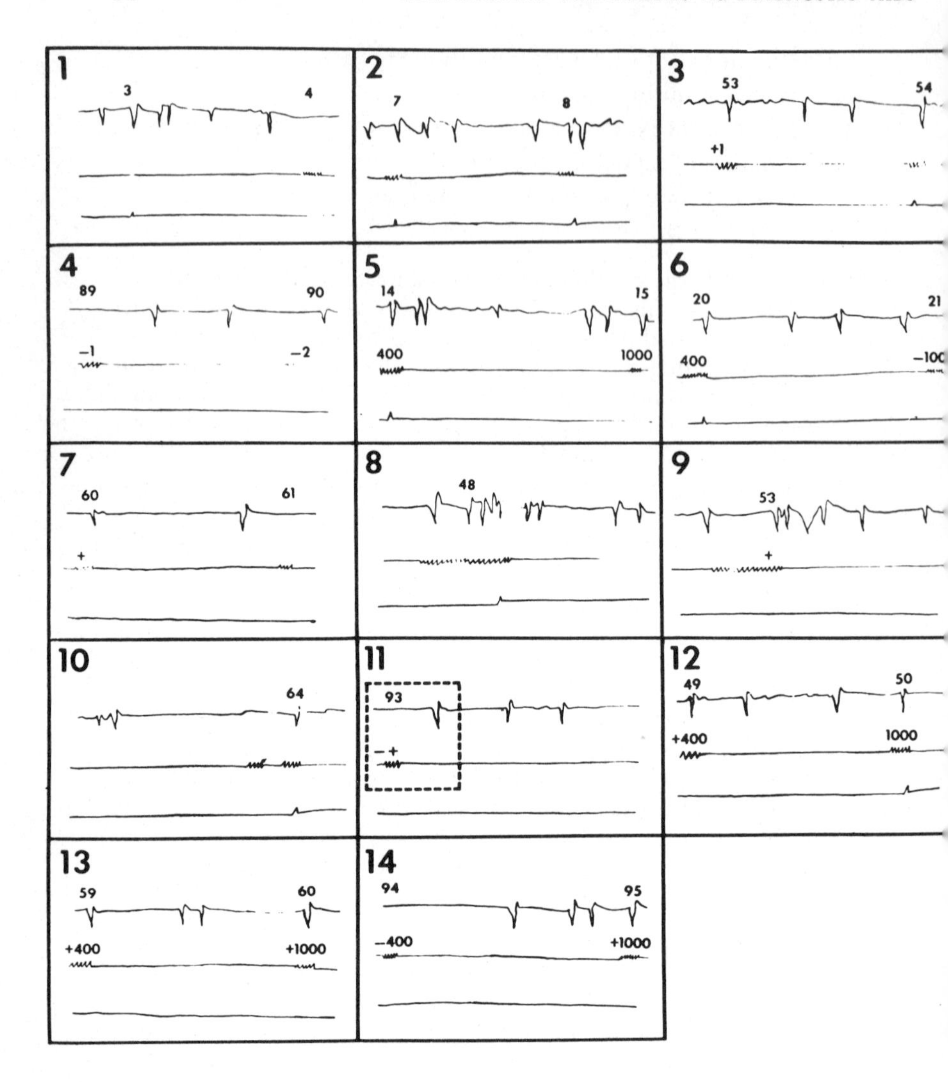

Epicrisis

According to the experimental observations presented in this paper, all the eight physiological parameters based on Pavlov's original experiments on animals can be established in a five-day experiment on human subjects by using the eyelid closure technique—using 100 stimulations daily. There is a significantly weak startle reaction or negative orienting reflex under physiological circumstances. The conditioned reflex can readily be established and distinguished. One notices that generalization of the conditional stimuli is present before differentia-

FIG. 1. The recording was done on 3 channels. On the upper channel the subject's eye blink, on the middle, the administration of the sound, and on the lower channel, the administration of the air puff was recorded.

1. The response to the 1.5 liter/sq. in. air puff (unconditional stimulus) and the response to the first administration of the 400 CPS sound (conditional stimulus) is recorded. There is no startle reaction or there is a negative orienting reflex.
2. Primary conditioning trials. An eye blink response to the 1010 milliseconds 400 CPS tone overlapped with 50 milliseconds by the 150 milliseconds air puff.
3. The established primary conditioned reflex—an eye blink response to the 400 CPS tone.

4. The extinguished primary conditioned reflex. No eye blink response to the 400 CPS sound.
5. Conditional stimulus generalization. After reinforcement of the positive conditioned reflex to the 400 CPS sound, there is a positive response to the 1000 CPS sound, which has never been associated with an air puff.
6. Intermediary stage in differentiation. There is no eye blink response to the 1000 CPS tone.

7. Differentiation is established. Positive response to the 400 CPS tone and negative to the 1000 CPS tone.
8. Conditioned reflex retardation. The first administration of the 8½ seconds 400 CPS tone at the end with 50 milliseconds overlapping 150 milliseconds air puff. Several eye blinks during the time of the lengthened conditional stimulus are seen. The first coincides in time with the primary conditioned reflex.
9. The conditioned reflex retardation is established. There is an eye blink only at the end of the lengthened conditional stimulus.

10. The secondary C.R. formation: the 400 CPS reinforced conditional stimulus is preceded by a 1000 CPS secondary conditional stimulus. The time interval between the primary and secondary conditional stimulus is 4½ seconds.
11. Secondary conditioned reflex is established. The eye blink occurs at the time of the primary conditioned reflex.
12. Testing of mobility of conditioned reflexes. Positive response to the non-reinforced 400 CPS tone and the association of the 1000 CPS tone with the air puff.

13. Intermediary stage in changing of stimuli. Positive response to both conditional stimuli.
14. Changing of stimuli established. Negative response to the non-reinforced 400 CPS sound and positive response to the 1000 CPS sound.

tion takes place. It is possible to obtain retardation of the conditioned reflex as well as the formation of secondary conditioned reflexes.

Another significant observation in regard to the mobility of the conditioned reflex is that under physiological circumstances formation of the positive conditioned reflex from the negative precedes the extinction of the conditioned reflex which was formerly positive.

Based on the findings of Moruzzi and Magoun, the conditional or unconditional stimulus at the level of the brain stem reticular formation stimulates these structures and blocks all cortical rhythms seen in desynchronization of all the induced cortical rhythms. According to this working hypothesis, in the eyelid closure test the conditional stimuli is conducted by the lateral lemnisci. In any conditioning procedure the activity of the thalamic reticular formation supersedes the brain stem reticular formation (4). Jasper (5) states that the stimulation of different parts of the ventral thalamic system acts only upon the corresponding region of the cerebral cortex. This indicates that the conditional and unconditional stimuli act principally on a localized part of the thalamic reticular formation. However, the function of closure may take place at any level within the central nervous system. According to Eccles (3), the function of closure results from synaptic convergence of heterogeneous impulses on the neurons. In this experiment, closure is manifested between the converging fibres of the trigeminal and of the lateral lemnisci. This is demonstrated by the fact that the sound stimulus becomes more effective and takes precedence over the blow of the air puff as a trigger mechanism. Shimbel states that the unconditional stimulus is capable of causing the neurons of the brain stem and thalamic reticular formation to discharge. Some of the peripheral manifestations of the unconditioned reflex depend upon this discharge, as originally the conditioned stimulus is not able to produce such a discharge. However, the succession at brief intervals of the conditional and unconditional stimuli are thought to create a spatial-temporal summation. This is manifested in this experiment by the fact that a stimulus of the auditory nerve results in activity in the facial nerve which causes the eye blink.

Using this modern neurological frame of reference, the replacement of the unconditioned reflex by the conditioned reflex implies the substitution of a system of thalamic alerting for one of mid-brain alerting. These facts indicate that two of the three main functional systems of the central nervous system, namely, the afferent sensory system and the ascending reticular system, are strongly interconnected. This would seem to support the accuracy of results obtained by conditioned reflex procedures in the exploration of functional activity of the central nervous system.

References

1. Ban, T. A.: *The Method of Conditioning and Its Application to Psychiatry,* Thesis, McGill Diploma Course, Montreal, 1960.
2. Cameron, D. E., Levy, L., Rubenstein, R., and Malmo, R. B.: *Am. J. Psychiat., 115*:985-991, May, 1959.
3. Eccles, J. C.: *The Neurophysiological Basis of the Mind.* Clarendon Press, Oxford, 1953.
4. Gastaut, H.: in Wonstenholme, G. E. W., and Connor, C. M., (ed.): *Neurological Basis of Behaviour.* J. and A. Churchill, Ltd., London, pp. 255-271, 1958.
5. Jasper, H.: in Jasper, H. H., Proctor, L. D., R. T., (ed.): *Recent Advances in Our Understanding of Ascending Activities of the Reticular Formation of the Brain.* Little, Brown and Co., Toronto, 1958.
6. Konorski, J.: *J. Ment. Sc., 104*:1100-1110, 1958.

4

PEEP-SHOW AUDIOMETRY

by M. R. Dix, M.D., F.R.C.S.,
and C. S. Hallpike, F.R.C.S., F.R.C.P.F.R.S.

The Peep-show, as first described (1), was designed to overcome the great practical difficulties of obtaining rapidly a reliable pure tone audiogram in young children with speech defects thought to be due to deafness.

The ages of the children were within the period 3 to 6 years, at which an accurate assessment of hearing capacity was urgently needed for the satisfactory prescription of the children's educational management.

In 1952 (2) a more comprehensive paper was published, giving results in a series of 260 cases, and in the course of this work the reliability of the findings was confirmed by a detailed follow up.

Since then the method has continued to give satisfactory results. Furthermore, the apparatus itself has been improved and simplified without, however, any departure from the very simple principles of construction and performance originally laid down.

Although the results obtained at Queen Square have continued to be satisfactory, and although good results have also been recorded by others (3), it would not seem that all who have attempted to use the equipment have been equally successful. Why this should be is not at all clear, but it would appear to have arisen from the use of Peep-show equipments incorporating various modifications of design and performance which must, in the light of experience, be deemed unsatisfactory and indeed permit little possibility of success.

In this situation, therefore, it has seemed that the present contribution could take no more useful form than a simple recapitulation of the essential principles of the test procedure, and a description of the Peep-show apparatus in its present very effective form.

The principles of the procedure are shown in Fig. 1. It is designed to avoid the two great difficulties which make conventional pure tone audiometry impossible with young deaf children.

Reprinted from the *Proceedings of the Third World Congress of the Deaf*, Wiesbaden, 1959, 77-83.

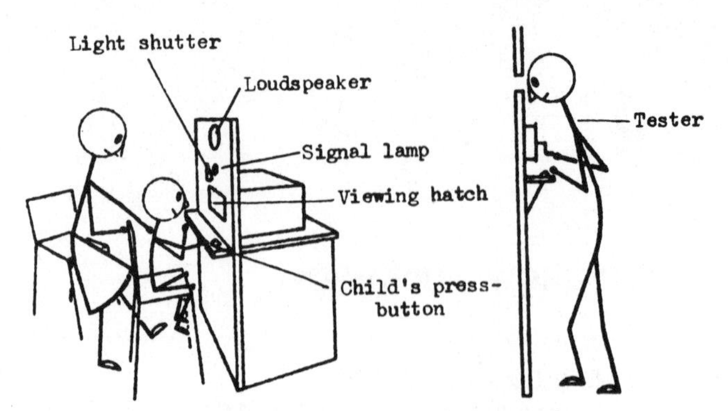

FIG. 1. Diagram of the Peep-show procedure.

In the first place otherwise meaningless pure tones are given an arresting significance. In the second place, the need for any explanation of the nature of listening and hearing is completely avoided.

The test procedure depends upon the conditioned response of the child to a series of short pure tone stimuli delivered from a loudspeaker. The pure tone stimuli are synchronised with the flashes of a signal lamp.

The child sits in front of the box, in which are displayed a series of attractive pictures. In order to see these pictures, the child must first illuminate them by the pressing of a button. Thereafter, he inspects them through a viewing aperture. This press-button mechanism works only when the synchronised light/sound stimuli are being delivered.

The stimulation mechanism is under the control of a tester, who observes the child closely from behind a screen. The pure tone stimuli are variable in frequency in fixed octave intervals from 250 to 4000 c.p.s. The intensity is calibrated in decibels above the threshold of hearing of a normal subject with his head in the position of the child. During the test, an instructor is seated by the child's side and performs the important functions of controlling him, encouraging him to co-operate in the test, and of changing the picture by the operation of a simple mechanism when necessary.

The test begins with the instructor focussing the child's attention on the viewing aperture. When the tester observes that this has been accomplished he applies the double signal; the signal lamp flashes and the loudspeaker emits synchronised impulses of sound. The instructor at once presses the button, illuminates the picture, and encourages the child to inspect it, which he usually does with every appearance of interest. When this has been accomplished, the tester withdraws the signal and the picture disappears.

After the demonstration has been repeated two or three times, the child soon learns to press the button and illuminate the picture when,

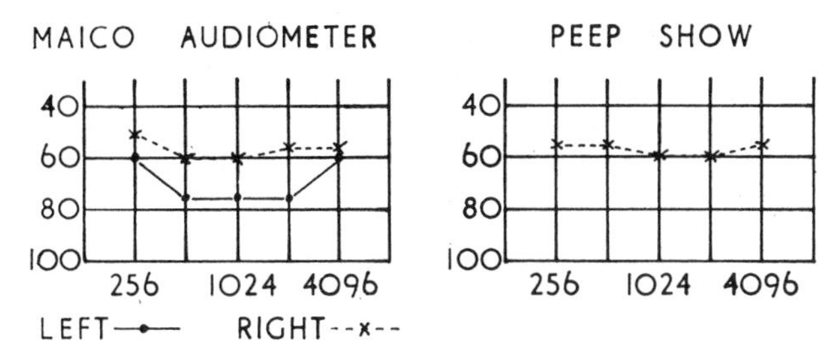

FIG. 2. Pure-tone audiogram and Peep-show test in a co-operative child aged 5.

and only when, the double signal has been given. As soon as this reflex has been established the next step is to eliminate the light signal in front of the box. This the instructor does by closing a simple shutter over the light. The test is then continued using the interrupted sound stimuli only, and thus becomes a test of hearing.

In children without hearing, this elimination of the light signal makes further response impossible. On the other hand, in children with sufficient hearing to detect the sound signal, the elimination of the synchronised light signal makes no difference to their response, and they continue to react to the sound signal alone. The intensity of the sound signal is then reduced progressively, until a threshold reading is obtained. The test frequency is then changed and the final result is a conventional audiogram.

On the right, in Fig. 2, is shown the Peep-show audiogram in a co-operative child of 5 years old. On the left is the conventional pure tone audiogram in the same subject. The close correspondence of the Peep-show audiogram to the hearing of the better ear is remarkable.

The present Peep-show apparatus, which was first demonstrated at the International Course in Paedo-audiology in Groningen in 1953, is shown in Fig. 3. On the right is shown the child's part of the apparatus with its loud-speaker, signal lamp and light shutter, viewing aperture and press-button. On the left is shown the tester's part of the apparatus, consisting of a sound generator and voltage supply for the lamps in the child's box. The equipment is simple to use and robust, suitable pictures are easily obtained from magazines and books, and are pasted upon rolls of tough fabric, each of which contain some 30 pictures.

The pictures are changed instantly and unobtrusively by the instructor by the pressing of the switch on the extreme right. The child's press-button is, by intention, made large and conspicuous, and the light shutter inconspicuous. Decorations are concentrated around the viewing aperture, and serve to maintain the child's attention upon this point.

The tester's part of the apparatus is simple. It consists of a pure tone oscillator giving frequencies fixed in octaves from 250 to 4,000 c.p.s. In

FIG. 3. The present Peep-show apparatus.

it is incorporated an attenuator giving outputs from 10 to 90 decibels above threshold. The interruption of the tone and the light is carried out electronically by means of a single central lever. The frequency of the sound pulses can be varied by a to and fro movement of this lever, thus lessening artefacts due to standing waves.

In addition to the small but important technical points outlined, great emphasis is laid upon the actual management of the child. It is essential that the children are not seen when they are tired or hungry, and they are always seen by appointment. It is also a mistake to attempt preliminary examination of the ears, nose and throat, and the wearing of white coats is avoided. The children are interviewed one by one in a quiet room with their parents. One examiner plays with the child with a few simple toys on a table, while the second examiner takes the history from the parents. This continues until it is seen that the intelligence of the child is sufficient for the test, and that his friendly co-operation has been assured. Not until this stage has been reached is the child taken to the Peep-show, which is presented to him as another very attractive toy. The whole examination, including this preliminary interview and subsequent examination of the ears, nose and throat, is completed within a matter of half-an-hour.

As previously said, various modification of the Peep-show equipment have been devised. Many of these seem to be unsound in principle, and must be unsatisfactory in use. Thus, in some equipments that have been examined the pictures are poor and badly illuminated. In others, the visual and auditory stimuli, instead of being intermittent, are sustained, leading inevitably to lack of attention. In still others, the apparatus has been modified to permit a single examiner to control the subjects and to operate the various controls. This, of course, is utterly impossible, and confusion speedily arises with disastrous results.

The rationale of the procedure presents no real novelty, being based as it is upon the system of performance and reward, which is the A.B.C. of all animal training.

In particular, the subject is at no time exposed to any unpleasant experience, such as is sometimes unavoidable with the psycho-galvanic test, and must make it difficult to secure a young child's willing concentrated co-operation. This must be a factor which at times seriously impairs the efficiency of the psycho-galvanic test. With the Peep-show, however, given a suitable selection of pictures, the child's interest is easily secured and maintained, and his responses receive a prompt and satisfactory reward, with the result that the necessary observations are made with remarkable speed and accuracy.

It is sometimes said to its disadvantage that the Peep-show cannot be used until a normal mental age of 3 years is attained, and that this defers the diagnosis and audiometric measurement of deafness beyond the critical speech-learning period of one to two years. The question of this critical period for speech development is certainly one of great importance, but accurate information upon it still seems hard to come by. There appears to be a widely held belief that this critical period is bound up with certain vital developments in the central nervous system. These are thought to be dependent upon normal hearing, and to take place in the first three years of life and, one might almost think, *at no other time.* Thus, a young child with a hearing defect uncorrected by means of a hearing aid, would suffer during this period an irreparable speech defect. If this could be accepted, then it would indeed be plain that what was lost in this period would be lost forever and, consequently, no efforts to diagnose and correct deafness in the first year or two of life could be too great. Without in any way wishing to counsel a policy of neglect, it does seem sensible to give some consideration to the possibility that this might not be quite the true picture, and that any latent speech development lost in this period might be later regained. If this were true, the great urgency for very early diagnosis and treatment would be lessened and results as good might, in the long run, be obtained if educational methods were deferred until the age of 3 or 3½ years, when they could be based upon accurate knowledge of the hearing loss derived from some such test procedure as Peep-show audiometry. It is not, of course, denied that a partially deaf child, intensively treated from the age of two or less, would at first appear at an advantage over a comparable child in whom similar treatment had been delayed until the age of 3 to 3½ years. This, however, is not the point. What is needed is a comparison between these children somewhat later, at the age of 10 years or so. If then no significant difference could be demonstrated in their speech or other attainments it would be necessary to conclude that the concentrated educational and other attentions received by the one child before the age of 3 had not been fully justified.

It is, therefore, hoped that this very necessary evidence which could only be derived from a long term systematic investigation, will, before long, become available.

When asked to see children at Queen Square under the age of 3, in whom Peep-show audiometry cannot be carried out, an explanation is generally given to the parents that no certain opinion can be given upon the state of their hearing and its relationship to their speech and other defects. It is explained that this cannot be done until the age of 3 or soon thereafter. In the meanwhile, the parents are advised that the possibility, or even the probability of a hearing defect has to be accepted. They are further advised that until the child has reached the age of 3 years or more, they should treat it as a case of partial deafness, that is, they should keep it with them, play with it as much as possible, and speak words to it clearly at close range, being sure always that the child can see their faces. The words should be simple, clearly articulated, and accompanied by suitable gestures. In this way it is felt that the child's progress would not be significantly delayed pending the further program of education based upon adequate audiometric tests usually possible between the ages of 3 to 4 years.

Peep-show audiometry has now been carried out at Queen Square upon 800 children, most of them in the age group 3-6 years. In all but a few cases a decisive result has been obtained in the course of a single visit, usually within a period of half-an-hour, including a preliminary interview.

In the absence of any special experience at Queen Square in the handling of children, these successful results could only be attributed to the careful attention paid to technical points of the kind outlined in the construction and use of the equipment, and in the management of the children before and during the Peep-show Test.

References

1. Dix, M. R. and Hallpike, C. S. *Brit. Med. Jour.* (1947) ii: 7, 19.
2. Dix, M. R. and Hallpike, C. S. *Brit. Med. Jour.* (1952) i: 235.
3. Statten, Page and Wishart, D. F. S. (1956) *Trans Amer. Otol. Soc.* XLIV: 141.

Discussion

Dr. Zaluk (Israel) asked:

1. Where could the "Peep-Show" apparatus be obtained? He had heard of Peters' model. Was there a satisfactory make?

2. What was Dr. Dix's opinion about conditioning to familiar sounds, instead of using pure tones?

3. What difference was obtained in "Peep-Show" audiograms repeated? He had often found less hearing loss if the "Peep-Show" test was repeated.

Dr. Hardy (Baltimore, U.S.A.) asked:

1. What experience had Dr. Dix had with deaf children with other defects?

2. He said there was plenty of evidence of the value of special education of very young deaf children.

Professor Prazic (Zagreb, Yugoslavia) said:

He could not appreciate the need for the "Peep-Show" apparatus, as children in 3-6 age group would co-operate with conventional pure tone audiometry.

In reply to Dr. Zaluk, Dr. Dix said she knew of no satisfactory commercial "Peep-Show" at present on the market. Pure tones were preferred to complex sounds since they provided a fuller analysis of the character of the deafness. Thus, if complex sounds were used, children with a sharp hearing loss for speech frequencies, but good hearing for low tones, were likely to give a false impression of good hearing.

If "Peep-Show" audiograms were repeated and showed detriment of hearing this might be a valuable indication of progress of the pathological process responsible for the deafness. On the other hand, if hearing was found to be improved at a later test this might indicate better attention. Alternately, Dr. Dix had seen cases of mixed conductive and nerve deafness in which, after removal of tonsils and adenoids the deafness had been much benefited by elimination of the conductive element.

In reply to Dr. Hardy, Dr. Dix said she had seen many difficult children but, provided that they had attained a normal mental age of about 3 years, it was usually possible to overcome the difficulties.

The "Peep-Show" was obviously inapplicable in cases of blind children. Children with partial motor defects, however, although unable to press the button efficiently, usually made efforts to do so well synchronised with the test signals when these were heard, and they were then helped by the instructor to complete the operation.

The "Peep-Show" was sometimes remarkably successful in withdrawn and uncooperative children suffering from psychological abnormalities. Dr. Dix noted with interest what Dr. Hardy had said about the availability of evidence upon the value of intensive special education of deaf children in the first 3 years of life. She thought that here some misunderstanding might well exist as to the kind of evidence that was really required. It was true that much had been written upon the subject. A great deal of this, however, seemed to be based upon insecurely founded impressions, and it was difficult to find any published account of carefully controlled investigations of the quality which was needed. If Dr. Hardy knew of any such publication she hoped he would be forward in providing some detailed references thereto.

In reply to Professor Prazic, Dr. Dix agreed that given the necessary time it might be possible to test co-operative children of 3-6 years by conventional pure tone audiometry. The great advantage of the "Peep-Show" however, was the possibility of obtaining accurate and reliable audiograms in difficult and unco-operative children in the course of a single visit.

PART II

EVALUATION AND PREDICTION

The effect of drugs upon conditioning can be of importance to the theoretician and the research investigator as well as the practicing clinician. For example, drugs may be used by the psychologist to manipulate drives experimentally and thus test predictions derived from learning theory. For the physiologist, knowledge of the effects of different drugs on different kinds and modalities of conditioning may make it possible to derive information and predictions about the sites of drug action. By combining conditioning and other techniques it is possible to study the relative peripheral and central effects of these drugs and, whenever pertinent, investigate the autonomic and central components of their actions.

For the clinician engaged in psychiatric practice, conditioning techniques may be helpful in the objective evaluation of the effects of drugs within the therapeutic setting. For the general practitioner or specialist in areas other than psychiatry, such techniques may likewise provide certain information concerning the presence and nature of some of the side effects of the drugs used to treat his patients. When drugs are ingested outside a medical setting (as, for example, in the case of the accidental or deliberate swallowing of large amounts of sedatives, or addiction to alcohol, narcotics, tranquilizers and other agents) the nature and permanence of some of the consequences may be better evaluated by including conditioning techniques among the assessment procedures. If alcoholism and addictions to drugs are to be treated by some form of conditioning procedure then it becomes all the more necessary to know just how these disorders have affected the conditioning process.

In the first paper Alexander shows how conditioning procedures can be applied to the evaluation of various kinds of drug and electroconvulsive treatments. It is probable that organically determined deficits may occur more often as a result of electric convulsive treatment than are clinically recognizable, and it is well known that central pathology can seriously interfere with the process of conditioning. Brown makes the important point that only the *complete absence* of conditionability is suggestive of cortical pathology; mere decrements in conditioning may be associated with reversible psychic factors. If psychotherapy can be used to reverse such factors, then conditioning techniques may be of value in the investigation of changes brought about by psychotherapy itself.

In the last two papers in this section Whitman, Brown and Gantt show how these techniques may be extended to a study of the aging process, and Vogel concerns herself with the attempt to evaluate individual differences in social drinking patterns by means of a technique of GSR conditioning applied in the laboratory. Such knowledge may be utilized not only in the selection of alcoholic patients for various types of conditioned aversion therapies (assuming that drinking alcoholic beverages is, in part, a learned response), but also in the selection of patients and specific techniques for other kinds of conditioning therapies.

5

OBJECTIVE EVALUATION OF ANTIDEPRESSANT THERAPY BY CONDITIONAL REFLEX TECHNIQUE

by Leo Alexander, M.D.

Certain clinical and physiological observations in patients suffering from depression suggested the interpretation that depression may be a state of inhibition resulting from supramaximal excitation (1, 2). This hypothesis was put to a test by means of the Pavlovian conditional reflex technique as elaborated in Dr. W. Horsley Gantt's laboratory (3, 4), utilizing his method of spacing and alternation of different stimuli. The stimuli and the responses were recorded continuously on a 5-channel Grass polygraph, as described previously (5). The results of our study confirmed the hypothesis. It was found (5-8) that the capacity to form conditional reflexes was significantly reduced in patients suffering from depression. The conditional psychogalvanic reflex showed reduction in magnitude and delay as well as impairment of differentiation between the excitatory and inhibitory stimuli, including paradoxical reversal of the responses in that inhibitory stimuli evoked greater responses than excitatory stimuli. (Pavlov's Paradoxical-Ultraparadoxical Phase.)

Among a recent series of 40 unselected patients suffering from depression, 32 of whom showed an inhibitory response pattern, were 11 who showed differentiation ratios less than 1; seven of these were paradoxical (differentiation ratios between 0.99 and 0.4; four were ultraparadoxical (differentiation ratios below 0.4); four showed equivalent reactions with equal responses to the inhibitory and the excitatory stimuli. We also found paradoxical reversal of the electrocerebral alerting response in depression, in that hypersynchrony occurred instead of the usual desynchronization (5). Gluck and Rowland (9) confirmed the interpretation of evoked hypersynchrony as a manifestation of inhibition. By introducing the inhibitory effects of delay and of a differentiated conditional stimulus, they were able to evoke hypersynchronous responses at exactly those phases of the responses at which

Reprinted with permission from *Diseases of the Nervous System,* Supplement, Vol. XXII, No. 5, May 1961, pp. 3-12.

inhibition was to be expected in the light of Pavlov's findings with the salivary response.

Absence or marked diminution of the positive conditional psychogalvanic reflex, with reduced differentiation between or paradoxical reversal of the responses to the excitatory and inhibitory stimuli, can be considered as an objective positive diagnostic sign of depression, provided the patient is not suffering from organic or toxic disturbance of the nervous system, or from chronic schizophrenia in which similar inhibitory phenomena may be observed (4, 10). By contrast, neurotic anxiety states showed enhanced responses with poor differentiation and other excitatory generalization phenomena. Acute schizophrenic reactions, however, were found to be associated with marked, precise responses with better than average differentiation between excitatory and inhibitory stimuli. While abolition or marked impairment of the positive conditional psychogalvanic reflex constitutes objective confirmation of a diagnosis of depression, preservation of the reflex does not exclude this diagnosis, especially in the case of psychasthenic-anhedonic depressions and in the case of acute situational depressive reactions. In many patients with psychasthenic-anhedonic depression there is a good deal of coexisting anxiety which may preserve or enhance this reflex response. In acute situational depressive reactions, the adaptive capacity of the patient may be unimpaired, hence the preservation of normal capacity for differentiation. Particularly in this clinical area, the test holds promise for usefulness in differential diagnosis, namely, in the distinction between crisis reactions, "people in crisis" (11, 12), as differentiated from actual depressive illnesses. These and other differential diagnostic aspects of the test will be reported elsewhere.

I have found the test clinically useful in the differential diagnosis between depressive somatization reactions in the form of pain, and physical pain states (8, 10). Patients suffering from psychalgic states incidental to depressive illnesses showed marked inhibition or abolition of the conditional PGR, as is characteristic of depressive states. Spontaneous PGR fluctuations, if present at all, also tended to be minimal. By contrast, patients suffering from physical pain showed marked spontaneous fluctuations of skin resistance corresponding to the waxing and waning of the physical pain, while the responses to the positive conditional stimuli remained uninhibited. Since the state of conditionability appears to be an objective parameter of depressive states, it is of interest to investigate its alteration concomitant with treatment.

Material and Method

The present study is based on 133 depressed patients whose conditional reflex responses were studied before and after administration of antidepressant therapy. Patients treated with electroconvulsive therapy were retested immediately after the completion of the electroshock series, and again at the time when optimal treatment benefits were established, after clearing of treatment-induced confusion, on the average 48 days after the last treatment. Patients treated with drugs were retested one hour after administration of the first test dose of the drug, and/or at the time of establishment of a clear-cut treatment result, either success or failure. In the case of the amine oxidase inhibitors, only the latter retest was used, while for the other drugs both the immediate response and the long-term effect were investigated.

The technique of the test is quite simple. After abolition of the orienting responses, a conditional reflex was established, according to the classical Pavlovian method, by pairing one of two tones with an electric shock to the tip of a finger during the fifth second of the sounding of the tone, while another tone, which was never so reinforced, was presented in regular alternation with the reinforced tone at one-minute intervals. For the purpose of quantitative comparison, only the psychogalvanic responses were utilized because they are easily and accurately measurable, and hence lend themselves readily to quantitative analysis. The well-known inherent difficulties encountered in attempting to analyze the electrocerebral alerting responses by quantitative methods prevented utilization of this portion of our data for this purpose.

Whenever an evoked psychogalvanic reflex response occurred, it was sharply defined and came within about 1.5-2.5 seconds after the beginning of the unconditional stimuli and within 2-3 seconds after the onset of the conditional stimuli. It consisted of an easily distinguishable drop in skin resistance, measured in ohms. Thus, the reaction to the excitatory tone and its overlapping shock stimulus consisted usually of two deflections: the first to the tone, classified as the excitatory or positive conditional response (CR+); the other to the shock, classified as the unconditional response (UR) (Fig. 1). The response to the never-reinforced, that is the inhibitory tone, was called the inhibitory conditional response (CR–). In cases of perfect differentiation, such a response was absent and counted as zero. When response to the inhibitory tone occurred, this was usually a response to the on effect, i.e., to the first second of the sounding of the tone, appearing about two seconds after the start of the sounding of the tone, classified as CR– (Fig. 2). This was sometimes followed by an additional response to the fifth second of the tone, occurring about one second after termination of the tone (Fig. 3), classified as a generalized time reflex (GTR), since it is obviously a generalization effect by means of a time reflex patterned after the excitatory tone and its overlapping unconditional stimulus (5).

These four psychogalvanic reflex responses were measured in ohms as the change in skin resistance for each pair of presentations of the tones for all patients before treatment and after treatment. Averages for the responses in each of these four categories were calculated in

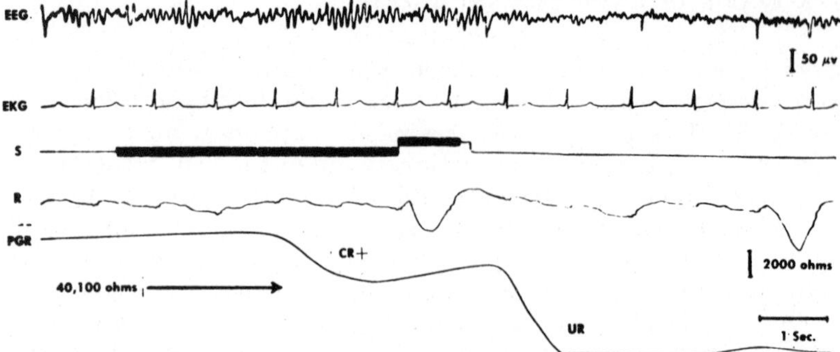

FIG. 1. Female, age 27, suffering from schizo-affective disorder. Polygraphic recording illustrating the psychogalvanic reflex responses to the fourth presentation of the excitatory (reinforced) tone and its overlapping shock stimulus. (EEG = electroencephalogram; EKG = electrocardiogram; S = signals (the thick black line denotes the sounding of the tone, the elevation of the base line of the signal channel denotes the shock stimulus to the index finger); R = respiration; PGR = psychogalvanic reflex.) Note conditional PGR response to the excitatory (reinforced) tone (CR+), consisting of a drop in skin resistance of 4000 ohms beginning 2 seconds after the onset of the tone and unconditional PGR response to shock (UR), measuring 7200 ohms, beginning 1.5 seconds after onset of the shock.

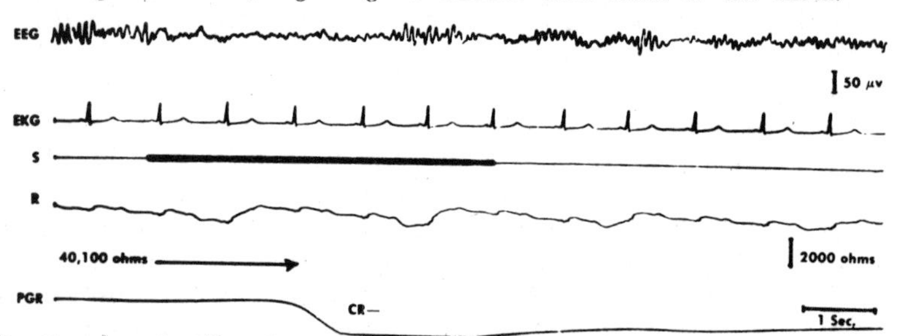

FIG. 2. Female, age 27, suffering from schizo-affective disorder. Polygraphic recording illustrating the psychogalvanic reflex response to the fourth presentation of the inhibitory (non-reinforced) tone (CR—) consisting of a drop in skin resistance of 2000 ohms beginning 2 seconds after the onset of the tone.

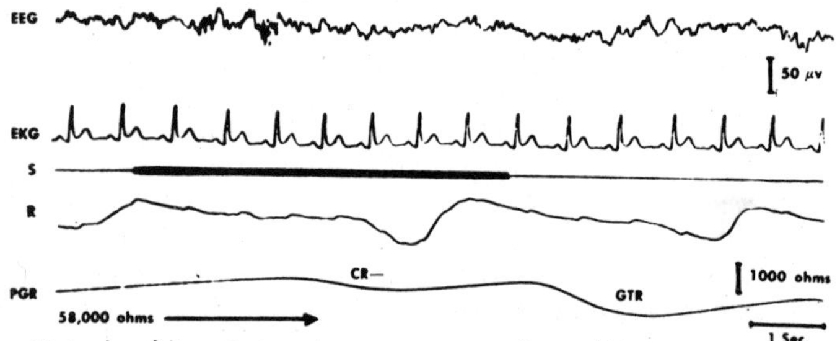

FIG. 3. Male, age 24, suffering from psychoneurosis, phobic reaction with obsessive features. Polygraphic recording illustrating a psychogalvanic reflex response to the inhibitory tone (CR—) occurring 2 seconds after the onset of the tone and an additional psychogalvanic reflex response beginning 0.8 seconds after the end of the tone interpreted as a generalized time reflex (GTR) patterned after the response to the excitatory tone and its reinforcing stimulus (compare Fig. 1).

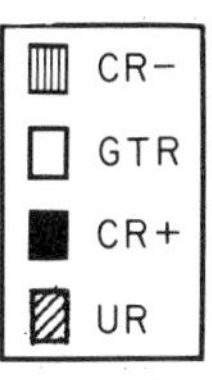

FIG. 4. Key to bar graphs shown in subsequent figures.

ohms for each conditioning session which uniformly consisted of 12 pairs of presentations. The bar graphs included in this paper represent the averages computed for each conditioning session. The key to these bar graphs is shown in Fig. 4.

Effect of Electroconvulsive Treatment

Thirteen patients were studied after electroshock therapy (7). There were eight psychotic depressions, four neurotic depressions, and one schizoaffective reaction in this group. On pretreatment examination, nine of these showed PGR responses to the excitatory tone which were less than 2000 ohms and hence belonged to the group which we classified as inhibitory types. In two of these nine patients, the response was ultraparadoxical in that the differentiation ratio was less than 0.4, namely, 0.28 and 0.37. All nine patients were suffering from depressive illnesses. There were eight psychotic depressions and one neurotic depression in the group. All of them recovered following treatment, four fully and five socially. When tested three and one-half hours to six days after the last shock treatment, the capacity to form conditional reflexes was completely abolished. Subsequently, enhanced but poorly differentiated activity came to the fore. Ultimately, when retested at the time at which optimal treatment benefits were established after clearing of the treatment-induced confusion (13 to 114 days after the last treatment, the average being 48 days), there was a significant increase in the responses to the excitatory signal (Fig. 5) from an average of 439 to an average of 1648 ohms (Table 1, $p = .008$). The expected corresponding improvement of the differentiation ratio was suggestive only; it improved from 1.08 to 2.03 ($p = .063$). This is due to the fact that the responses to the inhibitory signal sometimes increased also, although not to a significant degree (from an average of 303 to an average of 973 ohms, $p = .227$, Table 1). It is of particular

Table 1. Electroconvulsive treatment: Inhibitory subjects. N=9.

	PGR Averages in Ohms		One-tail
	Before ECT	After ECT	Chi-square Test P
CR−	303	973	.227
CR+	439	1648	.008
Ratio	1.08	2.03	.063
UR	2022	5395	.145
GTR	68	237	.344

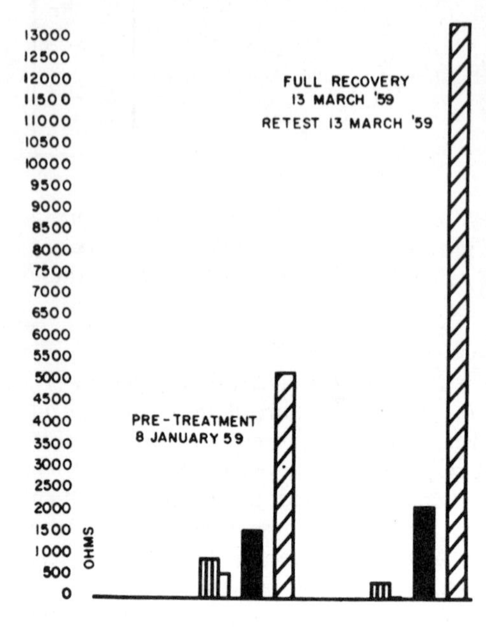

FIG. 5. Female, age 53, suffering from depressive reaction, psychotic, agitated, involutional (Issue: anticipated loss). Twenty electroshock treatments were administered between January 12, 1959 and February 23, 1959, resulting in full recovery. The bar graphs illustrate the conditional psychogalvanic reflex pattern before and after successful electroshock therapy. Note increase in psychogalvanic reflex responses to the excitatory conditional stimulus and decrease of those to the inhibitory stimulus, resulting in improved differentiation between responses to excitatory and inhibitory stimulus. The unconditional response was increased also. The generalized time reflex was abolished after electroshock therapy.

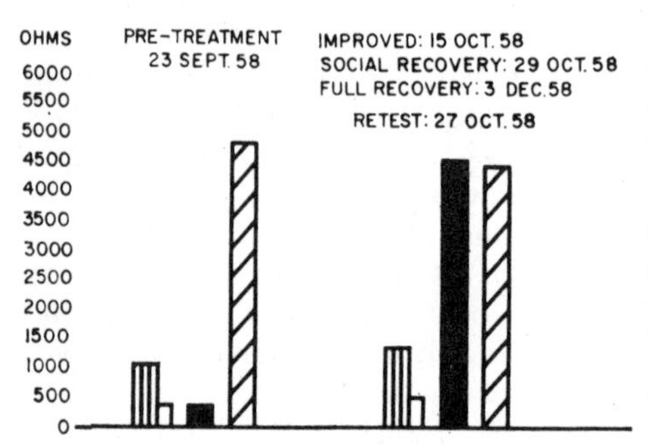

FIG. 6. Female, age 67, suffering from depressive reaction, psychasthenic type, psychotic borderline. Treatment with meprobamate-benactyzine combination from September 29, 1958 to December 21, 1958. Dosage 1600 mg. meprobamate and 4 mg. benactyzine q.d., gradually reduced to 400 mg. meprobamate and 1 mg. benactyzine q.d. at time of retest. Note ultraparadoxical pretreatment test pattern in that responses to the inhibitory stimulus greatly exceed those to the excitatory stimulus. Note change to normal relationship between these responses after five weeks of treatment, concurrent with clinical recovery.

interest, however, that the two patients whose responses had been ultraparadoxical before treatment showed a normal type of differentiation after treatment with differentiation ratio values of 1.33 and 2.44 respectively. The increase in positive conditional reflexes associated with a trend toward improvement in differentiation confirms the findings of Gellhorn (13) who showed that electroshock as well as insulin coma may bring about recovery of inhibited conditional reactions. He suggests as a possible reason for this phenomenon that these treatments increase the hypothalamic discharges to the cortex and thus may make subliminal cortical processes supraliminal.

The group of patients with pretreatment responses other than inhibitory (N = 4) is yet too small for evaluation. All psychotic depressions in our case material fell into the inhibitory group.

Effect of Meprobamate and Benactyzine in Combination

This test group comprised 39 subjects. Meprobamate and benactyzine in combination improved differentiation markedly, the differentiation ratio (Table 2) rising from 3.63 to 12.80 ($p = .006$). This significant improvement in differentiation was accomplished largely by decrease of the responses to the inhibitory stimuli ($p = .046$, Table 2). There also was a reduction in the generalized time reflex to the inhibitory tone in the majority of the cases. This was significant for the group of subjects with excitatory and average pretreatment test pattern ($p = .038$), but only suggestive when all cases were included ($p = .084$, Table 2). Changes in the magnitude of the psychogalvanic responses to the excitatory signal were insignificant ($p = .872$, Table 2).

The significant improvement in differentiation characteristic for the effect of meprobamate and benactyzine in combination is, of course, the more impressive the more abnormal responses were prior to treatment. Fig. 6 shows the pre-treatment and post-treatment responses of the only patient in this group whose pretreatment responses were ultraparadoxical (differentiation ratio = 0.34). Five weeks later, following recovery on this medication, the relationship of the responses was normal, the differentiation ratio having risen to 3.31.

Effect of Amine Oxidase Inhibitors

Fifteen patients were tested before and after treatment with amine oxidase inhibitors (14). Drugs used were iproniazid (eight cases), isocarboxazid, an analogue of iproniazid (three cases), and nialamide (four cases).

The times chosen for the post-treatment retests were those at which emergence of clinical signs of response to the drug appeared, or when treatment failure was established. Only those patients were included in this analysis in whom a clear-cut treatment result was achieved, either success (eleven cases: five, full recovery; six, social recovery) or failure (four cases: two improved short of social recovery; two unimproved). These retest times ranged from 20 to 284 days, the average being 70 days. Earlier retests were carried out from the sixteenth day onward in order to study the timing and gradual evolution of the change in conditional reflex activity, its relation to dosage, duration of its administration and clinical status of the patient. These will be referred to below.

Marked diminution of psychogalvanic reflex activity was an equally striking feature of the post-treatment pattern in all three sub-groups classified by the pretreatment test pattern (excitatory, average and inhibitory). Statistical analysis of the changes evident at the time of establishment of a clear-cut treatment result after treatment with amine oxidase inhibitors showed a significant quantitative reduction of responses to the inhibitory and excitatory conditional stimuli (p = .008), as well as reduction of the responses to the unconditional stimuli in the majority of the cases (p = .058) without significant change in the differentiation between excitatory and inhibitory stimuli (p = .608, Table 3). There was no significant change of the generalized time reflex. The three different drugs used all contributed equally to these results, the general quantitative reduction in the magnitude of responses being a characteristic of the action of all of them, although they are not entirely equivalent in terms of dosage and time required.

It is of interest that full or social recovery on treatment with amine oxidase inhibitors is consistent with marked reduction in responsiveness of the conditional psychogalvanic reflex, irrespective of whether or not this reflex was already inhibited before treatment. Fig. 7 illustrates this further reduction of responses in a patient whose pretreatment test pattern was markedly inhibitory with poor differentiation between the responses to the excitatory and to the inhibitory stimuli. Fig. 8 illustrates the reduction of the responses in a patient whose pretreatment test pattern was not inhibitory and whose differentiation between excitatory and inhibitory stimuli had been better than average. The post-treatment test, done at the time of consolidation of social recovery (which has remained sustained), shows the conditional psychogalvanic responses practically abolished and the unconditional responses greatly reduced in intensity.

The evolution of the change parallels that of the clinical result, and is related to dosage and to duration of its administration (14).

While marked diminution of the psychogalvanic reflex response appears closely linked with successful clinical result, a moderate degree of diminution of the reflex may precede clinical improvement in the same manner as the less readily quantifiable increase in tendon reflexes and thus be an indicator that clinical results are obtainable. The therapeutic result may then be accelerated by raising the dosage (Fig. 9), or initiated thereby if diminution in conditional psychogalvanic reflex responses had not been forthcoming before. However, the gradual cumulative effect of the drug itself without raising the dosage

Table 2. Meprobamate and benactyzine in combination. N=39.

	PGR Averages in Ohms Before Drug	After Drug	Two-tail Chi-square Test P
CR-	1272	938	.046
CR+	2925	2783	.872
Ratio	3.63	12.80	.006
UR	6010	4424	.330
GTR	303	186	.084

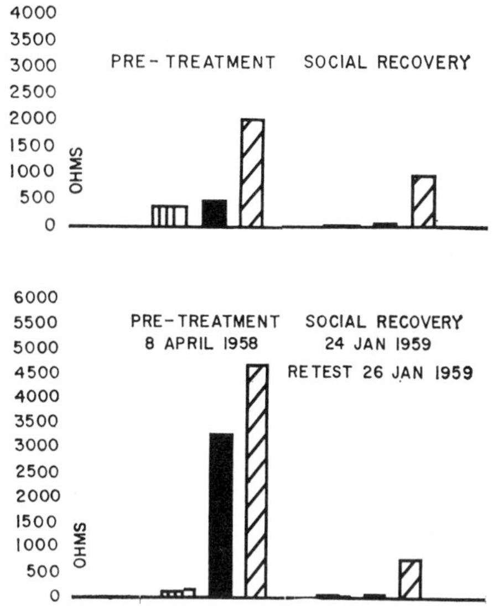

FIG. 7. Female, age 46, suffering from depressive reaction with anxiety, neurotic, psychasthenic, chronic (Issue: weakness—envy). Iproniazid treatment January 1958 to June 1958. Note marked reduction of psychogalvanic reflex responses at the time of social recovery on iproniazid therapy. Dosage 150 mg. daily at the time of the retest.

FIG. 8. Female, age 64, suffering from depressive reaction, neurotic, psychasthenic, chronic-recurrent (Issue: weakness—physical inadequacy). Treatment with isocarboxazid November 24th, 1958 to November 18th, 1959. Note marked reduction of psychogalvanic reflex responses two days after social recovery on isocarboxazid. Dosage 20 mg. daily at the time of the retest, 30 mg. daily until two days before the retest.

may be counted upon to bring about improvement in the course of time in less treatment-resistant patients, and this also reflects itself in the psychogalvanic reflex responses. Absence of change of psychogalvanic reflex responsiveness may be a helpful indicator of inadequacy of the initial dosage.

Conversely, when prolonged treatment with an adequate dose of an amine oxidase inhibitor is associated with maximal reduction in psychogalvanic reflex responsiveness, but clinical improvement fails to materialize, it may be taken as an indication that the patient is not likely to improve with continued administration or increase in dosage.

These observations are applicable for testing adequacy of dosage with amine oxidase inhibitors. Such an objectively quantifiable test for the effectiveness of dosage is highly desirable in this group of drugs because of the wide range of effective dosage and the wide range of duration of administration necessary to produce a successful result (15).

Table 3. Amine oxidase inhibitors (iproniazid, isocarboxazid, nialamide). N=15.

	PGR Averages in Ohms		Two-tail
	Before Drug	After Drug	Chi-square Test P
CR-	1254	986	.008
CR+	2974	2108	.008
Ratio	4.17	2.07	.608
UR	5126	3484	.058
GTR	293	144	.266

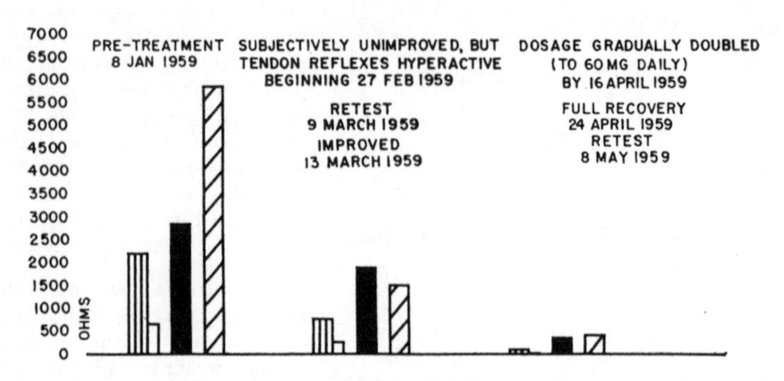

FIG. 9. Female, age 76, suffering from depressive reaction, manic-depressive, recurrent, psychotic (Issue: guilt, shame). Treatment with isocarboxazid January 15, 1959 to December 10, 1959. Note moderate reduction of psychogalvanic reflex responses prior to clinical improvement, ten days after tendon reflexes became hyperactive, on isocarboxazid, 30 mg. daily. Also note the marked reduction in psychogalvanic reflex responses after full recovery following raising of the dose to 60 mg. daily.

Effect of Chlorprothixen

This drug brought about a marked reduction in conditional PGR responses to the inhibitory and the excitatory stimuli in all but one of the seven patients studied. Responses to the unconditional stimuli were reduced in five of the seven patients. The differentiation ratio was reduced in six of the seven patients in contrast to the amine oxidase inhibitors where it remained unchanged. The generalized time reflex was reduced in all five patients in whom this response had been present before. The striking effects of this drug, associated with antidepressant and anxiety-relieving action were, however, in two of the seven patients studied, associated with neurocirculatory side effects which render this drug clinically impractical.

Effect of Imipramine

In the seventeen patients tested with this drug, the response patterns appeared to fall into two distinct groups, dependent upon treatment result. In all but two of the ten patients who failed to respond to this therapy, the post-treatment conditional responses were increased in magnitude. In all but one of the seven patients whose treatment resulted in recovery, the conditional responses decreased in magnitude in the course of treatment. Treatment success was predictable by means of retest one hour after the first test dose of 75 mg. p.o., since in all of the seven patients who recovered on this therapy decrease of the conditional responses manifested itself on that occasion.

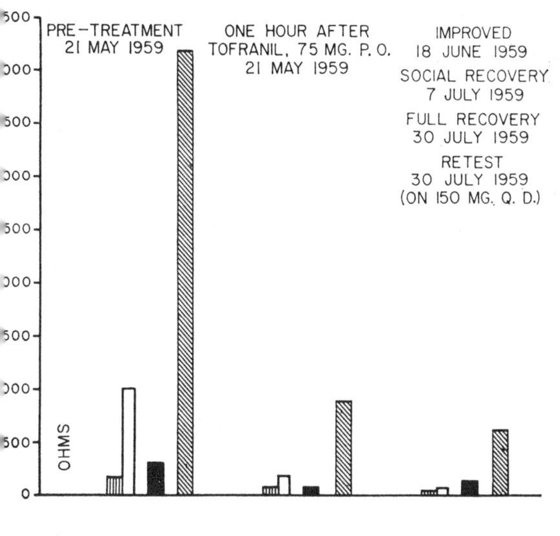

FIG. 10. Female, age 57, suffering from depressive reaction, psychotic, involutional, psychasthenic-anhedonie (Issue: loss, weakness, envy). Treatment with imipramine May 21, 1959 to April 11, 1960. Note reduction in psychogalvanic reflex responses one hour after first test dose and after successful treatment with imipramine.

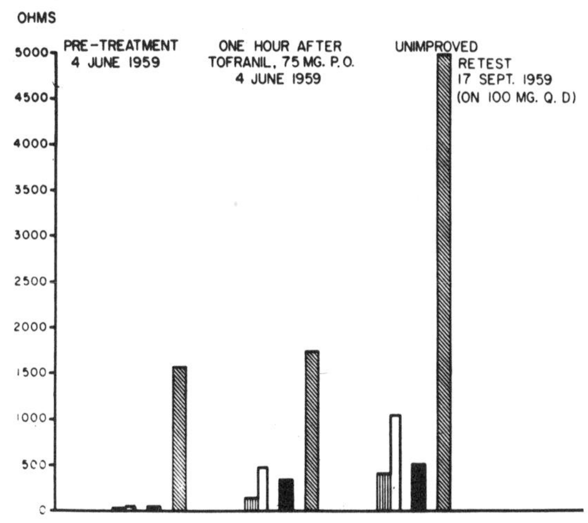

FIG. 11. Female, age 38, suffering from depressive reaction, psychotic, manic-depressive type, with hypochrondriasis and psychalgia (Issue: Loss). Treatment with imipramine July 20, 1959 to present. Note increase in psychogalvanic reflex responses one hour after first test dose and after treatment failure on imipramine.

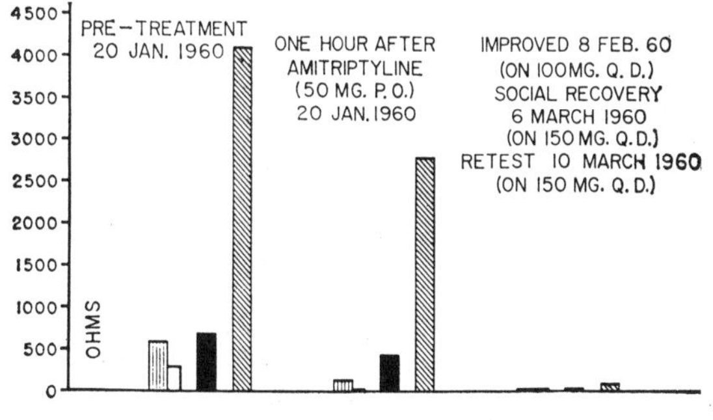

FIG. 12. Male, age 49, suffering from depressive reaction, neurotic, psychasthenic-anhedonic (Issue: power). Treatment with amitriptyline January 20, 1960 to March 16, 1960. Note reduction in psychogalvanic reflex responses one hour after first test dose and after successful treatment with amitriptyline.

The difference between treatment successes and failures with regard to the effect of the drug on conditional psychogalvanic responses may reflect critical levels of dosage requirements. The successfully treated patient (Fig. 10) showed a decrease in responses and dedifferentiation after the first test dose of 75 mg. p.o. On this occasion, the differentiation ratio declined from 1.90 to 1.00. On continuous medication of 150 mg. q.d., full recovery supervened seventy days later. When retested at this time, it was seen that the responses had remained low, but the differentiation ratio had improved to 3.69.

By contrast, the unsuccessfully treated patient whose test responses are illustrated in Fig. 11 showed an increase in responses, particularly of the GTR (denoting anxiety), without significant change in differentiation ratio (2.94 to 2.69) one hour after the first test dose of 75 mg. p.o. was administered. When treatment had failed, after three and one-half months on a dose of 100 mg. q.d., retest revealed that the responses had increased further (including the generalized time reflex) along with a decline of the differentiation ratio to 1.28 (Fig. 11).

In view of the findings emerging from this study, implying that increase of responses combined with dedifferentiation may reflect inadequate dosage, I have recently raised the dosage in the patient illustrated in Fig. 11 to 150 mg. q.d. She has since shown signs of improvement (still short of social recovery, however) concurrent with reduction of her galvanic skin responses.

Effect of Amitriptyline

Forty-two patients were studied before and one hour after the administration of amitriptyline, 50 mg. p.o. Seventeen of these patients were also studied after prolonged therapy with this drug. This drug produced a significant reduction in the conditional psychogalvanic responses, with a suggestive increase of the differentiation ratio (Table 4). Decrease of the responses to the inhibitory stimuli and decrease of the generalized time reflex were significant at better than the .01 level of confidence, while decrease of the responses to the excitatory stimuli and to the unconditional stimuli were significant at better than the .05 level of confidence. Increase in the differentiation ratio was suggestive only ($p = .15$, Table 4). The outcome of the

Table 4. Amitriptyline. N=42.

	PGR Responses After Drug Compared to Before				
	N Down	N Even	N UP	χ^2	P
CR−	31	0	11	9.52	<.01
CR+	28	0	14	4.67	<.05
Ratio	16	0	26	2.38	.15
UR	28	0	14	4.67	<.05
GTR	31	2	9	12.10	<.01

one-hour post-drug retest did not differentiate between the 22 patients in this group who recovered, and the 14 who did not recover (the outcome of the remainder is undecided at this time). There was evidence of cumulative effect in that there was further decrease in the responses after prolonged administration. This was significant for the responses to the inhibitory stimuli ($p = .04$). The change in the differentiation ratio, however, which had been suggestive for the one-hour post-drug retest, became definitely insignificant after prolonged administration when compared to the pre-drug test ($p = .227$). Fig. 12 illustrates a typical patient with an inhibitory pretreatment response pattern. One hour after the administration of amitriptyline, 50 mg. p.o., conditional responses were reduced, with improved differentiation, the differentiation ratio rising from 1.28 to 2.77. The unconditional response was likewise reduced. Four days after the achievement of social recovery, forty-eight days after the beginning of therapy, all responses were greatly reduced and the differentiation ratio had returned to 1.0.

Discussion and Summary

None of the drugs studied imitated the 2-phase effect of electroshock therapy which produces extinction of conditional reflex activity during the immediate post-treatment phase, followed during the recovery phase by a consistently significant increase of the positive conditional psychogalvanic reflex, with a trend toward improved differentiation in patients with inhibitory pretreatment response pattern. The drugs either changed the differentiation, or the magnitude of responses, or both. In those drugs which showed a 2-phase pattern of cumulative effect, the initial or mild effect tended to be associated with improved differentiation (disinhibition of differentiation) (see Figs. 9, 11, 12), while the late effects were reduced responses without change of or with reduced differentiation. This was the reverse of the sequence observed in electroshock therapy.

Meprobamate and benactyzine in combination improved differentiation largely by decreasing the responses to the inhibitory stimuli. The amine oxidase inhibitors (iproniazid, nialamide and isocarboxazid), as well as a number of other newer antidepressants, namely, chlorprothixen, imipramine, and amitriptyline, brought about marked and consistent decrease of the conditional psychogalvanic responses without significantly altering differentiation between the excitatory and inhibitory signals. While for amitriptyline and chlorprothixen, this decrease in magnitude of responses was general and did not discriminate between treatment successes and treatment failures, for the amine oxidase inhibitors and for imipramine, decrease of the conditional psychogalvanic responses was significantly associated with treatment success, absence of such decrease, or increase, with treatment failure. For the amine oxidase inhibitors, gradual decrease in conditional psychogalvanic reflex responses paralleled the clinical result and was related to dosage and to duration of its administration. This was utilized for testing adequacy of dosage with this group of drugs. A similar approach appears indicated for the regulation of the dosage of imipramine. The fact that amitriptyline brought about a significant reduction of the generalized time reflex (GTR, Table 4), in contrast to the amine oxidase inhibitors (Table 3) and the imipramine failures, may be related to the clinical observation that this drug tended rather generally to relieve anxiety in addition to its antidepressant action. It thus appears to occupy an intermediate position between imipramine, which it most closely resembles chemically on the one hand, and chlorpromazine (7) on the other. The mode of action of the inhibiting effect of the newer antidepressants (the amine oxidase inhibitors, imipramine and amitriptyline, on the conditional psychogalvanic reflex is obscure. It may be related to the autonomic effects of these drugs. This is particularly suggestive in the case of imipramine which is known to have a cholinergic effect in low dosage, and an adrenergic effect in large dosage. This fits in quite well with the observation that an ineffective dose increases, while an effective dosage decreases, the conditional psychogalvanic reflex. We cannot be entirely sure whether we are measuring a central effect or a peripheral manifestation of a central effect, but it is conceivable that the drug-induced inhibitory effect upon the conditional psychogalvanic reflex may be obtained by blocking the anterior hypothalamus and releasing the posterior hypothalamus.

The discharges from the anterior hypothalamus to the cortex may thus also be reduced by these drugs, thereby increasing the threshold for certain cortical responses, including those involved in depressive states.

Iproniazid is available under the trademark Marsilid®, isocarboxazid under the trademark Marplan, nialamide under the trademark Niamid, chlorprothixen under the trademark Taractan, imipramine under the trademark Tofranil®, amitriptyline under the trademark Elavil®, chlorpromazine under the trademark Thorazine®. Deprol® is a combination of meprobamate and benactyzine.

References

1. Alexander, L.: The therapeutic process in electroshock and the newer drug therapies. Psychopathological Considerations. *J.A.M.A. 162:* 966-969, 1956.
2. Alexander, L.: *"Objective Approaches to Treatment in Psychiatry."* Springfield, Ill., Charles C Thomas, 1958, pp. 1-139.
3. Gantt, W. H.: The Conditional Reflex Function as an Aid in the Study of the Psychiatric Patient, in Hoch, P. H. and Zubin, J. (Eds.): *Relation of Psychological Tests to Psychiatry,* New York: Grune and Stratton, 1952, pp. 165-188.
4. Gantt, W. H. (Ed.): *Physiological Bases of Psychiatry.* Springfield, Ill.: Charles C Thomas, 1958, I-XIII, 1-344.

5. Alexander, L.: Apparatus and Method for the Study of Conditional Reflexes in Man. Preliminary Results in Normal Control Subjects, in Mental Disorders and as a Result of Drug Action. *Arch. Neurol. & Psychiat., 80:*629-649, Nov. 1958.
6. Alexander, L.: Objective Approach to Psychiatric Diagnosis and Evaluation of Drug Effects by Means of the Conditional Reflex Technic, in Massermann, J. H. (Ed.): *Biological Psychiatry.* New York: Grune & Stratton, 1959, pp. 154-181.
7. Alexander, L., and Horner, S. R.: The effect of drugs on the conditional psychogalvanic reflex in man. *J. Neuropsychiat.* (In press.)
8. Alexander, L.: Effects of Psychotropic Drugs on Conditional Responses in Man. *Neuro-Psycho-pharmacology,* Vol. II. Amsterdam: Elsevier, 1961.
9. Gluck, H., and Rowland, V.: Defensive conditioning of electrographic arousal with delayed and differentiated auditory stimuli. *EEG Clin. Neurophysiol., 11:*485-496, August 1959.
10. Alexander, L.: New Diagnostic and Therapeutic Aspects of Depression, in Rogers, D. M. (Ed.), *Depression and Antidepressant Drugs.* Waltham, Mass. (Metropolitan State Hospital, Division of Mass. Dept. of Mental Health), 1960, pp. 23-33.
11. Caplan, G.: Practical steps for the family physician in the prevention of emotional disorder. *J.A.M.A., 170:*1497-1506, July 1959.
12. Parad, H. J., and Caplan, G.: A framework for studying families in crisis. *Social Work, 3:*15, July 1960.
13. Gellhorn, E.: Is restoration of inhibited conditioned reactions by insulin coma specific for Pavlovian inhibitions? *Arch. Neurol. & Psychiat., 56:*216-221, 1946.
14. Alexander, L., and Lipsett, S. R.: Effect of amine oxidase inhibitors on the conditional psychogalvanic reflex in man. *Dis. Nerv. System, 20:* (Suppl.): 26-33, August 1959.
15. Alexander, L., and Berkeley, A. W.: The inert psychasthenic reaction (anhedonia) as differentiated from classic depression and its response to iproniazid. *Ann. N. Y. Acad. Science, 80:* art. 3, 669-679 (Sept. 17) 1959.

6

CHANGES IN AVOIDANCE CONDITIONING FOLLOWING PSYCHOTHERAPEUTIC TREATMENT

by Clinton C. Brown, Ph.D.

The use of avoidance conditioning in human subjects as a method for the diagnostic determination of conditions adversely affecting the functional integrity of the cortex was proposed originally by Gantt as early as 1938. In a series of subsequent studies the method was advocated for the determination of Korsakoff's syndrome (1), generalized cortical pathology (2), and for the differentiation of psychogenic from organogenic psychoses (3).

The rationale for the clinical use of this test lies in the experimental observation that natural (human) or deliberately produced (animal) cortical lesions often result in the abolition of or decrement in previously established conditional reflexes and in a markedly increased difficulty in the formation of new conditioning. Gantt (1) found that patients with Korsakoff's syndrome failed to condition in a simple avoidance situation with visual CS's.

In a previous unpublished study performed on a group of elderly psychotic patients with and without neurological evidence of cortical damage, the following findings relevant to the question of validity were obtained:

1. All patients who had evidence of cortical pathology on the basis of EEG and neurologic examination failed to condition.
2. In another group matched for age and NP diagnosis but without EEG and neurological evidence of cortical pathology, approximately 50 per cent failures in conditioning were encountered.
3. Repeated neurological examination of the portion of this latter group who failed to condition did not reveal demonstrable signs of cortical pathology.

Reprinted from *The Journal of Nervous and Mental Disease.* Volume 125, No. 3, July-September 1957, pp. 487-489.

Two possible explanations of these findings were advanced:

a) Since all patients with clinically demonstrable signs of neurologic damage failed to condition and a portion of the group without these signs also failed to condition, the technique of conditioning may more sensitively reflect early or diffuse cortical damage than orthodox neurological procedures, or,

b) The failure of a patient to condition may be due to a *complex* of factors, among which is the factor of cortical pathology. If, for example, failure to condition reflects a lowered level of cortical efficiency, then cortical damage may only be considered a special case of irreversible degradation of function. Transient disturbances in cortical efficiency should be revealed by testing during disorder and following recovery.

The present study begins with the hypothesis that factors other than those of cortical pathology may influence conditioning and tests the validity of this assumption. The problem was that of determining changes in conditioning ability in a control and matched experimental group of psychiatric patients from a period prior to the beginning of group psychotherapy to a period immediately following the termination of the therapy. If changes in conditioning ability could be found in the experimental group (receiving psychotherapy) but were not found in the control group (resident on the ward, but not receiving psychotherapy), the hypothesis would be supported.

Method

Thirty-three chronic ward patients participated in the study. They represented the population of an entire ward except for evident cases of neurologic damage, epilepsy, etc. which were excluded from the study. The groups were divided randomly into seventeen controls and sixteen experimental patients. The latter group was subjected to various psychotherapeutic manipulations directed toward enforcing social interchange and the formation of small groups. This study was performed by other workers, and the results will be reported separately.

Conditioning procedures were performed on the entire thirty-three patients prior to the beginning of therapy. Following completion of the therapy in approximately three months the entire group was retested.

The procedures for conditioning are described fully elsewhere (4). They involve the presentation of paired light and tone stimuli at one-minute intervals alternately reinforced by a painful faradic shock of one-second duration to the right hand. A cradle for the right arm provides both a measure of motor reactivity and a means for avoidance of the shock. Continuous PGR recordings are made throughout the whole conditioning session. After 10 trials the subject is instructed to avoid shock by pressure on the right arm rest in anticipation of the shock. The stimuli are then continued, and a graded series of instructions are given after each successive failure in response until the final instruction is a clear and explicit direction to depress the rest at the presentation of a specific light and tone. The auditory stimulus was paired with the visual one to prevent the subject from disregarding the localized visual stimulus and failing thereby.

A final numerical score was obtained by summing separate scores for the following: 1) quality of CR formation, defined in terms of the trial number at which first evidence (autonomic or motor) of a CR appeared to the CS; 2) quality of differentiation between positive and negative stimuli, defined in terms of the differences in amplitude of the same responses to reinforced and unreinforced CS's; 3) verbal formulation of the procedure, defined in terms of completeness of formulation, whether such appeared after indirect questioning, etc.; 4) a general score, based upon a subjective estimate by the experimenter.

Results

A. The possible range of scores by the method employed was from zero to eight. The level of the pre-test score was subtracted from the post-test score for each of 16 experimental and 16 control group patients. Using a non-parametric statistic, the Sign Test, it was found that while no significant differences existed between the conditioning scores obtained by members of the two groups at the initiation of the study, the scores of the experimental group were significantly higher (p .001) following therapy when compared with their pre-therapy scores. The control group showed no significant increase for the same period. These findings are summarized in the following mean conditioning scores.

	Pre-therapy	Post-therapy
Experimental	2.8	3.6
Control	2.9	2.8

The control-experimental group difference is significant at .001 level.

B. The values of shock stimulus (US) necessary either to produce the first sensation of shock or to elicit a pain response also underwent some changes from initial to final tests. These show an increase in the amount of shock (voltage) necessary to elicit pain which was approximately equal for both experimental and control groups.

C. The level of shock necessary to elicit a barely perceptible sensation also increased in the same period and was approximately the same for both experimental and control groups.

D. A comparison was made of the changes in shock and pain sensitivity in individuals of both groups who showed increased (better) conditioning scores on the final test. There was a slight but statistically significant increase in both these levels evaluated by rank-order non-parametric statistics.

E. A summary analysis of the psychometric evaluation of therapeutic results including observational and rating scale methods failed to disclose significant changes in control and experimental groups.

Summary and Conclusions

Thirty-three chronic psychotics were employed as subjects in this study. They were first conditioned in a simple avoidance situation, divided into two groups, one of which was then given intensive group psychotherapy. After three months both groups were retested.

The results indicate a significantly increased level of conditionability for the experimental group and only random changes in the control group. Faradic pain appreciation and shock sensation levels showed a generalized but insignificant increase for both groups.

It is also apparent from previous studies that cortical pathology seriously interferes with new conditioning. For the diagnostic use of the conditional reflex procedures it is therefore suggested that only the *complete absence* of conditionability is suggestive of cortical pathology while decrements in conditionability may be associated with reversible psychic factors mainly affecting attention. It is not parsimonious to conclude that conditioning deficits, based on cortical pathology, could have been alleviated by three months of psychotherapy. It is more probable that any interferences in conditioning existing in the experimental group would be those adversely affecting the perception and interpretation of the stimuli or abstracting from them. This type of phenomena has been described by Pavlov as the class of "external inhibitors", external to the neural processes directly involved in conditional reflex formation.

In clinical applications the method of conditioning as a diagnostic procedure offers a number of distinct advantages over standard psychometric techniques. It is more objective in procedure and result, it is simple and brief in administration, and requires only minimal cooperation with the subject–an important advantage when working with mute or disturbed psychotic patients.

Any further exploration of the nature of these factors adversely affecting conditioning would necessarily be based upon the assumption that this information is of more diagnostic value than that obtained from clinical observation.

References

1. Gantt, W. H., and Muncie, W.: Analysis of the mental defect in chronic Korsakoff's Psychosis by means of the conditional reflex method. *Bull. Johns Hopkins Hosp., 70:* 467-487, 1942.
2. Gantt, W. H.: A method of testing cortical function and sensitivity of the skin: an aid in differentiating organic and psychogenic disturbances. *Arch. Neurol. & Psychiat., 40:* 79-85, 1938.
3. Gantt, W. H.: Impairment of the function of adaptability as measured by a simple conditioned reflex test in certain psychogenic contrasted with organic diseases. *South. M. J., 31:* 1219-1225, 1938.
4. Reese, W. G., Doss, R., and Gantt, W. H.: Autonomic responses in differential diagnosis of organic and psychogenic psychoses. *Arch. Neurol. & Psychiat. 70:* 778-793, 1953,

7

THE RELATIONSHIP OF GSR CONDITIONING TO DRINKING PATTERNS OF ALCOHOLICS

by Muriel D. Vogel-Sprott, Ph.D.

As defined by Eysenck (2, 3), "introversion-extraversion" has been related to individual differences in a variety of types of behavior displayed by normal and neurotic individuals (summarized in 3, *p. 28)* and these findings have been formulated into a general theory of personality. Hypotheses derived from Eysenck's theory have been employed by Vogel (4) in research on alcoholism. She found that "introversion," defined as E (extraversion) scores below the mean on the Maudsley Personality Inventory (MPI), was related to reports by male alcoholics of a steady drinking pattern, of solitary drinking, and of a longer time between the occurrence of first "blackout" and onset of frequent blackouts, while "extraversion" (E scores above the mean), was associated with reports of a periodic drinking pattern, of no solitary drinking and of a shorter time between first blackout and their frequent occurrence (5). A study of galvanic skin response (GSR) conditioning (6) in alcoholics showed that introversion, similarly defined, was associated with faster acquisition and slower extinction of the conditioned response as compared with extraversion. These studies could imply that the way alcoholics respond in a conditioning situation is related to their drinking practices, specifically with regard to steady or periodic drinking, solitary drinking and blackout experiences. The present study was designed to examine this implication, in the form of the following hypotheses:

1. A conditioned GSR is established in fewer trials, and is more resistant to extinction, in alcoholics who report solitary drinking than in those who report that they never drink solitarily.
2. A conditioned GSR is established in fewer trials, and is more resistant to extinction, in alcoholics who report a longer time between the first blackout and the increasing frequency of these blackouts, than in those who report a shorter time between these events.

Reproduced by permission from the *Quarterly Journal of Studies on Alcohol,* Vol. 22, pp. 401-410, 1961.

3. A conditioned GSR is established in fewer trials, and is more resistant to extinction, in alcoholics who report a steady drinking pattern than in those who report a periodic drinking pattern.

Method

Subjects

The sample consisted of 48 male inpatients of the Alcoholism Research Foundation Clinic. This treatment facility receives referrals from a variety of sources and admission is not restricted on any economic basis; Skid Row type alcoholics, however, are not usually obtained in this hospital population. The sample contained all the male patients admitted to the Clinic during the time the study was being conducted, provided they were able to read and write English sufficiently to complete a paper and pencil questionnaire.

Eight subjects in the sample failed to condition within the maximum number of acquisition trials permitted in the conditioning procedure. Since acquisition and extinction scores could not be obtained for these subjects, they were not included in the analyses of the conditioning measures but were retained for another investigation (7).

Procedure

The GSR conditioning procedure and measures have been fully described elsewhere (1) and may be summarized here briefly. Conditioning was conducted in a semi-soundproof room. The subject was told that the test was one of relaxation or repose, and that his task was to spell the syllables which were presented to him by a memory drum.

The conditioned stimulus (CS) was a nonsense syllable, "LAJ," which appeared 16 times, randomly placed among 35 other syllables of low association value (8). The memory drum presented a different syllable every 6 seconds. The unconditioned stimulus (US) was an unpleasantly loud-ringing door buzzer which reliably elicited the unconditioned response (UR) of abrupt change in skin conductance. The first presentation of the CS was followed in 0.5 sec. by the US. A 50-per-cent reinforcement schedule was employed so that alternate presentations of the CS were reinforced. Skin resistance was measured by a Lafayette 601-A GSR amplifier, using finger clamp electrodes and an Esterline Angus pen recorder which traced the GSR continuously. Every 6 sec., immediately before presentation of a new syllable by the memory drum, the GSR amplifier was balanced to the subject's skin resistance at that moment. This procedure automatically centered the Esterline Angus pen at zero on the record chart. The size of the pen deflection on the chart was a constant function of ohm change in resistance, and independent of the basal skin resistance level. This allowed the direct comparison of a subject's GSR responses to each syllable during the conditioning procedure. Accurate identification of the response to CS and US was permitted by a side pen which automatically marked the chart when these stimuli were presented.

The criterion of conditioning was similar to that employed by Welch and Kubis (9, 10), which required three consecutive conditioned GSR responses (CR) to the CS when unaccompanied by the US. A CR was defined as a change in skin resistance accompanying presentation of the CS which was larger than any change accompanying any intervening buffer syllables. The number of reinforcements (i.e., the number of presentations of the US) prior to achievement of this criterion constituted the count of trials to acquire the CR. A larger score thus indicated slower conditioning.

Vogel (6) noted that this conditioning procedure could not satisfactorily be continued much longer than 20 minutes because of increasing boredom or restlessness on the part of the subject. Slight shifts in posture, sighs, or comments aside to the experimenter all altered the skin conductance somewhat, and under such conditions a record of conditioning could not reliably be obtained. For this reason a limit of 15 min. was placed on acquisition trials. This duration permitted 24 presentations of the CS accompanied by the US, and 24 presentations of the unreinforced CS. A subject's maximum possible score was 24, and if conditioning had not then been achieved he was grouped with those who "failed to condition." These cases were examined in another study (7).

Extinction trials commenced immediately after a subject displayed the CR. The US was no longer presented, and he continued to spell syllables as they were presented by the memory drum. His GSRS were recorded and the number of CRS to the first 10 unreinforced presentations of the CS were counted. A CR again was defined as a GSR to the CS which was larger than any of his GSRS to the intervening neutral syllables. The score indicated the number of CRS during 10 extinction trials. The subject thereafter continued spelling syllables until "extinction" occurred. "Extinction" in this case was defined as 3 consecutive presentations of the unreinforced CS without eliciting a CR. In many cases this had occurred by the time the 10 standard extinction trials were completed. Two extinction scores thus were obtained from each subject: *a)* the number of CRS displayed in 10 unreinforced trials, and *b)* the number of CRS prior to extinction. In both cases a larger score was considered as indicating greater resistance of the CR to extinction.

All the subjects who underwent conditioning also completed a "research questionnaire." This questionnaire, which has been described in detail elsewhere (1), contained relevant items on drinking behavior as well as the MPI (2). The information obtained from the MPI is being reported in another study (7). Questions about drinking behavior were selected verbatim from Jellinek's Drinking History Questionnaire (11). Subjects were asked whether they drank solitarily, and whether they were more typically a "steady drinker" ("drinking

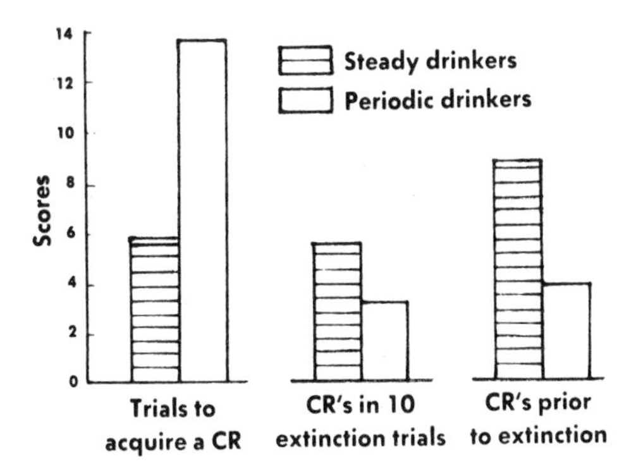

FIG. 1. Mean GSR Conditioning Scores of Two Groups of Alcoholics.

more or less the same amount at regular frequent intervals") or a "periodic drinker" ("drinking in bouts of 2, 3 or more days, either not drinking at all between bouts or only very moderately"). They were asked to state their age at first blackout,* and at the onset of frequent** blackouts.

The questionnaire replies revealed that 27 subjects reported solitary drinking and 13 stated that they never drank solitarily; 18 reported a steady drinking pattern and 22 reported periodic drinking. The difference between ages reported at first alcoholic blackout and at onset of frequent blackouts ranged from 0 to 23.5 years, with a median of 2.5. The sample was dichotomized in the following manner for each drinking behavior item:

A. Steady vs. periodic drinking.†
B. Solitary vs. no solitary drinking.
C. Difference of 2.5 or less between ages at first blackout and onset of frequent blackouts vs. difference larger than 2.5 years.

The results of previous research (5, 6) leading to the prediction of a relation between conditionability and the 3 drinking variables investigated in this study did not permit any hypotheses concerning the degree to which each of these variables separately might relate to conditionability. It seemed possible, therefore, that conditioning be-

* "Blackout" is described in Jellinek's questionnaire (11) as "Wake up in the morning after a party with no idea where you had been or what you had done after a certain point."
** "Frequent" is defined by Jellinek (11) as "at least two or three times out of ten drunks."
† The drinking behavior investigated in this study refers to the alcoholics' report of this behavior. However, the qualification "reported" is, for convenience, occasionally omitted from the text.

havior might depend on the particular combination of behaviors reported (i.e., an interaction effect). In order to investigate this possibility, a $2 \times 2 \times 2$ variance analysis (12) was performed using the 3 behavior variables categorized as *A, B, C,* above. In the cells of this threefold classification, the number of cases ranged from 2 to 8. Since the variance analysis presented by Lindquist (12) requires an equal number of cases (N) in all cells, and the smallest number of cases in any cell was 2, the N in other cells was reduced by a random selection of only 2 cases. This procedure resulted in a total of 16 subjects employed for each $2 \times 2 \times 2$ analysis.

Results

A $2 \times 2 \times 2$ variance analysis was performed for *a*) number of trials to acquire the CR; *b*) number of CRS in 10 extinction trials, and *c*) number of CRS prior to extinction. These analyses are summarized in Table 1. The similar finding in the three analyses permit an over-all summary of the results. No significant first- or second-order interaction effects are observed in the analysis of any of the three conditioning measures. Each analysis reveals only one significant main effect and in each case this is attributable to steady versus periodic drinking. Since the three analyses consistently failed to indicate any significant interaction effects among the drinking behavior variables, it might be assumed that these interaction effects are at least negligible. On this assumption, a separate investigation of each of the behavior variables was conducted employing the entire sample ($N = 40$).

Table 2 (*a*) presents the results of t tests of the differences in conditioning scores between alcoholics who reported steady drinking and those who reported periodic drinking. The groups differ significantly on all three conditioning measures. This evidence agrees both with the findings of the variance analyses and with the relevant experimental hypothesis. Group mean scores, presented in Figure 1, show that the conditioned GSR is elicited in fewer trials and is more resistant to extinction in alcoholics who reported steady drinking than in those who reported periodic drinking.

Table 2 (*b*) presents the results of t tests of the differences in conditioning scores between subjects who reported solitary drinking and those who never drank solitarily. Even when the entire sample is included in the test these two groups do not differ in measures of CR acquisition and extinction.

The conditioning scores of alcoholics who reported a shorter time between first and frequent blackout were compared with those subjects who reported a longer time between these events. The differences between these group mean scores were assessed by the t tests summarized in Table 2 (*c*). The groups do not differ significantly in trials to acquire or to extinguish the conditioned GSR.

Source	df	(a) Trials to Acquire a CR Sum of Squares	Mean Squares	F	(b) CRs in 10 Extinction Trials Sum of Squares	Mean Squares	F	(c) CRs Prior to Extinction Sum of Squares	Mean Squares	F
A	1	324.00	324.00	32.40*	33.07	33.07	11.25†	90.25	90.25	6.33†
B	1	1.00	1.00	0.10	5.07	5.07	1.72	4.00	4.00	0.28
C	1	2.25	2.25	0.23	0.07	0.07	0.02	1.00	1.00	0.07
AB interaction	1	20.25	20.25	2.05	7.55	7.55	2.57	30.25	30.25	2.12
AC interaction	1	1.00	1.00	0.10	0.05	0.05	0.02	6.25	6.25	0.44
BC interaction	1	1.00	1.00	0.10	7.55	7.55	2.57	0.00	0.00	0.00
ABC interaction	1	0.25	0.25	0.03	0.08	0.08	0.03	0.25	0.25	0.02
Within cells	8	80.00	10.00		23.50	2.94		114.00	14.25	
Total	*15*	*429.75*			*76.94*			*246.00*		

* With 1 and 8 df, $p<.01$. † With 1 and 8 df, $p<.05$.

Table 2. GSR conditioning scores among alcoholics who reported themselves as (a) steady or periodic drinkers, (b) solitary or nonsolitary drinkers, and (c) with more or less difference in age at first blackout and at frequent blackouts.

Alcoholic Group	N	Trials to Acquire a CR Mean	SD	t	CRs in 10 Extinction Trials Mean	SD	t	CRs Prior to Extinction Mean	SD	t
(*a*) Steady drinking	18	5.9	2.44		5.6	1.5		8.7	4.62	
				6.90*			3.97*			3.86*
Periodic drinking	22	13.7	4.12		3.3	2.05		3.8	3.19	
(*b*) Solitary drinking	27	10.26	5.15		4.26	2.10		5.93	5.04	
				0.101			0.176			0.138
No solitary drinking	13	10.08	5.23		4.39	2.24		6.15	3.51	
(*c*) 2.5 Years or less†	20	11.4	5.32		4.2	2.42		5.05	4.04	
				1.51			0.29			1.37
Over 2.5 years†	20	9.0	4.73		4.4	1.83		7.00	4.90	

* With 38 df, $p<.01$.
† Difference in years of age at first blackout and at beginning of frequent blackouts.

Discussion

There is some experimental evidence that alcohol ingestion produces a reduction in the strength of fear (13), and learning theorists have suggested that the alcohol drinking response may be explained in terms of reinforcement (14, *pp. 185-190*). A person who drinks alcohol when fearful or frightened would be "rewarded" by immediate drive reduction. The GSR has been used as a peripheral autonomic index of "emotionality," this term being used variously to mean startle, tension, anxiety or apprehension. To the extent that drinking is a learned drive-reducing response, and differences in GSR conditionability observed between alcoholics with a steady and a periodic drinking pattern indicate differences in general emotional conditionability, some hypotheses accounting for differing drinking patterns may be offered. More conditionable subjects may associate internal conditioned emotional responses to a wider variety or a greater number of fear-inducing stimuli. Mowrer's (15) two-factor learning theory suggests that autonomic fear responses act as stimuli to which instrumental drive-reducing behaviors (e.g., drinking) become conditioned. The drive-reducing response of drinking alcoholic beverages thus might be expected to be elicited more frequently, or with more regularity, in individuals who more readily develop and maintain autonomic conditioned responses. Conversely, people who acquire conditioned autonomic fear responses with more difficulty should have fewer or weaker internal fear stimuli to elicit a drive-reducing response like drinking. While alcohol ingestion may still be considered drive-reducing, this behavior might rather be predominantly elicited by the haphazard presentation of threatening stimuli in the environment. In another part of this research (5) periodic drinking behavior was found to be associated with extraversive personality test scores as defined by Eysenck (2). His suggestion that extraversion is associated with impulsive reaction to environmental rather than internal stimuli appears to be consistent with the above discussion. He comments, "the extravert is more dependent on external stimuli, rewards, punishments and the immediate group" (3, *p. 213*).

It has been suggested (1, 6) that the efficacy of conditioned aversion treatment of alcoholism may depend, in part, on the degree to which a conditioned autonomic nausea response to alcohol can be established and maintained in the patient. Since the GSR response has some autonomic components, the results of this study may offer a basis for identifying the more suitable patients for conditioned aversion treatment. To the extent that the conditioning of GSR and nausea responses may be comparable, the recognition of steady or periodic drinking patterns may be useful criteria by which to distinguish, in advance of trial, those alcoholics who would more readily develop and maintain a conditioned nausea response to alcohol.

No relation was observed between an alcoholic's report of solitary drinking behavior and his conditionability as measured in this study. Differences in time intervening between first alcoholic blackout and their frequent occurrence were not related to differences in GSR conditioning. The failure to discover a relation between conditionability and reports of solitary drinking or of blackout experiences must be interpreted with caution. While there is no reason to suspect that the drinking behavior reported by an alcoholic necessarily differs from that which he displays during drinking, it is important to note that validity evidence for the questionnaire form which was used has not yet been presented. Nonsignificant results could be obtained if the questionnaire responses are not valid (i.e., are not related to the actual behavior displayed during drinking), or if no relation between conditioning and this drinking behavior exists. The design of the present study does not permit any choice between these alternative interpretations.

Summary

This study was designed to investigate individual differences in drinking practices in relation to ease of galvanic skin response conditioning in male inpatients of an alcoholism clinic.

Conditioning was studied individually in 40 alcoholics. A bell which reliably elicited abrupt change in skin conductance (GSR) was employed as the unconditioned stimulus. The conditioned stimulus was a nonsense syllable placed in repeated random order in a list of nonsense syllables. The 6-second exposure time of each individual syllable was controlled by a memory drum. Alternate presentations of the conditioned stimulus were followed in 0.5 sec. by the unconditioned stimulus. The subject's changes in GSR to each syllable were measured by a GSR amplifier and traced continuously by a pen recorder. The definition of a conditioned GSR was based on the pen recordings. Measures on trials to acquire and to extinguish the GSR were obtained from each subject, who also completed a questionnaire containing 3 drinking-behavior items which were hypothesized to relate to conditioning.

Two questionnaire items, solitary drinking and blackouts, were found not to relate to ease of conditioning. The third item, steady versus periodic drinking, related to all three conditioning measures. Alcoholics who reported having a steady drinking pattern more quickly established the conditioned GSR and more slowly extinguished this response than did those who reported periodic drinking. Some implications of this finding were suggested. To the extent that drinking alcoholic beverages is a learned response, a relation between the drinking pattern and ease of conditioning might have practical application in the selection of patients for the conditioned aversion treatment of alcoholism, and for other therapy which employs conditioning principles in an attempt to develop and extinguish responses.

References

1. Vogel, M. D.: Alcohol Drinking Behaviour Related to GSR Conditioning and Personality Factors in Alcoholics. Doctoral dissertation (unpublished); University of Toronto; 1960.
2. Eysenck, H. J.: The questionnaire measurement of neuroticism and extraversion. *Riv. Psicol. 50:* 113-140, 1956.
3. Eysenck, H. J.: *Dynamics of Anxiety and Hysteria.* London: Routledge & Kegan Paul; 1957.
4. Vogel, M. D.: Alcohol, alcoholism and introversion-extraversion. *Canad. J. Psychol. 13:* 78-83, 1959.
5. Vogel, M. D.: The relationship of personality factors to drinking patterns of alcoholics: an exploratory study. *Quart. J. Stud. Alc. 22:* 394-400, 1961.
6. Vogel, M. D.: The relation of personality factors to GSR conditioning of alcoholics; an exploratory study. *Canad. J. Psychol. 14:* 275-280, 1960.
7. Vogel, M. D.: GSR conditioning and personality factors in alcoholics and normals. *J. abnorm. soc. Psychol.* [In press.]
8. Glaze, J. A.: The association value of nonsense syllables. *J. genet. Psychol. 35:* 255, 1928.
9. Welch, L. and Kubis, J.: Conditioned PGR in states of pathological anxiety. *J. nerv. ment. Dis. 105:* 372-381, 1947.
10. Welch. L. and Kubis, J.: Effect of anxiety on conditioning rate and stability of PGR. *J. Psychol. 23:* 83-91, 1947.
11. Jellinek, E. M.: Phases in the drinking history of alcoholics. Analysis of a survey conducted by the official organ of Alcoholics Anonymous. *Quart. J. Stud. Alc. 7:* 1-88, 1946.
12. Lindquist, E. F.: *Design and Analysis of Experiments in Psychology and Education.* Boston; Houghton, Mifflin; 1953.
13. Conger, J. J.: The effects of alcohol on conflict behavior in the albino rat. *Quart. J. Stud. Alc. 12:* 1-29, 1951.
14. Dollard, J. and Miller, N. E.: *Personality and Psychotherapy.* New York: McGraw-Hill, 1950.
15. Mowrer, O. H.: *Learning Theory and Personality Dynamics.* New York: Ronald Press, 1950.

8

APPLICATION OF CONDITIONING PROCEDURES IN THE STUDY OF AGING

by James R. Whitman, Ph.D., Clinton C. Brown, Ph.D.,
and W. Horsley Gantt, M.D.

This is a brief report on the results obtained from two studies investigating the changes in conditionability occurring with age. Other investigators have usually selected subjects as representative of contrasting age groups, and they have compared these different groups on the basis of the measures obtained for the purpose of specifying differences which may be associated with increasing age. Responses which have been conditioned have been the eye blink and hand withdrawal, and the findings are to the effect that with increasing age there is some impairment in conditionability. The present studies were concerned mainly with correlation of measures of conditionability with intelligence test scores and clinical findings, and with respect to age the subjects selected represented a homogeneous group.

Materials and Methods

The method of conditioning used was that standardized by Gantt as an examination useful in the clinical study of the psychiatric patient. The general procedure consists of presenting to the subject a series of pairs of two different tones, one of which is always followed by a shock to the subject's hand. The subject's task is to learn the relationship between the shock and the tones and to state this in his own words. The subject is also instructed to press a bar or bulb which prevents his receiving a shock.

Normal subjects learn the relationship between the tones and the occurrence of the shock during the first series of trials and are able to verbalize this relationship. Such a performance is given a rating of "A." Subjects who do not learn the relationship with this amount of practice are given additional practice with increasing amounts of information or hints as to what the relationship is. If

Reprinted with permission from *Recent Advances In Biological Psychiatry, Volume* 4, Plenum Press, New York, 1962.

after 25 pairs of tones, for the last 5 of which the information is given that one tone is always followed by a shock and the other is not, a subject shows no evidence of conditioning, his performance is rated "D." Ratings of "B" and "C" indicate intermediate degrees of difficulty experienced by a subject.

Two different groups of subjects were given this examination. The first group consisted of six patients in a neuropsychiatric hospital who were not capable of conducting their affairs or of taking care of their personal needs. The clinical diagnosis of each of these subjects was chronic brain syndrome. They were selected by the ward psychiatrist as being patients exhibiting the symptoms of senility without other complications. The subjects ranged in age from 60 to 72 years (median age 67.5 age years); and they had been hospitalized for from three to twelve years at the time of the study. There was nothing in a review of their educational or occupational history which indicated that the subjects had been deficient in either of these areas. Intelligence test scores from the Wechsler Adult Intelligence Scale did not reveal gross intellectual deficiencies, except that in one case the score was below the normal range (IQ score 71). In each case the history suggested a gradual onset of the symptoms which led to hospitalization. On admission and at the time of the experiment, an examination revealed no striking deep-tendon reflex abnormalities.

The performance of each of these subjects in the conditioning experiment was rated as "D." That is, after repeated presentations of the tones and the shock with one of these tones, no one in this group was able to anticipate the shock or to state the relationship between the tones and the shock. There was no evidence that any form of conditioning had occurred.

The second group of subjects studied were 24 domiciliary residents without a diagnosis of CNS damage. These subjects were not patients as were those in the first group. They were able to lead a normal life in the domiciliary residence, and all reported for the examination without assistance. In this group over half of the subjects achieved "A" scores; the others either had difficulty with or were unable to form the conditional reflex. Those who failed ("D" scores) gave responses which did not differ from those reported for the first group.

Results and Conclusions

The relationships between performance on this examination, IQ scores, and age are shown in Table 1. In terms of IQ scores, the group achieving "A" scores did not significantly differ from the group which was not able to do so. High IQ scores were found among both groups, and this result as well as the data from the first group suggests that conditionability is not a direct expression of the type of intellectual function measured by the standard measure of intelligence.

Neurological examinations were completed on most of the subjects. A relationship between the findings of the neurological examination and the performance on the conditioning examination was not evident. It appears that what is being measured is an aspect of human functioning not directly measured by the neurological examination.

Table 1. Description of performance groups according to age and IQ score

Performance Group	Age		IQ Score	
	Range	Median	Range	Median
A (13 patients)	40-72	65	80-121	102
B, C, and D (11 patients)	62-76	68	71-126	97
Both Groups (24 patients)	40-76	65	71-126	97

Note: Difference between groups not significant, $P > 0.05$, median test.

Summary of Conclusions

The results from the conditioning experiment with the two groups of subjects led to the following conclusions:

1. Age in itself is not always accompanied by an impairment in the ability to form conditional reflexes.
2. The ability to form conditional reflexes is not correlated with intelligence test scores obtained from the standard intelligence test.
3. Impairment in the ability to form conditional reflexes may appear in the absence of neurological findings and therefore may be a precursor of these.

PART III

THE. CONDITIONED REFLEX IN CLINICAL RESEARCH

In clinical research, as in clinical practice, it is often necessary to work with individuals who are mute, only partially cooperative, limited in their ability to sustain interest or attention, or distracted in other ways. For such patients the method of conditioning has many advantages over the more usual psychometric procedures since it is usually short and simple to administer and requires little in the way of cooperation from the subject. It is, in addition, objective, minimally dependent upon the examiner and readily amenable to quantification and recording. For such reasons conditioning procedures can be usefully applied to almost all subjects and at every age level, ranging from before birth to old age.

It is often suggested that many neurotic traits and psychosomatic reactions of later life owe their origin, at least as far as the predisposition is concerned, to early conditioning experiences. Conditioning techniques offer a method whereby such speculations may be usefully explored.* If characteristics such as thumb-sucking, nose-picking, nail-biting and various allergies can be shown to be learned responses then perhaps they can also be treated by techniques derived from conditioning and learning theory. Although of a complex nature, stuttering and certain other speech disorders also may profitably be analyzed in such terms.

Of the many possible areas for study we have selected four. Wells, while cautioning the reader against the premature clinical application of his test, shows how the EEG may be effectively applied to the *research* study of groups of patients suffering from diseases involving

* An interesting example of the clinical possibilities inherent in such an approach is provided in a short paper written almost 15 years ago by Seitz. He presents both clinical and experimental evidence to suggest that hairpulling in a 2½ year old girl may have originated during the first two weeks of life as a result of some form of nasal-cutaneous conditioning while nursing at a hirsute breast. Such findings certainly raise the question of what other neurotic and psychosomatic reactions may be conditioned in this way (Seitz, P.F.D. Psychocutaneous conditioning during the first two weeks of life. *Psychosom. Med.*, 1950, *12,* 187-188.)

the brain stem and the central hemispheres. Birch and Demb skillfully integrate Pavlovian principles and data obtained from a study of mongoloid and normal children to show how the various kinds of behavior displayed by brain-injured children might be understood as the "result of disturbances in normal cerebral functioning which modify the effective equilibration of excitation and inhibition." This has important implications for the differential management and training of hyperactive and non-hyperactive brain-injured retarded children. Also of pertinence in this respect is a more recent project of Franks and Franks * in which it was shown that, among *not* obviously brain-injured mental defectives, those with inferior vocational adjustments are also relatively poor at forming conditioned eyeblink responses in the laboratory. Thus, if properly developed, conditioning techniques can be of value in the selection, management and training of defectives of both endogenous and exogenous origin. There is a compelling need for more clinical research in this area.

Dekker, Pelser and Groen show how asthmatic attacks in man may be deliberately induced by conditioning procedures. They point out that there is now a need for a form of specific deconditioning therapy which would make the conditioned asthmatic response disappear in much the same way it came. Finally, Efron shows how uncinate seizures may be voluntarily arrested by the application of the method of conditioning. In the case reported by Efron, the patient was initially able to avert his seizures by an appropriate olfactory stimulus. After conditioning, visual stimuli or even the thought of such stimuli were equally effective in averting the seizures. Further research is required into possible methods of arresting seizures by conditioning techniques in other patients who do not possess this initial—but presumably conditioned—ability.

* Franks, Violet and Franks, C. M. Classical conditioning as an index of vocational adjustment among mental defectives. *Percept. Mot. Skills,* 1962, *14,* 241-242.

9

CONDITIONED CEREBRAL RESPONSES IN NORMAL SUBJECTS AND IN PATIENTS WITH CENTRAL NERVOUS SYSTEM DISEASES

by Charles E. Wells, M.D.

B. Pavlov and his collaborators (quoted by Rusinov and Smirnov, (12)) utilizing positive and negative conditioned motor responses, demonstrated that the proper response following a positive conditioned stimulus was associated with diminution in alpha activity while that following a negative stimulus was associated with a reinforcement of this rhythm. Jus and Jus (6) have carried out even more elaborate testing procedures, utilizing the method of Ivanoff-Smolenski. This method theoretically promotes the formation of a "temporary cerebral connection" by association of an indifferent stimulus with a simple movement performed by the subject in response to the experimenter's verbal command. They demonstrated formation of conditioned cerebral responses to both positive and negative stimuli of this type, as well as their inhibition.

The awakened interest in cerebral conditioned responses resulted in a cooperative investigation by scientists from the United States, the Netherlands, Poland, and France. These studies (4) revealed that early in the course of conditioning, the electrographic response to the conditioned stimulus developed over wide areas of the cortex (the "startle" response). Later, the response to the conditioned stimulus became localized to the region where the unconditioned response would be expected to appear. Based on these and previous investigations, the authors postulated development of conditioned cerebral responses to be the result of a "temporary link" made in the thalamic reticular formation.

A major question persists as to what to term this phenomenon whereby a previously indifferent stimulus, by temporal association with a stimulus whose effect upon the electroencephalogram is predictable, acquires the ability to provoke this same predictable electro-

---

Reprinted with permission from the chapter "Alpha Wave Responsiveness to Light in Man" from *EEG and Behavior,* ed. by Gilbert H. Glaser. Basic Books, New York, 1963

graphic response. Early investigators regarded this simply as another form of conditioned reflex, differing from those described by Pavlov in the absence of motivation and of overt response. The alpha blocking response (alpha attenuation, arousal reaction, alpha desynchronization) was regarded by many as the electrographic manifestation of the orientation reflex or, as Pavlov (11) called it, the "What is it?" response. When, by a "conditioning" procedure, a previously indifferent stimulus provoked this alpha attenuation, it was assumed that this represented another form of conditioned reflex. As early as 1941, Knott and Henry (7) questioned this interpretation, suggesting that this might represent a conditioned anticipatory response instead of a true conditioned reflex. The observation of Jasper and Shagass (5), however, seemed to favor these as representing conditioned reflexes in the Pavlovian sense.

Following publication of Morrell and Ross's paper in 1953 (10) a rebuttal (17) appeared, maintaining that these responses could best be interpreted in non-Pavlovian terms rather than in terms of conditioning and inhibition, a view vigorously opposed by Morrell (9). Later, Lilly (8) also deprecated the use of standard Pavlovian terms for changes in cerebral function detected by electroencephalographic means. More recently still, Stern et al. (13) and W. Grey Walter (16) have advanced further objections to entitling these phenomena "conditioned cerebral responses." This reluctance to employ Pavlovian terms for electrical events has led to their being called "temporary cerebral connections," "electrical correlates of conditioning responses," "contingent alpha blocking," and so on.

This study is concerned predominantly with the development of these phenomena in groups of human subjects, not with the physiological interpretation of this particular response. For this reason and because it is a term readily understood by most scientists familiar with the field, the term "conditioned cerebral response" has been utilized throughout this paper. It is not meant to imply that these "conditioned cerebral responses" necessarily represent true conditioned reflexes in the Pavlovian sense, but alternative terms serve only to expand an already imprecise nomenclature.

One of the continuing problems in electroencephalography is the occurrence of a normal electroencephalogram in certain individuals with patently obvious cerebral disease. Since the early papers of Berger (2) and of Adrian and Matthews (1), many studies have been devoted to this problem and to means by which an abnormality might be stimulated to appear in the electroencephalogram of patients known to have cerebral disease but whose resting electroencephalograms are normal. Thus a number of activation procedures have been designed to reveal abnormalities where none were observed or to accentuate them where few were found. Hyperventilation, sleep, water loading, stimulation with rhythmically flashing light, injection of cerebral stimulants, injection of sedative drugs—all have been found of some value as activating measures. Hyperventilation, sleep, and rhythmic photic stimulation have proved sufficiently useful to constitute a routine part of the electroencephalographic examination in most laboratories.

It was well known from the studies previously described that by the use of paired sound and light stimuli alpha activity demonstrated conditioned cerebral responses satisfying many of the criteria for Pavlovian conditioning. It was also known that subjects with lesions of the cerebral hemispheres failed to develop conditioned responses of the classic Pavlovian type as well as did normal subjects (18). The question then arose whether the development of conditioned cerebral responses could be quantitated to evaluate the functional capacity of the cerebrum of man. Since the studies of Travis and Egan (14) and of Knott and Henry (7), almost no quantitative figures regarding the development of conditioned cerebral responses have been presented. It was therefore necessary to study these conditioned cerebral responses in normal human subjects to determine whether their development could be quantitated. Further investigation of these conditioned cerebral responses in the brain-damaged individual might: 1) demonstrate whether formation of conditioned cerebral responses is impaired in the individual with disease of the cerebral hemispheres, and 2) throw light upon the functional and anatomical substratum necessary for development of these conditioned responses in man.

Some preliminary observations (3) have already been published. These studies, performed in 15 normal subjects and 26 subjects with known cerebral damage, indicated that individuals with gross structural brain damage developed significantly fewer conditioned cerebral responses than did normal subjects. No correlation could be established between the location of the brain lesion and impaired ability to form conditioned cerebral responses. Recently reported studies by Visser (15), who utilized similar techniques, are in accord with these observations. He noted formation of significantly fewer conditioned cerebral responses in patients with "organic psychosis" than in normal subjects and in patients with other psychiatric diagnoses. He further found a close positive correlation between the alpha frequency and the "intensity" of the conditioned cerebral response. This section reports studies on formation of conditioned cerebral responses in a large number of normal and brain-damaged subjects.

Methods and Material

Studies were carried out in a quiet and semidarkened room with the subject separated by a partition from the examiner, the recording equipment, and the device for triggering sound and light stimuli. Needle scalp electrodes were placed bilaterally in the frontal, parietal, temporal, and occipital areas, and bipolar recordings were made by means of a Grass Model III Electroencephalograph. Auditory stimulation, produced by a Beltone Audiometer, was delivered through earphones to one ear at a frequency of 500 c./sec. at 40 to 50 decibels above the level of audibility. In the earlier experiments, a low masking sound was delivered to the opposite ear, but this was discontinued when better isolation facilities were developed. Visual stimulation was provided by a 150-watt bulb with white reflector placed approximately 12 inches in front of the patient's closed eyes.

Before testing began, the experimental procedure was explained to the subject in general terms to allay apprehensions regarding the study. During the testing period, the subject was seated with eyes closed. He was presented first with the light stimulus, 3 sec. in duration, repeated once or twice to show that light initially suppressed the alpha activity (Fig. 1). Auditory stimuli then followed, 4 sec. each in duration, repeated until the alpha activity became habituated to the sound—an arbitrarily defined state where five successive presentations of the tone failed to provoke any change in the background activity (Fig. 2). Paired sound and light stimuli were then presented to the subject, the light appearing 0.8 to 1.0 sec. after the sound. Both sound and light then continued together for 3 sec. before stopping simultaneously. The interval separating the appearance of sound and light was timed automatically and remained constant in each subject. The paired sound-light stimuli were presented to each subject 50 times, at irregular time intervals to avoid cyclic conditioning. The experimenter tried to present the stimuli when alpha activity was most prominent. On an average, one sound-light stimulus was given every 15-20 sec. A total of 50 paired stimuli was chosen because it was almost impossible to maintain alertness for any longer period of study.

The usual response to the paired sound-light stimulus is illustrated in Fig. 3. Sound generally had no effect upon alpha activity, but light was usually followed by prompt disappearance or marked attenuation of the alpha waves. A conditioned cerebral response was considered to have occurred whenever the alpha rhythm was obliterated or strikingly attenuated following presentation of the auditory stimulus but before the appearance of the visual stimulus. Figs. 4 and 5 demonstrated typical conditioned cerebral responses. The number of conditioned cerebral responses occurring out of the 50 paired sound-light presentations was determined for each subject, the author evaluating the records without knowledge of the patient's name or clinical status.

The formation of conditioned cerebral responses has been studied by these methods in 153 subjects. Thirty-eight of these were excluded from statistical evaluation because the poor quality or absence of alpha activity in their electroencephalogram precluded demonstration of these conditioned responses. They are not further considered here. The remaining 115 presented well-developed and well-regulated alpha activity, present for over 50 per cent of the recording

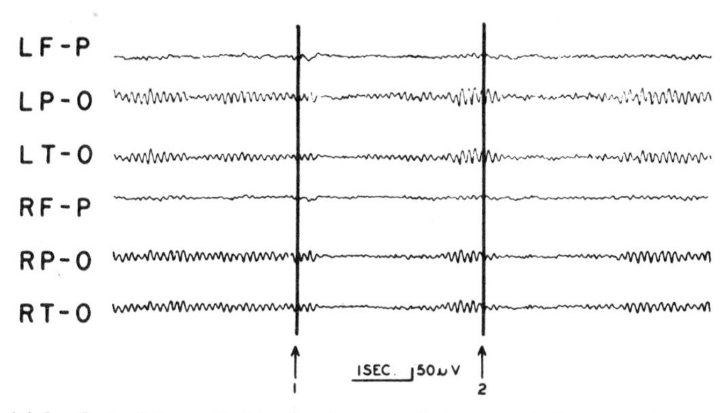

FIG. 1. Initial effect of 3-sec. light stimulus on electroencephalogram. Arrow 1 = appearance of light. Arrow 2 = disappearance of light.

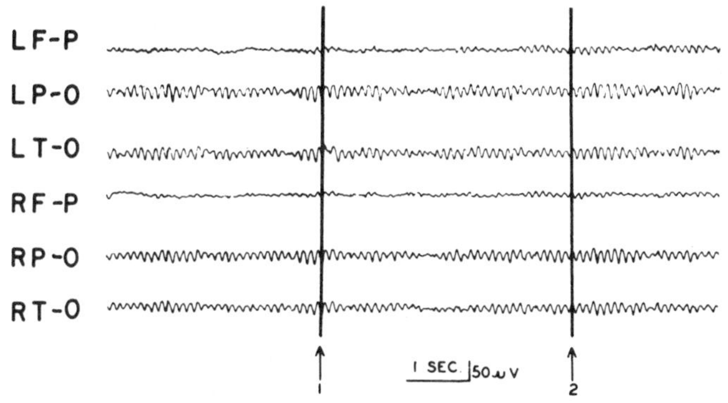

FIG. 2. Electroencephalogram of subject habituated to the effect of 4-sec. sound stimulus. Arrow 1 = appearance of sound. Arrow 2 = disappearance of sound.

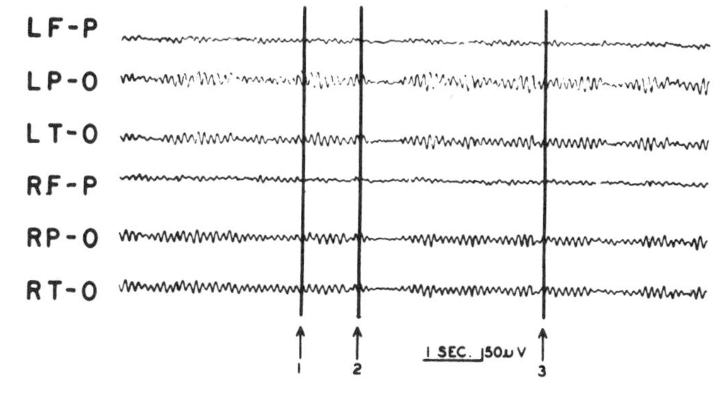

FIG. 3. Usual response to paired sound-light stimulus. Arrow 1 = onset of sound. Arrow 2 = onset of light. Arrow 3 = disappearance of sound and light. Note that sound alone has no effect upon the electroencephalogram, while light is followed by disappearance of alpha activity.

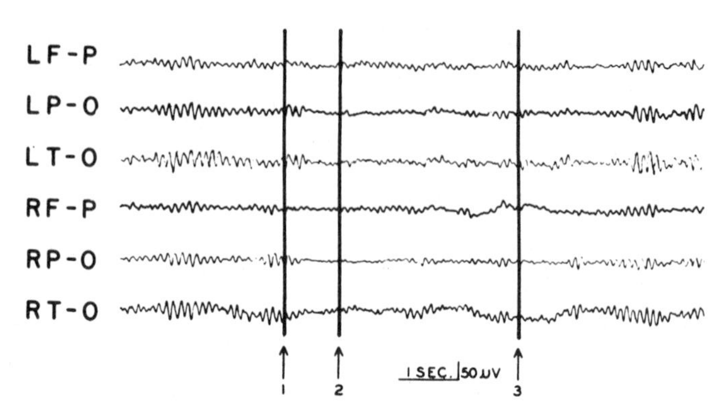

FIG. 4. Conditioned cerebral response. Sound. arrow 1, is followed by disappearance of alpha activity before light appears, arrow 2. Arrow 3 = disappearance of sound and light.

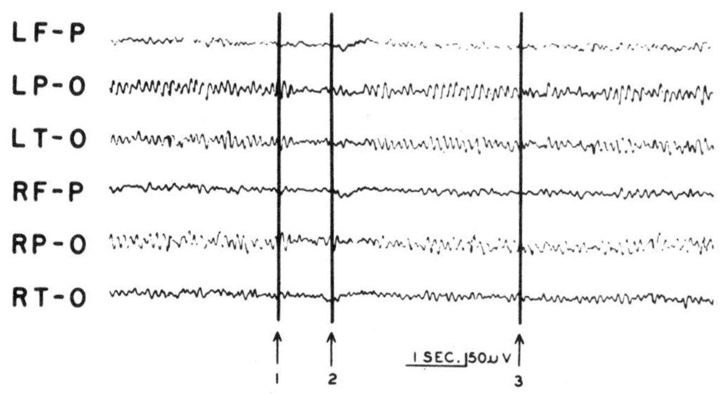

FIG. 5. Conditioned cerebral response. Sound, arrow 1, is followed by disappearance of alpha activity before light appears, arrow 2. Arrow 3 = disappearance of sound and light.

in all subjects and over 75 per cent in most subjects. These 115 subjects included 46 control subjects who had no suggestion of any disease involving the cerebral hemispheres or brain stem. These control subjects were predominantly medical students, house-staff physicians, and laboratory personnel but also included some patients admitted to the hospital for diseases not involving the brain stem or cerebral hemispheres.

Sixty-nine patients with diseases of the cerebral hemispheres or brain stem were studied. Their diagnoses are listed below.

DIAGNOSIS	NUMBER
Intracranial Neoplasms	20
Meningiomas–6	
Arteriovenous Abnormalities–6	
Primary Intracerebral Neoplasms–4	
Pituitary Adenomas–2	
Carcinoma Metastatic to Cerebrum–2	
Cerebral Vascular Disease	14
Seizure Disorders	10
Disseminated Sclerosis	9
Degenerative Cerebral Diseases	8
Cerebral Emboli	4
Central Nervous System Syphilis	1
Central Nervous System Sarcoidosis	1
Cerebellar Degeneration with Chronic Alcoholism	1
Parkinson's Disease	1
Total	69

The only criteria for choice were that the patient be capable of sitting for the required period and that he be sufficiently cooperative to permit a satisfactory examination. A number of the "patients" (notably several with seizure disorders and with multiple sclerosis) had no evidence on clinical neurological examination to suggest a structural lesion of the brain stem or cerebral hemisphere. They were included in the group of patients, however, because their clinical diagnoses made it impossible to exclude such a lesion. The group was thus somewhat weighted in the direction of normal by inclusion of these subjects.

Results

The number of conditioned cerebral responses which occurred in the 50 paired sound-light presentations for the control and for the patient group is shown graphically in Fig. 6. The 46 control subjects developed a mean of 10.2 conditioned cerebral responses out of 50 presentations, with a standard deviation of ±2.9. The 69 patient subjects developed a mean of 6.1 conditioned cerebral responses out of 50 presentations, with a standard deviation of ±3.8. The difference between the number of conditioned cerebral responses in the control and in the patient group is highly significant, the statistical likelihood of its occurring by chance being less than 1 per cent.

The diagnosis and the result of the routine clinical electroencephalogram in the 21 patients who developed eight or more conditioned cerebral responses are listed below.

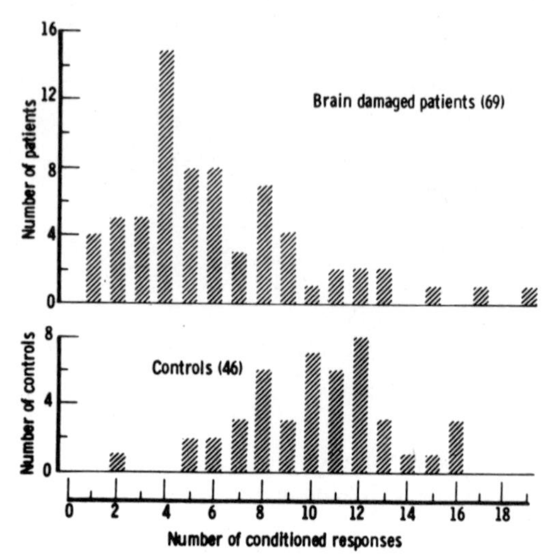

FIG. 6. Comparison of number of conditioned cerebral responses formed by the control subjects and the patients with neurological disease.

DIAGNOSIS	EEG
Disseminated Sclerosis	Rare Spikes
Rt. Frontal Astrocytoma (3 years post surgery)	RF Delta and Theta
Rt. T-O Arteriovenous Malformation (5 years post surgery)	RT-O Theta
Left Cerebral Embolus	Left Hemisphere Delta
Left Cerebral Embolus	Left Hemisphere Delta
Left Hemisphere CVA	Left Hemisphere Delta
Cerebral Degeneration	LF-T Delta
Seizure Disorder	Rare Spikes During Sleep
Seizure Disorder	Normal
Seizure Disorder	Normal
Pituitary Adenoma	Normal
Cerebral Vascular Insufficiency	Normal
Cerebral Vascular Insufficiency	Normal
Brain Stem Vascular Accident	Normal
Brain Stem Vascular Accident	Normal
Ant. Fossa Meningioma	Normal
CNS Sarcoidosis	Normal
Disseminated Sclerosis	Normal
Disseminated Sclerosis	Normal
Disseminated Sclerosis	Normal
Disseminated Sclerosis	Normal

The routine clinical electroencephalogram was normal in 13 of these 21 subjects, while in seven it was abnormal. Six of these patients had normal neurological examinations and normal electroencephalograms. They were included in the patient group because it was impossible to exclude a cerebral lesion in the presence of their clinical diagnosis. Six patients with fewer than eight conditioned cerebral responses had normal clinical electroencephalograms.

Although the average age between the two groups is significantly different (mean age in the control group was 30.8 years; mean age in the patient group, 44.9 years), there was nothing within the groups to suggest that the number of conditioned cerebral responses was correlated with age.

Discussion

The development of conditioned cerebral response has been shown to be a quality which can be quantitated. Although there is a wide variation in response among different subjects, these studies clearly demonstrate that the group of patients suffering from diseases involving the brain stem and the cerebral hemispheres developed significantly fewer conditioned cerebral responses than did the group of normal control subjects. Furthermore, on the basis of evidence obtained in an earlier portion of this study, impairment of the ability to develop conditioned cerebral responses is not related to the location of the cerebral lesion, impairment occurring with lesions of the brain stem as well as with lesions involving any portion of the cerebral hemispheres. Nor can the degree of impairment be correlated with size of the lesion—not a surprising observation when a function manifests such wide variation even among normal subjects.

Although the difference in formation of conditioned cerebral responses in the two groups is statistically very significant, for a variety of reasons the test lacks clinical applicability. Perhaps the most significant factor limiting its clinical use is the wide overlap in results between the control group and the patient group (see Fig. 6). Among the patients who developed as many conditioned cerebral responses as did most of the controls, there were a number whose routine electroencephalogram was within normal limits and whose neurological examination gave no evidence for a focal cerebral lesion (primarily patients with multiple sclerosis or seizure disorders). On the other hand, six patients with known disease of the cerebral hemispheres had normal routine electroencephalographic studies but developed fewer conditioned cerebral responses than did the normal group. Thus, while the test for development of conditioned cerebral responses may occasionally reveal abnormalities of function where none was apparent on the routine electroencephalogram, in general the percentage of abnormality unearthed by this test is no better than that found on the routine electroencephalogram while its interpretation is considerably more difficult and time-consuming.

Several other factors limit the clinical applicablity of this test. First, it is hard to administer since the patient must remain alert throughout the paired presentations, a situation frequently difficult to obtain. Further, it is of use only in subjects who have a well-regulated and well-developed alpha activity over at least one hemisphere; thus a significant number of subjects are excluded before the test even begins. Lastly, the records are hard to interpret. The normal fluctuation in alpha activity is such that it may be impossible to judge whether a diminution in alpha wave amplitude is a response to a stimulus or a physiological variation. Even after several years of careful attention to the details of this test, instances continue to arise in some number where the author just cannot be certain whether or not a cerebral conditioned response had occurred. Since all records in the present series have been read by one person without knowledge of the clinical status of the subject at the time of interpretation, it can be assumed that these uncertainties are averaged out over the two groups as a whole.

Summary

Development of the conditioned cerebral response was studied in 153 subjects by the presentation of 50 paired sound-light stimuli, the sound preceding the light by 0.8-1.0 sec. The records of 38 subjects were excluded because of the poor quality or the absence of alpha activity at rest. The remaining 115 subjects included 46 controls and 69 patients with diseases of the cerebral hemispheres or brain stem. The 46 control subjects developed a mean of 10.1 conditioned cerebral responses out of 50 presentations; the 69 patients developed a mean of 6.1 conditioned cerebral responses out of 50 presentations. The difference between the number of conditioned cerebral responses developing in the two groups is highly significant, the likelihood of this difference occurring by chance being less than 1 per cent.

References

1. Adrian, E. D. and Matthews, B. H. C.: The Berger Rhythm; Potential changes from the occipital lobes in man. *Brain, 57*:355-385, 1934.
2. Berger, H.: Über das Elektrenkephalogramm des Menschen. *Arch. Psychiat, Nervenkr., 87*:527-570, 1929.
3. Chapman, L. F. and Wolff, H. G., The cerebral hemsipheres and the highest integrative functions of man. *Arch. Neurol., Chicago, 1*:357-424, 1959.
4. Gastaut, H., Jus, A., Jus, C., Morrell, F., Storm van Leeuwen, W., Dongier, S., Naquet R., Regis, H., Roger, A., Bekkering, D., Kamp, A., and Werre, J.: Étude topographique des réactions électroencéphalographiques conditionées chez l'homme. *Electroenceph. clin. Neurophysiol. 9*:1-34, 1957.

5. Jasper, H. and Shagass, C.: Conditioning the occipital alpha rhythm in man. *J. exp. Psychol., 28*:373-388, 1941.
6. Jus, A. and Jus, C.: Les méthodes bioélectriques dans l'expérience conditionnelle clinique. *Electroenceph. clin. Neurophysiol.,* Suppl. *6*:25-37, 1957.
7. Knott, J. R. and Henry, C. E.: The conditioning of the blocking of the alpha rhythm of the human electroencephalogram. *J. exp. Psychol., 28*: 134-144, 1941.
8. Lilly, J. C.: Discussion, in Brazier, M. A. B. (ed.), *The Central Nervous System and Behavior,* Trans. First Conference, Josiah Macy, Jr. Foundation, New York, 1958.
9. Morrell, F.: Further discussion of a note on Morrell and Ross's 'Central inhibition in cortical conditioned reflexes.' *Arch. Neurol. Psychiat., Chicago, 75*:563-565, 1956.
10. Morrell, F. and Ross, M. H.: Central inhibition in cortical conditioned reflexes. *Arch. Neurol. Psychiat., Chicago, 70*:611-616, 1953.
11. Pavlov, I. P.: *Conditioned Reflexes. An Investigation of the Physiological Activity of the Cerebral Cortex*, Anrep, G. V. (trans. and ed.), Oxford University Press, London, 1927, 430 pp.
12. Rusinov, V. S. and Smirnov, G. D.: Quelques données sur l'étude électroencéphalographique de l'activité nerveuse supérieure. *Electroenceph. clin. Neurophysiol.,* Suppl. *6*:9-23, 1957.
13. Stern, J. A., Das, K. C., Anderson, J. M., Biddy, R. L., and Surphlis, W.: A study of 'conditioned' alpha desynchronization. *Science, 134*:388, 1961.
14. Travis, L. E. and Egan, J. P.: Conditioning of the electrical response of the cortex. *J. exp. Psychol., 22*:524-531, 1938.
15. Visser, S. L.: Correlations between the contingent alpha blocking, EEG characteristics and clinical diagnosis. *Electroenceph. clin. Neurophysiol., 13*:438-446, 1961.
16. Walter, W. Grey.: The vocabulary of psycho-physiology. *Electroenceph. clin. Neurophysiol., 13*:447-448, 1961.
17. Weiss, B.: Morrell and Ross's 'Central inhibition in cortical conditioned reflexes.' *Arch. Neurol. Psychiat., Chicago, 74*:171-173, 1955.
18. Wells, C. E. and Wolff, H. G.: Formation of temporary cerebral connections in normal and brain-damaged subjects. *Neurology, 10*:335-340, 1960.

10

CONDITIONING AS A CAUSE OF ASTHMATIC ATTACKS; A LABORATORY STUDY

by Egbart Dekker, M.D., Henk E. Pelser, M.D.,
and Juda Groen, M.D.

Introduction

A number of authors have written on the role which conditioning may play as a cause of attacks of asthma. Their evidence, however, was mostly indirect, mainly based on clinical histories as obtained from the patients. Some of our former observations on asthmatic attacks provoked by emotional stimuli under controlled laboratory conditions also seemed in line with a conditioning mechanism although they did not represent classical examples of such a mechanism.

Strictly speaking, a conditioned attack of asthma should contain the following elements:

1. One or more attacks of asthmatic dyspnoea.
2. A conditioning stimulus or situation, which originally does not in itself produce an attack but coincides with these attacks.
3. The occurrence of attacks after exposure to the conditioned stimulus or the conditioned situation alone.

In this paper, observations on two patients are presented which seem to fulfil these requirements. In both patients the conditioning took place under experimental conditions in the laboratory and the effect could be measured by the standard technique used in the former investigation.

Methods

The experiments were carried out in the course of investigations during which patients were exposed to allergic and emotional stimuli. To register the effect, we used a modification of the method developed by Herxheimer (16, 17) and ten Cate and Orie (4, 5) for the detection of inhalation allergy by provocation tests. In this method the vital capacity is

Reprinted with permission from *J. Psychosomatic Res.*, 1957, Vol. 2, pp. 97-108. Pergamon Press Ltd., London.

used as the parameter. The patient is seated in front of a spirograph. Every 4 min. the vital capacity is determined; between these determinations, the patient is not connected to any apparatus. After the vital capacity has been registered a number of times and a baseline value has been obtained, the patients are exposed to various stimuli. During the experiment the determination of the vital capacity is continued every 4 min. for at least 20 min., as far as the condition of the patient allows.

For the present investigation into the possibility of the production of asthmatic attacks by conditioning under laboratory conditions, an unconditioned stimulus was provided by the inhalation of nebulized allergens to which the patients were hypersensitive.

An aerosol† of grass-pollen extract (5000 Noon units per ml.) was administered to the first patient; the second patient inhaled an aerosol of a 5% solution of house-dust extract as prepared in the University of Groningen (5).

The allergens were nebulized in glass atomizers‡ by means of a stream of oxygen with a flow-rate of 4 l./min. The atomizers were placed, hidden from the patient's view, in a wooden box. The box contained a number of holes through which rubber tubing carried the aerosol to the patient. The tubes from any atomizer could be made to leave the box through any hole; this prevented the patient from knowing what substance he or she was given to inhale. The inhalation took place by means of an exchangeable glass-tube mouthpiece, held loosely between the half-opened lips through which the patient was quietly breathing outside air.

A regularly progressive decrease of the vital capacity of more than 10% of the mean of the baseline values was accepted as a positive reaction, according to the standards laid down by ten Cate and Orie (4, 5).

The figures give the mean value for all the determinations of the vital capacity during a 20-min. observation after the end of the provocation or, in other instances, up to the moment when an attack had to be stopped by drugs. The effect of drugs has been indicated as the maximal increase in the vital capacity which was observed.

After one or more positive reactions to the inhalation, we gradually changed the inhalation situation and studied the influence of these changes on the effect. These "fragments" of the inhalation situation acted as conditioned stimuli. Registration and evaluation of these reactions took place in the same manner as those of the allergic reactions. This determined the sequence of the experiments described below.

Observations

Case 1. *A.*

A 37-year-old unmarried housekeeper suffered from serious bronchial asthma. Skin reactions to grass pollen and tree pollen were strongly positive.

26 April: First control inhalation test with the neutral solvent of the allergen extracts,* caused a slight subjective dyspnoea and a decrease of the

† Trademark: LIFA, Groningen. ‡ Trademark: Wiesbadener Doppelinhalator.

* Coca solution: A watery solution of sodium chloride, sodium bicarbonate with a trace of phenol.

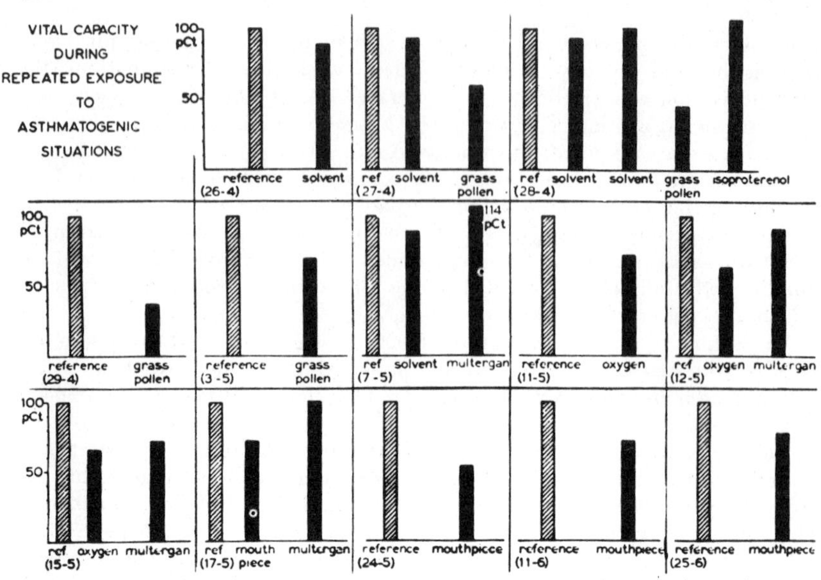

FIG. 1 (Patient *A*). Diagram of vital capacity measurements. The mean values of the baseline determinations, indicated by the shaded areas, are the reference level, put at 100%. The black areas indicate the means of the vital capacities after each test, expressed in percentages of the corresponding reference values.

vital capacity to a mean of −11% (Fig. 1). The patient showed manifest anxiety for the examination. After reassurance the vital capacity increased to −4%.

27 April: A second inhalation of an aerosol of the neutral solvent caused no dyspnoea and no decrease in vital capacity. The inhalation of a solution of grass-pollen extract however, had to be stopped after 6 min. because of an attack of asthma during which the vital capacity decreased to a mean of −40%. The attack was stopped by administration of an aerosol of isoprenaline.

28 April: The experiment was repeated in exactly the same way. The investigator took care to use exactly the same words for his instructions to the patient. Inhalation of the neutral solvent caused no reaction. From the same opening in the atomizer box from which the patient had received the pollen aerosol on 27 April, the neutral solvent was administered for a second time; again there was no reaction. Inhalation of a grass-pollen aerosol, however, once more caused an impressive attack of asthma with a mean decrease of the vital capacity to −54%; inhalation of isoprenaline stopped this attack within a few minutes.

To test the possibility that the patient believed that the first solution she was given to inhale was always innocuous, she was made to inhale grass-pollen extract without preliminary control on 29 April and 3 May. Each of these inhalations was followed by a clear-cut attack of asthma.

This convinced us that the positive reactions to the inhalation of grass-pollen extract could not be ascribed to emotional factors; the patient obviously met the criteria of ten Cate and Orie for the presence of a manifest inhalation allergy to grass pollen.

On 7 May another inhalation test with the neutral solvent was carried out. To our amazement, the patient reacted this time with subjective and objective dyspnoea and wheezing during the inhalation. The vital capacity dropped to −11% after 10 min. inhalation.

Several explanations for this phenomenon seemed possible: fatigue caused by the repeated measurements of the vital capacity, an allergic reaction to minute amounts of allergen in the apparatus, or a reaction to psychological influences.

The dyspnoea and wheezing had begun already during the inhalation. This made fatigue seem improbable. Moreover, a series of vital capacity determinations during 60 min., without preceding inhalation, caused no decrease of the vital capacity, so that this possibility seemed excluded.

The possibility of an allergic influence was next studied by a series of control experiments. To rule out the presence of an allergen in the solvent, a stream of oxygen was administered through an empty new atomizer. This caused a typical attack of asthma with a decrease of vital capacity to −27%. The attack disappeared 20 min. after the intramuscular injection of thiazinamine.*

To exclude contamination of the rubber tubing by traces of allergen as the cause of these attacks, new rubber tubes were built into the apparatus. Oxygen inhalation through these tubes on the 12 May caused another attack. In view of the possibility that the patient may have become sensitive to substances in the rubber, plastic tubing was used. The glass mouthpieces were exchanged for new ones. All these measures did not prevent the patient from developing an impressive attack of asthma on the inhalation of oxygen through this new material. The vital capacity decreased to a mean value of −34%.

Next, the presence of allergens in the oxygen had to be excluded. On 17 May with this purpose, the patient was placed before the atomizer box as usual. After the baseline determinations, the nose clip was applied and the glass mouthpiece given between the lips. The patient herself remarked that the mouthpiece was not connected to the tubing and the atomizer. The investigator replied that this was not necessary. Within 5 min. after inhaling ordinary room air through and past the glass mouthpiece, she developed an attack of asthma which gradually increased in severity; the vital capacity decreased to a mean of −27%. Obviously the patient had now reached a state where it was possible to provoke an attack of asthma within a few minutes by simply asking her to hold a piece of glass tube in her mouth.

Our last, admittedly somewhat far-fetched, allergic hypotheses were that some substance in the laboratory or on the body of the observer might be responsible for the phenomenon.

With this in mind the experiment was repeated on 24 May in the ward, where the patient at that period had no "spontaneous" attacks. A severe attack was produced by putting the glass tube in her mouth for a few minutes; the vital capacity fell to a mean of −46%.

* Trademark: Multergan.

A different investigator was asked to perform the next experiments. He abandoned the use of the nose-clip and provoked clear-cut asthmatic attacks on different occasions on 11 June and 25 June by the simple introduction of the mouthpiece alone. All these attacks could be stopped by the injection of thiazinamine. Representative curves from this series of observations are reproduced in Fig. 2.

Case 2. *B*.

A 37-year-old female shop assistant suffered from severe bronchial asthma. Skin tests for house dust and tree pollen were positive.

A similar series of observations as in the first case were done in this patient (Fig. 3).

1 September: the investigation for inhalation allergy was started. Administration of an aerosol of the "neutral" solvent gave a mean decrease of the vital capacity to −9%. Inhalation of a mist of tree-pollen extract of 25,000 Noon units per ml. caused an irregular decrease of the vital capacity of an average of 12%. The inhalation of house-dust extract, however, was followed within 4 min. by a severe asthmatic attack and a decrease of the vital capacity to −59%. The attack was suppressed by inhalation of isoprenaline.

This strongly positive reaction made a manifest inhalation allergy to house-dust extract highly probable. Its existence was confirmed in a series of later investigations not included in this paper, which regularly gave positive reactions to the allergen extract.

During the next investigation on 7 September the control inhalation of the neutral solvent was also followed by a clear-cut attack of asthma and a decrease of the vital capacity to a mean of −40%. This made us interrupt the further investigation of the inhalation allergy and begin a series of investigations into the cause of the asthmatic attacks following the inhalation of the indifferent solvent.

On 14 September the patient inhaled oxygen instead of an aerosol. It caused a slight subjective and objective dyspnoea. The vital capacity decreased by a mean of 20%. A detail worth mentioning was that during this dyspnoea the patient's nose secreted a watery fluid, as had happened during many of her "spontaneous" attacks. Oxygen, administered through plastic tubes, caused a similar decrease in vital capacity the next day. On 22 September inhalation of oxygen through plastic tubing caused another attack, this time even more severe. There was typical wheezing and the vital capacity dropped to a mean of −60%. When the tubes were disconnected from the oxygen supply, she still reacted to the introduction of the mouthpiece with the plastic tubes attached, by a decrease of the vital capacity of 30%.

On 29 September the vital capacity dropped 23% of the mean of the first three determinations when the patient was simply seated in front of the atomizer-box without any inhalation or imitation thereof.

It must be pointed out, however, that this patient was less suitable as a subject for this kind of examination than patient *A*. During the baseline period the variation of her vital-capacity determinations often somewhat exceeded the 10% limit. In addition she was the habitual user of a handspray apparatus with the proprietary preparation "respifral." The possibility that

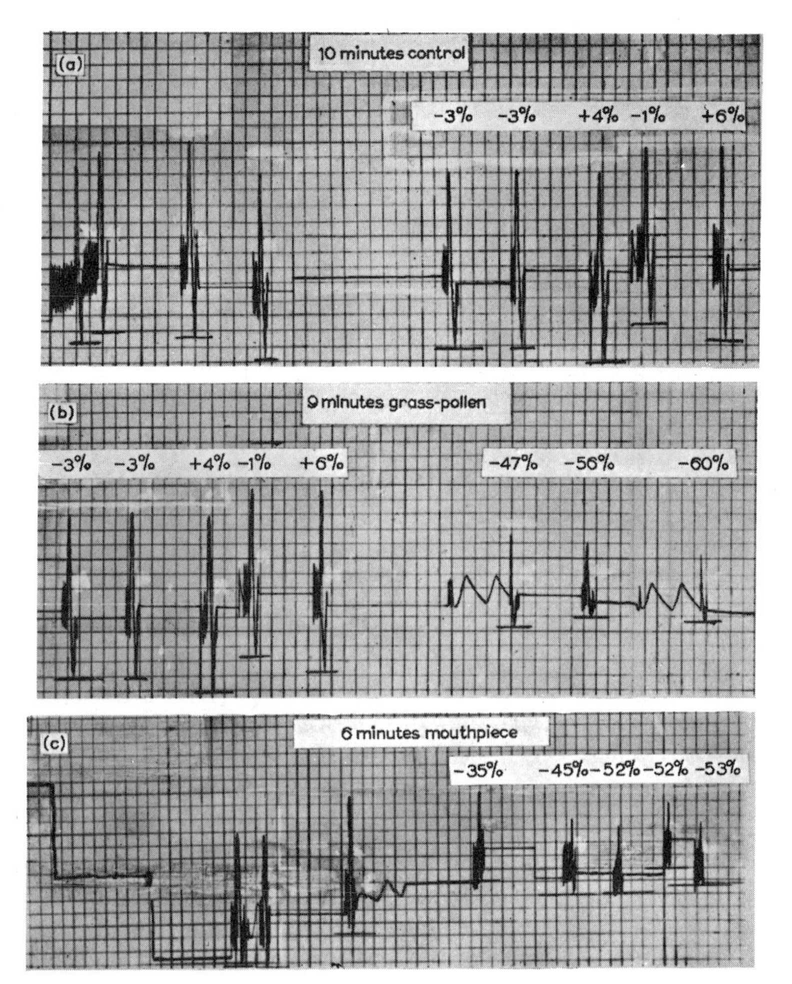

FIG. 2. (Patient *A*). Spirographic records of the reactions of the vital capacity of patient *A*.
(a) To the inhalation of the neutral solvent.
(b) To the inhalation of grass-pollen extract.
(c) To the introduction of the glass mouthpiece after conditioning. (This record is reproduced on a more reduced scale than the other two.)

the asthmatic breathing and the reduction of the vital capacity might result from the wearing off of the pharmacological activity of the drug could not be definitely excluded. However, the change in vital capacity and the onset of asthmatic attacks followed so regularly after the inhalation situation, and this could be repeated so often, that the assumption of a causal relation seemed convincing to two observers and to the patient.

VITAL CAPACITY DURING REPEATED EXPOSURE TO ASTHMATOGENIC SITUATIONS

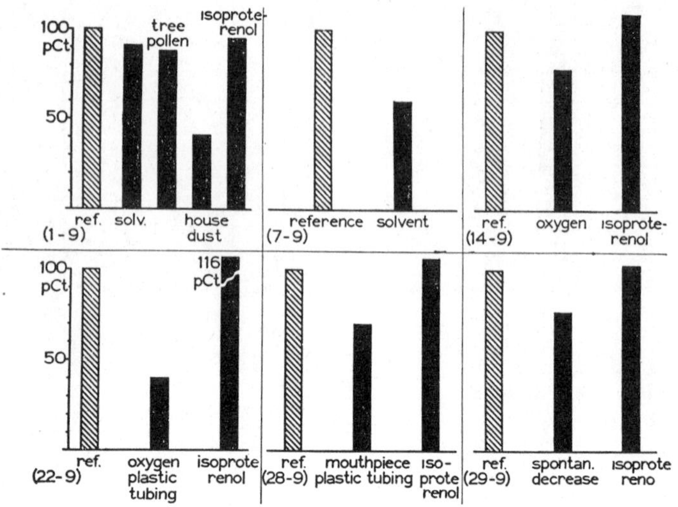

FIG. 3. (Patient *B*). Explanation in legend, Fig. 1.

These experiments concerned two asthmatic patients, who had positive skin reactions to grass pollen and house dust respectively and who reacted by typical attacks of asthma when they were given these allergens to inhale in the laboratory. The inhalation of the neutral solvent of the allergen extracts initially caused no reaction.

In the course of further inhalation experiments, however, the reaction patterns of the patients changed. They began to react also to the inhalation of the indifferent solvent with attacks of dyspnoea. Later it was found that the inhalation of pure oxygen in the laboratory caused attacks of asthma, and finally it was sufficient to introduce the mouthpiece of the apparatus or to imitate a connection of the mouthpiece with the inhalation apparatus, to provoke severe paroxysms of asthma. These attacks, once developed, could not be distinguished from those which appeared after inhalation of allergens or from spontaneous attacks: more specifically they reacted favourably to inhalation of isoprenaline or injection of Multergan.

These observations gave the impression that the patients had become conditioned by the allergic attacks to the inhalation situation and later even to certain "fragments" thereof.

In the next series of experiments an attempt was made to cure the patients.

During a number of interviews with patient *A*, her fears for the investigations and her actual life difficulties were discussed. During these interviews the investigator tried to give her support and reassurance. He explained that the introduction of a piece of glass tube could not possibly be harmful. After a number of interviews he gave her the mouthpiece to hold between her lips for a few seconds only. This gave no reaction. Under constant reassurance the time during which the patient held the mouthpiece between the lips was gradually increased. However, when an exposure time of 4 min. had been reached, the patient got a severe attack of asthma which had to be stopped by isoprenaline.

This attempt at deconditioning by verbal and "personal" influence therefore did not succeed.

In patient *B* the therapeutic effect of a combination of supportive psychotherapy with suggestion was studied. The patient was seen in regular interviews; she also took part in group psychotherapy. In the meantime the inhalations were continued. Preceding each inhalation, the patient was given an intramuscular injection of thiazinamine; in the course of the succeeding investigations the dose of thiazinamine was gradually decreased and finally the drug was substituted with saline. Strict precautions were taken so that the nature of the injections was unknown to the patient. In a third period the preceding injections were altogether omitted.

Table 1 summarizes the effects on the mean vital capacity during the first 20 min. after each inhalation under these circumstances. Thiazinamine produced a considerable increase in vital capacity, even in low doses. It also gave considerable protection against the attacks of asthma after the inhalation of oxygen. On 8 October the inhalation of oxygen was tolerated without a

Table 1. Patient B. Effect of gradually diminishing doses of thiazinamine followed by saline (0) and omission of the injection (—), on "provocation test" by inhalation of oxygen or neutral solvent. Doubtful deconditioning.

Date	Dose thiazinamine (mg)	Inhalation and time		Mean effect on vital capacity in per cent
5/10/55	25	O_2	10 min	+13
6/10/55	12·5	O_2	10 min	+18
7/10/55	6·25	O_2	10 min	+32
7/10/55	0	O_2	10 min	−22
8/10/55	—	O_2	10 min	+1
12/10/55	—	solvent	10 min	−27
13/10/55	12·5	solvent	10 min	+14
14/10/55	6·25	solvent	10 min	+40
16/10/55	0	solvent	10 min	−27
19/10/55	—	solvent	10 min	−11
20/10/55	50	solvent	10 min	+86
21/10/55	—	solvent	10 min	−10

preceding injection. There was no decrease of the vital capacity. But on 12 October inhalation of the neutral solvent was followed by a renewed decrease in vital capacity. This effect could be prevented by a preceding injection of thiazinamine, but not by injection of saline.

The inhalations were continued, and on 19 October the decrease in the vital capacity after inhalation of the solvent was 11%, on 21 October it was 10%. On 8 November inhalation of the solvent caused no decrease any more. At this stage, after a long series of "deconditioning," the patient reacted as she did in the beginning: the inhalation of the neutral solvent did not produce an attack.

In a next series we attempted to desensitize the patient in a similar manner to the inhalation of the house-dust extract (Table 2). Thiazinamine proved to be effective in preventing attacks from the allergen. However, when this premedication was omitted, on 23 November house-dust extract caused a severe attack of asthma, just as it did in the beginning. After the patient had undergone this "unconditioned" attack, two inhalations of the neutral solvent again provoked attacks of asthma with decreases in vital capacity of 49% and 27% respectively. Apparently the effects of the deconditioning procedure broke down very easily after the experience of a single severe attack in the inhalation situation.

At this moment the inhalation experiments were interrupted.

The patient was re-examined eleven months later. In the meantime she had been treated by occasional individual and regular group psychotherapy. An obvious change in her personality and behaviour towards doctors and fellow patients had taken place in the meantime. She still was rather timid and easily disturbed, but she was far different from the withdrawn, extemely sensitive, and overtly fearful person she had been at the time of the previous investigation. Inhalation of the neutral solvent produced no reaction (Table 3); inhalation of house dust still caused attacks. A series of inhalations of

Table 2. Patient B. Effect of thiazinamine, followed by saline (0) and omission of th injection (—) on effect of provocation-test by inhalation of allergen or neutral solvent On 8/11 the result indicated the possibility of deconditioning by this procedure: after th severe attack of 23/11 this had disappeared.

Date	Dose thiazinamine (mg)	Inhalation and time		Mean effect on vital capacity in per cent
22/10/55	25	House-dust	10 min	+28
1/11/55	2·5	Solvent	10 min	+76
8/11/55	0	Solvent	10 min	+2
9/11/55	25	House-dust	10 min	−8
23/11/55	—	House-dust	5 min	−51
25/11/55	—	Solvent	5 min	< −12
7/12/55	—	Solvent	10 min	−49
14/12/55	—	Solvent	10 min	−27

gradually increasing doses of house-dust extract was now given in an attempt to desensitize her against this allergen (Table 4). To these inhalations she reacted by attacks of widely varying severity. The impression was obtained that this depended not only on the dose or duration of the inhalation, but also on the emotional attitude of the patient as a result of the life situation she happened to be in at that very moment. From time to time, an inhalation of neutral solvent was given between the inhalations of the allergen extract. It was found now that although she had a great number of "unconditioned" attacks, a positive reaction to the inhalation of the solvent occurred only on rare occasions. Apparently the "preparedness" of the patient to become conditioned by the experience of attacks in the laboratory situation, had become less. It was surmised that this change in "conditioning behaviour" was related to her changed attitude to the doctors and the laboratory situation in general, but this could not be proven.

Discussion

In these two patients the occurrence of asthmatic attacks was observed under similar circumstances as in conditioned responses de-

Table 4. Patient B. Results of consecutive inhalation tests using either various allergen extracts or the neutral solvent. In the beginning of the series some reconditioning appeared to take place, but it was irregular and later disappeared altogether.

Date		Result
12/11/56	Feathers	+
14/11/56	Solvent	—
15/11/56	Solvent	—
16/11/56	Hay dust	+
17/11/56	Solvent	—
18/11/56	Kapok	+
19/11/56	House dust	+
21/11/56	Tree pollen	+
22/11/56	Solvent	+ !
23/11/56	Solvent	—
24/11/56	Kapok	+
25/11/56	Feathers	—
28/11/56	Solvent	+ !
30/11/56	Cat's hair	—
1/12/56	House dust	++
6/12/56	Solvent	+ !
7/12/56	Solvent	+ !
8/12/56	Solvent	—
9/12/56	Solvent	—
10/12/56	Solvent	—
10/12/56	House dust	+
12/12/56	House dust	+
13/12/56	House dust	+
14/12/56	House dust	++
21/12/56	Solvent	—
22/12/56	Solvent	—
23/12/56	Solvent	—

Table 3. Patient B. Results of inhalation tests demonstrating the disappearance of the conditioning after 11 months.

Date	Inhalation of	Result
9/11/56	Solvent	—
10/11/56	Solvent	—
11/11/56	Solvent	—
12/11/56	Solvent	—

veloped in certain animal experiments. Both patients were simultaneously exposed to an inhaled allergen and a certain situation (observer, laboratory room, apparatus, tubes, mouthpiece, etc.). After one or more exposures, the experimental situation (or, part of it) alone, provoked an attack. It seems justified to regard this newly formed way of production of asthmatic attacks as changes in behaviour patterns, developed as a consequence of a conditioning process.

Several investigators in the literature have mentioned the possibility of conditioning as a cause of attacks of asthma, and case histories have been reported that even seem to point to a conditioning mechanism as a frequent cause of attacks. We have been unable, however, to find any report where the development of such a conditioning has been studied and demonstrated under laboratory conditions.

Between 1927 and 1930 Hansen (14, 15) drew attention to the possibility of conditioning superimposed upon unconditioned allergic attacks of asthma. Both he and Vaughan (29) cite as an illustration the story, endlessly repeated in this literature, of the lady who, being hypersensitive to roses, developed an attack of asthma when she was shown a paper rose. This lady even found her way into textbooks of internal medicine (19). According to Urbach and Gottlieb's textbook of allergy (28), attacks of asthma caused by a conditioned reflex mechanism occur in many cases. But no evidence for this thesis is presented. Kallos (21) mentions the occurrence of asthmatic attacks as a conditioned reflex, following the experience of attacks, for example, after exposure to pollens. He gave no arguments for this contention. Herxheimer (16, 17) also considers the possible significance of conditioning as the mechanism of psychogenic attacks of asthma, but without contributing factual material. Kremer (22) described patients who, after having experienced asthmatic attacks due to dust from their beds, later got an attack as soon as they entered their bedroom and saw their beds. He regarded this as a conditioned reflex. Groen (10) described a patient with attacks of asthma due to contact with horses. This patient also got a feeling of oppression on seeing horses from the window of the train. Many other of Groen's case histories reveal instances of attacks under circumstances that suggest conditioning. Hunt (20) described a patient who got an attack when he saw horses on a motion picture. Groen and Bastiaans (2, 12) have postulated on the basis of clinical observations that the coincidence of shortness of breath, of whatever cause, with an oppressive life situation, may produce a conditioning to the effect that at a later date either "organic" irritation of the airways or the psychic effect of an oppressive interhuman conflict situation, may bring about the asthmatic type of breathing. These authors give several examples to illustrate their hypothesis. On reviewing these data, it appears that the concept of conditioning as a cause of attacks of asthma has been accepted both by allergological and psychosomatic investigators, but on the basis of remarkably few observations.

Physiologists have contributed considerably to our knowledge of the conditioned reflexes of the respiratory tract in the experimental animal (8) and even in the human (3). Especially changes in depth and frequency have been recorded, but these changes cannot be identified with attacks of asthma. The observations of Noelpp and Noelpp-Eschenhagen (25, 26, 27) seem, however, of special significance in this respect. These investigators exposed guinea-pigs a number of times to the simultaneous influence of a sound stimulus and to an aerosol of a protein to which the animals were sensitized. In some experiments a histamine spray was used. After a number of simultaneous exposures it was possible to register an asthmatic type of breathing after the exposure to the sound stimulus alone.

These results in the guinea-pig seem clearly related to our clinical observations. They provide an argument in favour of the possibility of conditioning as a cause of human asthma of the same order as the results of the allergic investigations in this animal supporting the hypothesis of allergic mechanisms in the human.

In this connection, attention should be drawn to the changes in rate, rhythm, and patterns of respiration that occur when experimental neuroses are produced in animals by the use of conditioned reflexes (1, 23). Especially noteworthy are the experiments of Masserman and Pechtel (24), who described severe asthmatic attacks, lasting for hours, in several of their neurotic monkeys, and the observations of Gantt (9) in his experimentally neurotic dog Nick, who developed "a loud raucous breathing with quick inspiration and laboured expiration, . . . accompanied by a loud wheezing as if the animal were hoarse." "Examination of the dog by an internist showed that there was no true bronchial constriction except in the large bronchi." This description is the more interesting, as constriction of the large bronchi has been shown by us to be a regular occurrence in severe asthmatic attacks (7). It is also noteworthy as an experimental counterpart of the observation in our patients that "this loud forced breathing would usually begin when the dog was brought from the paddock, and increase as the experimental room was approched, disappearing in reverse order. However, it was sometimes present in other situations when he became excited." This, together with those of Noelpp's, is the best description to our knowledge of "conditioned asthma" in experimental animals.

What is the significance of our observations as a contribution to the knowledge of the cause of attacks in general, and more specifically of psychogenic attacks? Are they incidental observations or is a similar mechanism responsible for the provocation of a considerable number of so called "spontaneous" attacks of asthma? The occurrence of conditioning during the investigations for the presence of inhalation allergy is by no means the rule. We have exposed other patients to much greater series of inhalations of allergens, to which they were hypersensitive, in the same room, with the same apparatus. They reacted to these exposures by attacks, but no conditioning to the situation developed, although our attention was constantly directed to its eventual occurrence. Apparently the possibility of becoming conditioned by this technique was restricted to relatively few patients. Of further importance in this respect is the observation that patient *B* (case 2) lost her ability to be conditioned by this method, after 11 months, during which she was treated mainly with group psychotherapy. Her personality changed considerably during this time and apparently it also changed her preparedness to develop conditioned attacks in the particular laboratory setting. This seems to show that the preparedness to conditioning may fluctuate during life, and is not solely dependent on the individuality of the patient or on the nature of the environmental setting. Both patients greatly feared the allergic investigations at the time when they developed their conditioned attacks, and it may well be that the emotional attitude of an individual towards a given situation, in this case the laboratory investigation, may be an important factor in determining whether he will become easily conditioned or not. The influence of anxiety as a factor in the development of conditioned responses is familiar to most animal experimenters in this field; it has been shown to be of decisive importance in the establishment of experimentally induced conditioned reflexes in man (30). However this may be, it is obvious that the technique which we have used for the demonstration of conditioning as a cause of asthmatic attacks is not suitable for the majority of patients. The question whether all psychogenic attacks of asthma can be interpreted as conditioned responses, cannot be answered from the evidence here presented. Neither is it possible to give any experimental support to the hypothesis that a large number of so-called spontaneous attacks are in reality the results of conditioning of some kind. As no other exact investigations are at present available, it is only possible to speculate on the subject.

The problem of how important may be the role of conditioning as a cause of ordinary asthmatic attacks is intimately connected with the question of whether other psychological functions like memory, learning and habit formation are accepted as fundamentally based on the neurophysiological mechanism of conditioning. Even if this is the case, we have to admit that the quantity of component conditionings and the complexity of their interrelation may become so great that originally simple conditioned responses develop into intensely integrated reaction patterns that are widely different from the simple conditioned reflex. If this applies to the conditioned asthmatic attack, one can expect that the environmental stimuli become integrated with stimuli of an allergic, chemical, physical, or bacterial nature, whereas the preparedness for further conditioning or deconditioning depends on hereditary and acquired constitutional, neurophysiological, and endocrine factors, upon which are imprinted the events of the life history of the patient. For this concept it is immaterial whether the unconditioned stimulus is furnished by an allergen or by an emotionally oppressive situation, as hypothesized respectively by allergological or psychosomatic investigators. But the question remains whether conditioning as a cause of attacks is a rare or frequent mechanism.

In order to answer this question it seems methodologically necessary not to give too wide a meaning to the "conditioned" attack and to reserve the use of this word to those instances in which a chain of events, containing the simple components of a) an attack, b) a simultaneous exposure to an originally ineffective stimulus, which c) consequently becomes effective when applied alone, are discernible. We are at present occupied with devising a better method by which to study the possible importance of conditioning in the production of asthmatic attacks, based on this principle.

Our observations also raise some therapeutic problems. The rigidity with which the patients remained attached to their conditioned behaviour was no less impressive than the rapidity with which it developed. A therapeutic appeal to their logical insight failed. The effect of our first attempt at "personal" psychotherapy, including a discussion of their life conflicts and aimed at giving the patients strong support, was not very impressive. Long-term group psychotherapy appeared to have a favourable effect in one case. It seems that there is a need for a more specific deconditioning therapy that makes the conditioning disappear in the same way in which it came.

Summary

Two patients suffering from severe bronchial asthma who had a skin sensitivity to grass-pollen and house-dust extract, respectively reacted to the inhalation of an aerosol of these allergens, in the laboratory, with an attack of asthma. After these exposures they also showed attacks of asthma after the inhalation of the neutral solvent, or of oxygen, or even after the introduction of the glass mouthpiece, when this was not connected to the inhalation apparatus.

These phenomena were interpreted as a result of conditioning by the simultaneous exposure of the patient to the inhalation of the allergen and to the situation in which this took place. Deconditioning by psychotherapeutic supportive interviews proved diffcult and its success was temporary.

The relative importance of conditioning in the genesis of attacks of asthma in general and of psychogenic attacks in particular is discussed.

References

1. Anderson, O. D. and Parmenter, R. (1941) Experimental neurosis in the sheep and dog. *Psychosom. Med. Monograph* Vol. II. Nos. 3 and 4. p. 41. Washington.
2. Bastiaans, J. and Groen, J. (1954) Psychogenesis and psychotherapy of bronchial asthma. Desmond O'Neill *Modern Trends in Psychosomatic Medicine* p. 242. Butterworths, London.

3. Bykov, K. M. (1953) Zeitweilige kortikale Verbindungen bei der Täitgkeit des Atemapparates, *Grosshirnrinde und innere Organe* p. 65. V.E.B. Verlag Volk und Gesundheit, Berlin.
4. ten Cate, H. J. and Orie, N. G. M. (1953) Positieve intracutane reacties voor allergenen bij asthmalijders, vergeleken met de resultaten verkregen door inhalatie van allergeenextracten. *Ned. Tijdschr. Geneesk., 97,* 598.
5. ten Cate, H. J. (1954) Onderzoek bij asthmapatiënten naar overgevoeligheid voor verstoven allergeenextracten. Doctoral Thesis, Gröningen, Holland.
6. Dekker, E. and Groen, J. (1956) Reproducible psychogenic attacks of asthma. A laboratory study, *J. psychosom. Res., 1,* 58.
7. Dekker, E. and Groen, J. Compression of the trachea and major bronchi as a cause of wheezing in bronchial asthma. (In preparation.)
8. Freedman, B. (1951) Conditioning of respiration and its psychosomatic implications. *J. nerv. ment. Dis., 113,* 1.
9. Gantt, W. H. (1944) *Experimental Basis for Neurotic Behaviour* pp. 77, 117. Hoeler, New York and London.
10. Groen, J. (1950) *Asthma bronchiale seu nervosum. Een psychosomatische studie* p. 48. Scheltema and Holkema, Amsterdam.
11. Groen, J. (1953) Treatment of bronchial asthma by a combination of A.C.T.H. and psychotherapy. *Acta Allergol.* Suppl. III, 21.
12. Groen, J. and Bastiaans, J. (1953) Psychosomatische en allergische opvattingen over de ontstaanswijze van het asthma bronchiale: een poging tot synthese. *Psyche en Allergische Ziekten Stenfert Kroese* p. 43. Leiden.
13. Groen, J. and Pelser, H. E. Experience and results of 4 years group psychotherapy with asthmatic patients. (In preparation.)
14. Hansen, K. (1927) Analyse, Indikation und Grenze der Psychotherapie beim Bronchialasthma. *Dtsch. med. Wschr., 53,* 1462.
15. Hansen, K. (1930) Zur Frage der Psycho- oder Organogenese beim allergischen Bronchialasthma und den verwandten Krankheiten. *Nervenarzt, 3,* 513.
16. Herxheimer, H. (1951a) Bronchial obstruction induced by allergens, histamine and acetyl-beta-methylcholinechloride. *Int. Arch. Allergy, 2,* 27.
17. Herxheimer, H. (1951b) Induced asthma in man. *Lancet, 1,* 1337,
18. Herxheimer, H. (1951c) Bronchial hypersenitization and hyposensitization in man. *Int. Arch. Allergy, 2,* 40.
19. Hijmans van den Bergh, A. A., de Lange, C. D., and Snapper, I. (1941) *Leerboek der Inwendige Geneeskunde* Deel II. p. 285. Scheltema and Holkema, Amsterdam.
20. Hunt, C. L. (1954) Cronic asthma. *Canad. med. Ass. J., 70,* 666.
21. Kallos, P. (1950) Some aspects of allergy. *Ann. Allergy, 8,* 251.
22. Kremer, W. (1953) Is asthma een psychosomatisch of een allergisch verschijnsel? *Psyche en Allergische Ziekten, Stenfert Kroese* p. 72. Leiden.
23. Liddell, H. (1951) The influence of experimental neuroses on respiratory function. Aramson, H. A. *Somatic and Psychiatric Treatment of Asthma* p. 126. Williams and Wilkins, Baltimore.
24. Masserman, J. H. and Pechtel, C. (1953) Neuroses in monkeys. *Ann. N.Y. Acad. Sci., 56,* 253.

25. Noelpp, B. and Noelpp-Eschenhagen I. (1951a) Bedingte Reflexe beim Asthma bronchiale. Ein experimenteller Beitrag zur Pathogenese des Asthma bronchiale. *First Internat. Congr. for Allergy, Zurich* p. 783.
26. Noelpp, B. and Noelpp-Eschenhagen, I. (1951b) Die Rolle bedingter Reflexe beim Asthma bronchiale. Ein experimenteller Beitrag zur Pathogenese des Asthma bronchiale. *Helv. med. Acta, 18,* 142.
27. Noelpp, B. and Noelpp-Eschenhagen, I. (1951c) (1952) Das experimentelle Asthma bronchiale des Meerschweinchens. *Int. Arch. Allergy, 2:* 308, 321, *ibid. 3,* 108, 207.
28. Urbach, E. and Gottlieb, P. M. (1946) *Allergy* 2nd Ed. p. 570. Grune and Stratton, New York.
29. Vaughan, W. T. (1939) *Practice of Allergy* p. 128. Henry Kimpton, London.
30. Welch, L. (1953) Human conditioning and anxiety. *Ann. N.Y. Acad. Sci., 56,* 266.

11

THE CONDITIONED INHIBITION OF UNCINATE FITS

by Robert Efron, M.D.

Historical Background

It has been repeatedly observed, since ancient times, that a specific sensory stimulus could arrest epileptic fits, but the physiological explanation of this phenomenon is still unknown.

Similarly, seizures spontaneously arrested during the aura (aborted for reasons which cannot be ascertained, but not *apparently* by sensory stimulation) are reported by almost every epileptic from time to time. In one of the rare references to this phenomenon in the last twenty years, S. A. K. Wilson (33) noted that the grand mal fit sometimes "fails to evolve according to rule . . . the process becomes arrested at some point, for reasons difficult to fathom." He called these abortive fits "fragments."

It has also been observed that spontaneous arrests during different stages of the aura are more frequently noted after treatment with anti-convulsant drugs, especially phenytoin. (The suggestion so often made when a spontaneous arrest or "fragmentary" fit occurs—that the "threshold for the spread of the fit was not achieved at that moment" is mere tautology.)

This phenomenon of seizure-arrest, known for so long, has not been seriously investigated in the laboratory or clinic although hundreds of papers have recently been published on methods of precipitating fits. This neglect is surprising since a study of naturally arrested seizures is both of theoretical interest and pertinent to therapy.

In the last and most exhaustive study of the phenomenon of sensory arrest of seizures, Gowers (4) pointed out that the repeated arrest of Jacksonian fits by ligatures could permanently alter the subsequent development of the fit. He reported the case of a "patient whose fits always commence in the hand by a sensation which passes up the arm, and could be arrested by the ligature applied just above the elbow. After employing the ligature in this manner for some months, he found

Reprinted with permission from *Brain,* Vol. 80, Part II, 1957, pp. 251-262.

that the fits, commencing in the same way, stopped of their own accord at the spot at which they had been repeatedly arrested by the ligature. They never stopped thus before the patient commenced the use of the ligature, which appeared to have produced a permanent increase of resistance at a certain part of the unstable nerve tissue."

Another case of permanent cure by application of the ligature, reported originally by Lysons (10) was mentioned by Gowers. In Lysons' patient, the fits began in the foot and were arrested by repeated applications of a tight garter at the knee at the onset of each fit. "The fits afterwards became weaker, and the same means being used, whenever notice was given of their approach, they were at last entirely cured without medicine."

Lysons did not indicate, however, whether or not his patient continued to experience the early phases of the fit. Gowers' patient continued to have fits which were spontaneously arrested without any *apparent* sensory stimulus from a ligature.

Present Investigation

In reading these case reports one is forcibly struck by the resemblance of this phenomenon to the establishment of conditioned reflexes in animals and man by the repeated temporal association of a non-specific (conditioned) stimulus with a specific (unconditioned) stimulus. Indeed, Gowers' own language—"permanent increase of resistance . . . of the unstable nerve tissue"—is almost identical to that used by I. Pavlov (14) in explaining the behavior of his dogs. To use this analogy: we may say that the ligatures (specific unconditioned stimuli) became linked, as a result of repeated temporal association, with a non-specific stimulus—which in turn became as effective in arresting the fit as was the original "specific" ligature itself. We cannot determine, from the reports of Gowers and Lysons, what the non-specific stimulus might have been in their patients.

In a previous paper by the author (3) a case of temporal lobe epilepsy was reported which was characterized by depersonalization, forced thinking, olfactory hallucination, auditory hallucination and adversive head movement preceding the *grand mal* climax. These attacks had persisted for twenty-six years and the sequence had been identical for each fit. No arrested seizures had ever occurred; once the first part of the aura had begun, a stereotyped fit was inevitable. Application of a specific sensory stimulus (an unpleasant odor) prior to the stage of forced thinking, invariably arrested further development of the aura and prevented the occurrence of the tonic and clonic seizure. Application of the unpleasant odour at the appearance of the stage of forced thinking, resulted in bizarre fragments of adversive seizures, gyratory epilepsy and epilepsia cursiva. Further delay in administration of the stimulus failed to alter the pattern of the seizure in any way.

The patient has since been able to arrest every seizure by inhaling from a vial the odors of various aromatic chemicals or essential perfume oils. The frequency of her attacks has remained unchanged. The only failures to arrest seizures have been at night when she slept throughout the early phases of the aura (which on other occasions had awakened her) and had no opportunity to inhale the essence. For details concerning the lysis of the aura as a result of these stimuli, the reader is referred to the original report.

In attempting to explain, in physiological terms, the effectiveness of the olfactory stimulus in our patient, the activation of a widespread inhibitory system by the unpleasant (nociceptive) olfactory stimulus was predicated. It was assumed that the nociceptive stimulus activated this inhibitory system in a "reflex" or automatic fashion. Yet, Gowers' patient was eventually able to inhibit his fit *without* the application of a nociceptive stimulus. It thus seemed possible to produce an activation of this reflex fit inhibition (originally produced by a nociceptive stimulus) by a conditioned, non-specific stimulus, in the same way that a dog may eventually be led to salivate by hearing a tuning fork.

It is the object of this paper to report the arrest of seizures not only by a conditioned, non-specific visual stimulus but also by a second order conditioned reflex (2° C.R.) which was concurrently, but inadvertently, established.

Methods

Every fifteen minutes (approximately) for a period of eight days, two stimuli were simultaneously presented to the subject. The first was a concentrated odor of jasmine which had previously been found effective in arresting the uncinate seizures. The second was an inexpensive silvered bracelet. She was instructed to stare intently for 15-30 seconds at the bracelet while sniffing a vial of essence of jasmine.

The patient was permitted seven hours sleep at night and the conditioning was begun anew each morning lasting until bedtime. Five different persons* exposed her to the sight of the bracelet and to the jasmine odor during the eight-day period, so that the response would not depend on the presence of any particular person. Similarly, the double stimulation was performed in the patient's hospital room, the day room, during walks in the hospital grounds, and while reading, etc., to avoid unrelated conditioning by specific aspects of her environment. Except for the 15-30 second interval during which the stimuli were simultaneously applied, the subject was not exposed to either of them.

* T/Sgt. R. Koran, U.S. Air Force; T/Sgt. C. Martin, U.S. Army; HM2 M. Cassidy, U.S. Navy; HM3 M. Shepherd, U.S. Navy; HN J. Cohill, U.S. Navy.

Twice during the eight-day conditioning period the patient developed spontaneous seizures, each of which was arrested by the use of the odor alone. This unintentional failure to reinforce the conditioning process occurred because the attacks developed at night after the bracelet had been removed from her room.

Interpretation of Results

At the end of eight days of conditioning the bracelet alone was presented to the patient and she experienced the odor of the concentrated jasmine in a vivid fashion. The olfactory hallucination persisted while the bracelet was exposed and receded in a few seconds when it was removed from her sight.*

For the next week the patient was exposed only twice a day . . . to the bracelet and the jasmine, a programme instituted to maintain reinforcement. During the second week *a spontaneous seizure occurred which was arrested by the patient's merely staring at the bracelet for a few seconds.*

This seizure began in its stereotyped form and the patient reported its arrest as a gradual lessening of the intensity of the depersonalization, remoteness and dreamy state. There were two significant subjective differences, however, in the response to the specific stimulus (essence of jasmine) and the one to the non-specific conditioned stimulus (bracelet). The patient reported that the "dissolving" of the seizure began later after exposure to the bracelet, than it usually did after exposure to the essence of jasmine. This increased latency of response is a finding usually noted in conditoned reflexes as compared to unconditioned reflexes. In addition, she described the lysis itself as more "abrupt" when terminated by the essence of jasmine. When the bracelet was used, the fit "faded away" more slowly, and this appeared to be a consistent finding in further arrests with the bracelet. As the lysis of the depersonalization was gradual in both cases and persisted for about "half a minute," it was difficult to be certain of the precise moment the lysis began and the exact moment normality was achieved. For this reason, measurements of the latency and the duration of the lysis were impossible to obtain with any accuracy.

Following this success, the patient was permitted to go home with only the bracelet to control her seizures. (Anticonvulsant medication had been discontinued after the initial success with aromatic chemicals some months previously.) The patient entirely discontinued the use of the vials of aromatic chemicals, and successfully used the bracelet

* This type of response to conditioning is not unusual. The work of C. and N. A. Popov of Paris (1953, 1954, 1955) showed that visual hallucinations (after-images) can be easily induced by Pavlovian techniques. Further reference will be made to their work in the discussion.

to arrest seizures for a period of eight months. Further formal reinforcing conditioning has not proved necessary, as each arrested seizure appears to serve as a reinforcement.

On three occasions, shortly after the intial success with the bracelet, the patient was instructed to delay the exposure of the bracelet until later in the aura (just prior to the olfactory hallucination) to see if any forms of larval epilepsia cursiva or gyratory epilepsy would develop —as they had when applications of the primary olfactory stimulus was delayed. In the first two of these attempts, the patient experienced such passivity and inertia at this late stage of the seizure, that she was unable to get up to take the bracelet out of her purse. She experienced a complete *grand mal* seizure both times.

On the third occasion, at the earliest stage of the aura, she removed the bracelet from her purse (without looking at it), and placed it on a table in front of a chair. Then, with head averted, and eyes open, she sat in front of it, having only to turn her head to bring the bracelet into view. The patient reported that in performing these activities she was extremely conscious of the existence of the bracelet at all times, and was puzzled as to the slowness with which the aura developed in this particular fit. However, she finally reached the stage of forced thinking, impending olfactory hallucination, and passivity, when she turned her head and looked at the bracelet. She experienced the smell of jasmine and the fit rapidly subsided without the development of the *grand mal* component. This was the first time that success had been achieved at such a late phase in the fit.

Following this, no further delays were suggested and the patient continued, *without fail,* to arrest seizures by staring at the bracelet in the early phase of her attacks. She had attacks at about the same frequency as before. With continued practice, she became more socially adept at controlling her fits in varying situations. On one occasion, while performing at a theatrical benefit, she was forced to leave her purse in a distant room. Fearing the possibility of a seizure while performing before a large audience, she put the bracelet on her wrist, and covered it with a kerchief. During her song, she began to experience the characteristic depersonalization of her attacks. She also noted that the conductor was signalling for her to slow down. (Her disturbed time sense in an early stage of the aura has been previously reported.) She uncovered her bracelet while singing. The hallucination of jasmine and the lysis of aura occurred, and she finished her performance uneventfully. Only the conductor knew that "something had gone wrong."

Electroencephalographic Studies

In the previous investigations of this patient, EEG confirmation of an arrested seizure (aborted by B.A.L.) was obtained with the aid of metrazol activation. On one occasion 75 mg. metrazol induced a self-sustained seizure and on another 50 mg. did so. A third attempt was made to perform the experiment using the bracelet as the arresting stimulus. Sphenoidal electrodes were placed by a modification of the techniques of Arellano and MacLean (1) and adequate control tracings were secured. Metrazol was administered intravenously in the dosage of 30 mg. over a two second period every thirty seconds. Once the aura was precipitated the metrazol infusion was discontinued. The whole procedure was similar to prior procedures, including the placing of the sphenoidal electrodes with local cocaine anaesthesia. The single difference was that where, in the earlier experiements, the patient was told that the vial of aromatic chemical would be placed beneath her nostrils at the critical moment—on this occasion she was instructed to open her eyes at the critical moment in order to see the bracelet about two feet away.

Two very surprising things happened. In the first place, injection of 60-90 mg. metrazol failed to precipitate even the earliest stages of the patient's specific aura. It was found that rapid injection of 150 mg. was necessary to "switch" from the fright and lightheadedness that normally follows a metrazol injection, to the patient's own characteristic type of depersonalization, dreamy state, etc. . . . the hallmarks of her fit. Secondly, the fit did not progress as it had on previous occasions. Even though the bracelet had not yet been viewed, the patient reported that the aura was "hung up," meaning by this that the subjective intensity was not worsening, that the depersonalization and dreamy state were static. After being "hung up" in such a fashion for about two to three minutes she reported that the fit was subsiding. After she experienced, for the first time in her life, four such *spontaneously* abortive attacks, it was realized that the threshold for metrazol had changed in two respects. Firstly, more was required to precipitate an attack. Secondly, the aura, once precipitated did not sustain itself and progress into a full-blown fit. Because of this resistance to metrazol, an attempt was made to sustain the aura, and cause it to progress by continuous infusion of metrazol.

After a five-minute rest period, the patient was given 150 mg. metrazol over a one-minute period of 50 mg. every 30 seconds thereafter. She reported the onset of a fit, in the usual fashion, and even at this rate of continued metrazol infusion the aura remained almost motionless, with perhaps the slightest progression, for ten minutes. She received a total of 1,150 mg. over this eleven-minute period. Opening her eyes and viewing the bracelet resulted in a rapid lysis of the subjective sensations of the fit *despite* the fact that metrazol was still being slowly infused. The patient was made extremely anxious by this procedure, and in view of the large quantities of metrazol administered (1,350 mg. in thirteen minutes), the procedure was discontinued.

Although five different fits were induced, only the earliest psychic stages could be precipitated, there being an obvious resistance offered by some mechanism to the development of a self-sustaining fit. The EEGs showed no localized or generalized abnormality during the stage of the aura. When the patient was reporting the lysis of a seizure, either by use of the bracelet or spontaneously, some bursts of high voltage 30 cps activity were recorded from the bisphenoidal electrodes.

Development of a Second Order (2°C.R.) Conditioned Reflex

On questioning the patient subsequently about her reactions during the metrazol infusions, it emerged that she was thinking almost continuously about the bracelet, whether it would really be presented to her in "time," and whether it would "work," etc.

It seemed plausible that the alteration in the patient's sensitivity to metrazol was caused by a *premature activation* of the "inhibitory" mechanism—precipitated by *thinking* about the bracelet. This might serve not only as an explanation for the results of the experiment with metrazol but for the earlier success of the bracelet in the late stage of the aura just prior to the olfactory hallucination.

It thus became essential to prove that the patient's seizures could be arrested by having her think of the bracelet when a spontaneous fit developed. The test was made and *the act of thinking intently about the bracelet proved sufficient to inhibit the seizure.* When the patient merely thought of the bracelet she also developed the olfactory hallucination of jasmine.

The patient reported that it took even longer for the fit to begin to subside when she was thinking of the bracelet than it did when she actually looked at it. She was not certain that there was any change in the time taken to return to normality.

For a period of six weeks the patient continued to arrest her seizures by thinking of the bracelet as the seizure developed. During this period, she observed that on several occasions, when she did *not* think of the bracelet, a spontaneous odor of jasmine suddenly enveloped her. This occurred once at night during this early period and awoke her from sleep. However, at these times she had no subjective manifestations of her seizure.

The spontaneous hallucinations of jasmine, lasting for one to one and a half minutes became increasingly frequent over the next three weeks, during which time she experienced fewer seizures. Those seizures which did develop were arrested by thinking of the bracelet. For *fourteen* full months, the patient has had no seizures at all. She developed no episodes of depersonalization and did not need to rely upon any external method of arresting attacks: she experienced only spontaneous, abrupt (one minute) hallucinations of smell. At these times, she did not "smell" the original odor which was associated with her uncinate discharges, but, instead, was "overwhelmed" by the odor of jasmine.

For the first four to six months these hallucinations occurred at the same frequency (seven to fifteen a month) as did her original uncinate seizures. This six-month period of frequent olfactory hallucinations (but no seizures of any type) was followed by another eight-month period during which she was still free of seizures, but had only three episodes of hallucination. Two of these were at night and awakened her, the third occurred while she was singing.

Although she was at first extremely anxious and preoccupied about her experiences, she soon adjusted to her hallucinations of jasmine, and now that she has no seizures or hallucinations she has returned to a full-time singing career. She considers herself "cured" as she had not, in the previous twenty-six years, been free of seizures for more than a fortnight.

Discussion

In our attempt to "explain" the case reports of Gowers and Lysons, it had been assumed that a conditioned reflex had been established in their patients which then served to arrest the focal seizures as the ligatures had done previously. In this patient, a conditioned stimulus (bracelet) arrested uncinate seizures just as successfully as did the primary unpleasant olfactory stimulus. Furthermore, the thought of the bracelet was later sufficient to arrest a seizure.

Hudgins (5) has shown that the pupillary reflex in man could be conditioned to the sound of a bell, and that a second order conditioned response could then be established between the bell and the spoken verbal command, "constrict." Finally, the spoken command was conditioned, by frequent repetition to the thought "constrict." Upon completion of this complex series of conditioning experiments, Hudgins' subjects could constrict their pupils by merely thinking the word "constrict." The latency of the response was about seven to ten times longer than the latency of the direct pupillary response to light.

Similarly, Jasper and Shagass (7, 8), Shagass (29, 30) Laufberger (9), as well as Travis and Egan (31) conditioned the alpha blocking reaction in the human EEG to a sound. Following Hudgins, they then conditioned the blocking response to the verbal command "block" and finally to the thought "block." Laufberger (9) conditioned the alpha blocking response to a phoneme and showed that the thought of the phoneme would similarly block the alpha rhythm. In these experiments the investigators were conditioning an electrical response of the cortex to stimuli which were ineffective in altering the EEG pattern prior to the conditioning procedure. Jasper and Shagass (8) described in detail how every type of conditioned reflex in dogs, as described by Pavlov, could be similarly established in the human EEG by using the alpha blocking response as the test indicator. They were able to produce simple conditioned reflexes, delayed, differential, differential delayed, and cyclical conditioned reflexes. They also showed tracings which clearly depicted "anticipation" of the conditioned blocking response in cyclical conditioning. There seems to be little difference between "anticipation" as seen in Jasper and Shagass' records and the "premature activation of the inhibitory mechanism" which we have just postulated.

Morrell and Jasper (12) have gone even farther and have convincingly demonstrated in monkeys that not only alpha-blocking responses could be conditioned, but that certain occipital augmentation rhythms (photically activated) could be conditioned in identical fashion. They found that a photic flicker rate of eight cycles per second produced a frequency-specific occipital response, and that this cortical response could be produced by the conditioned stimulus after a suitable number of paired stimuli. Similarly, a cortical response to a twelve cycle per second flash could be conditioned to a 500 cycle per second tone and the frequency of the cortical response to that tone was at 12 cycles per second. Sounding a 1,000 cycle per second tone would not evoke any occipital augmentation pattern.

The work of the Popovs (15-28) is also most interesting. They, too, have conditioned the alpha-blocking response to a sound stimulus, but they have been primarily studying after-images. They have found that at the time when the alpha rhythm blocks to the specific conditioning sound stimulus, the subject reports seeing after-images—identical to those after-images experienced following the original light flash. They have thus claimed that the after-image is not primarily a retinal reaction, such as might be due to regeneration of visual purple, but, rather a purely cerebral response as it can be produced without light by a conditioned reflex.

These experiments in human beings (Hudgins, Shagass, Jasper, the Popovs, Travis and Egan, Laufberger, etc.) and in lower animals (Jasper, Morell and Jasper, Morell and Ross (13), the Popovs) in which *normal* neurophysiological responses have been conditioned to an indifferent stimulus, and finally (in man) to the thought of the indifferent stimulus, closely parallel our attempt similarly to condition a *pathological* response of neural tissue—a fit.

That pathological neural responses (fits) *can* be conditioned has been known for many years. James Dunsmure (2) presented a case of a boy whose fits could be readily elicited by patting him on the head. However, if he was prepared for the stimulus, a fit did not occur. Jackson (6) similarly described a patient whose fits were always precipitated if his face were touched, especially if there was an element of surprise in the touch. If he thought that his face would be touched, the stimulus would not evoke the fit. In this case, the reflex epilepsy could be inhibited. Wilson (32) described another such case.

In recent years, Mitchell, Falconer and Hill (11) reported the case of a fetishist with temporal lobe epilepsy who would precipitate fits (auto-erotically) by staring at a safety-pin. He found that scissors and paper clips were also effective, but less satisfying methods of producing his fits. Following temporal lobectomy which cured him of both fits and fetish, he told how, previous to surgery, merely "phantasizing" a safety-pin in his mind was an adequate stimulus to produce an attack. In this case, the displacement from the specific stimulus to the intellectual or symbolic conception of it, was still sufficient to "trigger" the mechanism.

We now find an analogy in our patient who was eventually "cured" of her seizures by repeated arrests by sensory stimuli or by their conditioned equivalents. Review of the literature does not reveal a similar case although it is strongly suspected that Gowers' (4) case may have been due to an identical mechanism. Similarly, the "cure" of focal seizures by repeated application of the ligature which Lysons (10) described is probably explicable on this basis.

In the case of our patient, the spontaneous hallucinations of jasmine which occurred for six months at the same frequency as did the original seizures, and then disappeared, probably represents an extreme degree of "anticipation" . . . that is, the inhibitory mechanism, once conditioned, is now being activated almost immediately after the initial epileptic discharge commences. With the activation of the reflex fit inhibitory mechanism occurring prior to the development of any *subjective manifestations* of the fit, the patient experiences only the manifestations of the inhibitory reflex (hallucination of jasmine). She would most likely be unaware that a fit had started and might have matured, had this hallucination not occurred. It is not clear, at the present time, why even the hallucinations of jasmine have disappeared. It may represent even a further degree of anticipation, or may possibly reflect a decay in the conditioned reflex as a result of lack of reinforcement.

Recalling S. A. K. Wilson's (33) remarks about the high frequency of fragmentary seizures in all epileptics, we may wonder if these, too, are not examples of fit inhibition, either by an undetected sensory stimulus, or perhaps by an intellectual event. It is not infrequent to hear a patient describe twice as many aurae as fits and to have him claim that he "fights off" half of his attacks. Such methods of arresting seizures in other of our patients currently under treatment are: "intense concentration on the conversation or on the radio," "rapidly putting my head between my knees," "getting up to walk it off," and "eating a piece of chocolate" (sugar is not effective). In a child of 6 years, his mother has found that his focal, adversive attacks which are followed by complete immobility can be arrested by tickling him at the onset of the adversive movement. Sometimes his fits stop when he sees his mother approach to tickle him. The family of a 19-year-old boy has discovered that a quick jerk of his head in a direction opposite of the first adversive movement will abort a *grand mal* seizure.

Reflex fit precipitation (musicogenic, photogenic, etc.) has been studied extensively, as it has been thought by some to be frequent if specifically looked for, whereas reflex fit inhibition has been almost totally neglected in recent times as it is considered to be extremely rare. Yet we may be fairly certain that the mechanism of one is closely related to the other. They must both represent converse aspects of the process of excitability of neural tissue. This would seem to be a fruitful area for therapeutically oriented research.

Summary

(1) A patient who had been able to arrest uncinate seizures by a properly timed, unpleasant olfactory stimulus was conditioned (Pavlov) to a nonspecific visual stimulus. After conditioning, seizures were as successfully arrested by the visual stimulus as they had previously been by the olfactory stimulus.

(2) It was discovered that the "intellectual" act of thinking about the visual stimulus was equally effective in arresting seizures.

(3) Metrazol activation studies following conditioning showed a marked decrease in sensitivity to this drug.

(4) The clinical literature referable to conditioned inhibition and conditioned precipitation of seizures is reviewed and the physiological studies of electronecephalographic conditioning are described.

(5) An analysis of the physiological mechanisms is attempted.

References

1. Arellano, A., and MacLean, P. D. (1949) *Electroenceph. clin. Neurophysiol., 1,* 251.
2. Dunsmure, J., Jr. (1874) *Edinb. med. J., 20,* 173.
3. Efron, R. (1956) *Brain, 79,* 267.
4. Gowers, W. (1881) *Epilepsy and Other Chronic Convulsive Diseases.* London.
5. Hudgins, C. V. (1933) *J. gen. Psychol., 8,* 3.
6. *Jackson, J. Hughlings (1887) *Trans. med. Soc. Lond., 10,* 78. [On a case of fits resembling those artificially produced in guinea-pigs.]
7. Jasper, H., and Shagass, C. (1941*a*) *J. exp. Psychol., 28,* 373.
8. ———. (1941*b*) *J. exp. Psychol., 28,* 503.
9. Laufberger, V. (1950) *C.R. Soc. Biol., Paris, 144,* 467.
10. Lysons, D. (1772) *Practical Essays upon Intermitting Fevers.* Bath.
11. Mitchell, W., Falconer, M. A., and Hill, D. (1954) *Lancet, 2,* 626.

* Other papers in this volume by Hughlings Jackson: "Random symptoms from cerebral syphilis." p. 306; "Case of facial monoplegia of cortical or subcortical origin." p. 307.

12. Morrell, F., and Jasper, H. H. (1956) *Electroenceph. clin. Neurophysiol., 8,* 201.
13. ———, and Ross, M. H. (1953) *Arch. Neurol. Psychiat., Chicago, 70,* 611.
14. Pavlov, I. P. (1928) *Lectures on Conditioned Reflexes.* New York.
15. Popov, C. (1954) *C.R. Acad. Sci., Paris, 239,* 1859.
16. ———. (1955*a*) *C.R. Acad. Sci., Paris, 240,* 1268.
17. ———. (1955*b*) *C.R. Acad. Sci., Paris, 240,* 1929.
18. ———. (1955*c*) *C.R. Acad. Sci., Paris, 241,* 249.
19. ———. (1955*d*) *C.R. Acad. Sci., Paris, 241,* 335.
20. ———. (1955*e*) *C.R. Acad. Sci., Paris, 241,* 1414.
21. Popov, N. A. (1950*a*) *C.R. Soc. Biol., Paris, 144,* 906.
22. ———. (1950*b*) *C.R. Soc. Biol., Paris, 144,* 1667.
23. ———, and Popov, C. (1953*a*) *C.R. Acad. Sci., Paris, 237,* 930.
24. ———, ———. (1953*b*) *C.R. Acad. Sci., Paris, 237,* 1439.
25. ———, ———. (1954*a*) *C.R. Acad. Sci., Paris, 238,* 1912.
26. ———, ———. (1954*b*) *C.R. Acad. Sci., Paris, 238,* 2026.
27. ———, ———. (1954*c*) *C.R. Acad. Sci., Paris, 238,* 2118.
28. ———, ———. (1954*d*) *C.R. Acad. Sci., Paris, 239,* 1243.
29. Shagass, C. (1942) *J. exp. Psychol., 31,* 367.
30. ———, and Johnson, E. P. (1943) *J. exp. Psychol., 33,* 201.
31. Travis, L. E., and Egan, J. P. (1938) *J. exp. Psychol., 22,* 524.
32. Wilson, S. A. K. (1930) *Brit. med. J., 2,* 1.
33. ———. (1935) *In* Bumke, and Foerster's *Handbuch der Neurologie,* Berlin. Vol. 17, p. 1.

12

THE FORMATION AND EXTINCTION OF CONDITIONED REFLEXES IN "BRAIN-DAMAGED" AND MONGOLOID CHILDREN

by Herbert G. Birch, Ph.D.
and Howard Demb, M.A.*

The terms "brain-damaged" or "brain-injured" when applied to children refers to a combination of psychologic functions that are presumed to originate in pre-natal, peri-natal or infantile insults to the cerebrum. The category is entirely behavioral (4, 5) and implies that any of a number of kinds of cerebral damage will result in a common pattern of behavioral disturbance. Locus of injury, nature of the lesion and the temporal course of the illness are usually not considered in the designation, and the non-behavioral, neurologic confirmation of the fact of anatomic insult has been conspicuous by its absence. These considerations make it clear that the term "brain-damaged" refers to a behavior syndrome and not to the fact of brain damage as such.

The identification of a pathological pattern of behavior, characterized by difficulties in figure-ground perception, abnormal distractibility, perseverative tendencies, conceptual rigidity, emotional lability, and hyperactivity, by Strauss and Werner (4-16) was an important contribution to the more refined differential diagnosis and treatment of psychologically disturbed children. However, the unfortunate characterization of the pattern as *the* "brain-damaged child" has led to confusion in two directions. First, Strauss (5) has declared that the syndrome is pathognomonic of brain damage and has assumed behavior problems to have such an etiology even in the absence of any clearly substantiating neurologic or historical data. Second, it has come to be

* The research here reported was carried out at the Morris Solomon Clinic for Retarded Children, The Jewish Hospital, Brooklyn, N.Y.

Reprinted from *The Journal of Nervous and Mental Disease.* Volume 129, No. 2, pp. 162-170.

widely assumed that the behavior syndrome described is the typical consequence of organic brain damage in childhood. Neither of these extensions appears to be warranted by experience. In earlier discussions (1, 2) one of us has pointed to a variety of patterns of behavioral alteration that may occur as the consequence of organic brain damage in infancy and childhood and has argued that the syndrome described by Strauss and his colleagues represents only one of many different types of behavioral alteration that may be associated with cerebral lesions in children. However, to define the numerous distinct behavioral syndromes which may occur as consequences of infantile cerebral damage is beyond the scope of the present report. It is concerned, rather, with a more limited and specific inquiry into the behavioral sequellae of brain damage. Basic to the present study is the view that a population of children who are known to have cerebral injury may, at the very least, be divided into two groups, one of which contains children who exhibit hyperactivity and/or distractibility and a second whose members do not show either of these characteristics. Possible underlying differences in the central nervous system organization in each of these groups can then be analyzed through the use of both psychologic and physiologic techniques.

The use of conditioned reflex methods for such analysis seems especially desirable since conditioned reflex theory (3) permits the formulation of some quite specific hypotheses concerning the nature of the functional alterations in central nervous system activity that may underlie hyperactivity and distractibility, two prominent and readily discerned features of the behavior occurring in some of the children who have sustained cerebral damage. From the point of view of Pavlovian theory the behavioral phenomena of distractibility, hyperactivity and even of perseveration can be conceptualized as manifestations of defective equilibration between the processes of cortical excitation and inhibition. If this conceptualization is correct, one should find differences in the character of the processes of cortical excitatory and inhibitory activity in normal and hyperactive groups. For this reason the present study is concerned with a comparative examination of the conditioning and extinction process in hyperactive and/or distractible brain-damaged children and in brain-damaged children who exhibit neither hyperactivity nor distractibility. It includes as well an analysis of the functioning of a sample of mongoloid children and of a small number of normal children.

Method

Subjects

In examining the records of children in a pediatric psychiatric installation, it was possible to obtain records of eighteen children who showed unequivocal evidence of central nervous system trauma acquired either perinatally or as a consequence of meningitis or encephalitis in infancy. Supportive evidence included the presence of seizures, and/or of neurological signs such as pathologic reflexes and abnormal EEG. The presence or absence of stereotyped behavioral characteristics was not used as a variable in the selection. The sex, I.Q. and age of the subjects are presented in Table 1.

Behavioral analysis of these 18 children showed that ten of them were hyperactive and/or distractible, whereas the remaining eight included six normoactive and two hypoactive children. For comparative purposes eight mongoloid children with no history of central nervous system trauma, and four normal children who were convalescing from non-neurologic illness were studied.

Apparatus and Procedures

The unconditioned stimulus used was a mild electric shock adjusted by means of a Variac supplied by a 120 volt, 60 cycle AC source. The shock was administered through two polished copper electrodes which were taped to the inside of each forearm. A 7½ watt white frosted bulb served as the conditioned stimulus. It was placed on the wall five feet in front of the subject, who was seated in a cushioned chair provided with broad wooden arm rests. Continuous recordings of the skin resistance were taken by means of a C.E.M. Research Laboratories Physiological Recording Galvanometer, model #650. Extraneous visual stimuli were minimized, but no control over auditory stimuli was maintained.

Table 1. Classification, sex, age and I.Q. of subjects.

Brain-Damaged								Mongoloid			
Non-H and Non-D				Hyperact. and /or Distract.							
Subj.	Sex	Age	I.Q.	Subj.	Sex	Age	I.Q.	Subj.	Sex	Age	I.[illegible]
J.E.	M	8-5	85	S.P.	F	10-5	85	E.P.	F	6-2	68
J.J.	M	10-2	68	L.G.	F	8-6	80	L.L.	M	6-2	67
S.B.	M	15-1	60	A.M.	F	13-2	63	A.S.	F	9-8	54
S.S.	M	12-2	55	C.H.	F	12-10	60	L.D.	F	8-5	48
J.S.	F	16-9	51	M.S.	F	10-6	60	L.C.	M	6-9	38
B.W.	M	17-5	50	C.C.	M	12-4	57	C.K.	F	15-0	36
J.M.	M	12-10	48	V.M.	M	13-1	54	B.H.	F	13-0	35
R.A.	M	15-1	42	S.H.	M	10-8	54	G.H.	F	11-7	33
				W.B.	M	15-11	49				
				W.W.	F	14-0	30				
Mean I.Q.*			57.4				59.2				47
S.D.			12.8				15.3				13

* There is no statistically significant difference between the mean I.Q.'s of these groups.

Since any new stimulus can affect the GSR, at the beginning of each child's first session the light was presented alone for approximately 1½ sec. once every 30 sec. This was done until there was no measurable response to three consecutive presentations of the light. Then the intensity of the shock was built up to a level which resulted in a decrease in skin resistance equivalent to an increased current flow of at least 0.039 milliamperes. This amplitude was chosen because it was of greater magnitude than 90 per cent of the observed random fluctuations in skin resistance. After the desired level of shock was attained, the light alone was again presented every 30 sec. to the criterion of three consecutive zero responses, in order to eliminate the possibility of "pseudo-conditioning," *i.e.* the creation by shock alone of a hypersensitive nervous system which could produce a high level of response to any subsequent neutral stimulus. In no case were the responses to the light alone following the determination of the proper shock level of sufficient duration and amplitude to warrant the possibility that the criterion for conditioning could be reached without true conditioning taking place.

Following a second extinction of the skin response to the light the conditioning series itself was started. This consisted of alternate presentations of the light and shock in combination and then light alone. The interval between each step in the sequence was 90 sec. so that any two successive presentations of either light alone or of the light shock combination occurred at three minute intervals. When the stimuli were paired, the onset of the light would precede the shock by ½ sec. and would be present for a total time of 1½ sec.

The alternate presentations of light paired with shock and light alone continued until there were three successive responses to the light alone which were either equal to, or greater than 0.039 milliamperes in amplitude. The extinction series began ninety seconds after the third consecutive CR. For the extinction series, the light alone was presented every 90 sec. until three consecutive zero responses to this stimulus were produced.

In the majority of cases the entire process could not comfortably be completed in a single session. Therefore, each experimental period was limited to one hour. The only exception to this rule occurred after the conditioning criterion had been reached and the extinction series was initiated. Since extinction was sometimes prolonged, the final session lasted for between one and two hours.

Results

Quantitative Features of the C.R. Formation

When the course of conditioning is examined, it is found (Table 2) that the hyperactive and/or distractible group of brain-damaged children required a significantly greater number of trials ($p = .02$) to reach the criterion of conditioning than did the non-hyperactive and non-distractible brain-damaged group. The mean number of trials required was 31.2 for the typeractive and 10.6 for the non-hyperactive children. In only one case is there any overlap between the number of trials required to reach conditioning by the individuals in the two groups. It is of further interest to note that whereas it was possible to complete the conditioning of all the non-hyperactive children 40 per cent of the hyperactive children could not achieve criterion levels of conditioning despite prolonged training periods.

Table 2. Number of presentations of light paired with shock necessary to reach criterion conditioning.

Brain-Damaged						Mongoloid		Normal	
Non-H and D		H and/or D							
		Completed		Inc.					
Subj.	No. of Trials	Subj.	No. of Trials	Subj.	No. of Trials	Subj.	No. of Trials	Subj.	No. Tri
J.J.	4	A.M.	13	S.P.	31+	C.K.	4	D.T.	4
J.M.	7	W.B.	19	C.H.	37+	G.H.	4	S.S.	5
S.S.	8	W.W.	21	M.S.	40+	L.D.	19	B.A.	6
J.E.	9	V.M.	30	L.G.	78+	A.S.	25	E.R.	10
J.S.	9	C.C.	48			B.H.	36		
B.W.	14	S.H.	56			L.L.	40		
R.A.	17					E.P.	45		
S.B.	17					L.C.	91		
Mean	10.6		31.2				33.0		6
S.D.	4.5		15.5				26.5		2

The scores of the subjects who did not reach the criterion for conditioning are indicated by a + were not included in the calculation of the means.

t scores and corresponding probability values that the null hypothesis regarding the differe between the mean number of presentations of light paired with shock necessary to criterion for conditioning can be rejected.

	H and/or D		Mongoloid		Normal	
	t Score	*p* Value	*t* Score	*p* Value	*t* Score	*p* Value
Non-H and Non-D	2.87	2%	2.20	5%	2.03	10%
H and/or D			0.15	50%	3.53	1%
Mongoloid					2.64	5%

The p values were calculated by using Fisher's t for small samples.

The mongoloid group performs significantly more poorly than does the non-hyperactive and non-distractible brain-damaged group (p = .05). The mongoloid children require approximately the same number of trials to achieve the conditioning criterion as do those of the hyperactive and/or distractible subjects who could be conditioned. It is possible that this elevation in number of trials required by the mongoloid children is largely the contribution made by the three youngest children of the group, all of whom were under seven years of age. If these young children are eliminated from consideration the conditioning of the remaining mongoloid children tends to become significantly more efficient than that of the hyperactive and/or distractible children, who were conditionable.

When the performances of the four normal children are analyzed it is found that they required significantly fewer trials to reach the criterion for adequate conditioning than either the hyperactive and/or distractible ($p = .01$) or mongoloid group ($p = .05$). However, they do not condition at a level which is significantly different from the performances of the non-hyperactive and non-distractible subjects ($p = .10$).

In order to determine whether the differences among the retarded children with respect to conditioning rate is in any way a reflection of differences among these children with respect to intellectual capacity as measured by I.Q., a correlation was made between these two variables. The product-moment correlation was $r = -.07$, which suggests that for the children in this study the I.Q. and the formation of the conditioned reflex are independent measures. Thus, for the children in this study the measure of the number of reinforced trials necessary for conditioning is not merely another means of demonstrating those consequences of brain damage which may be reflected in a modified I.Q.

Qualitative Features of the C.R. Formation

There were marked differences in the behavior of the children of the different groups during the conditioning series. The two groups of brain-damaged children showed the most extreme differences in behavior. The group of hyperactive and/or distractible children could only cooperate for a short time. Their capacities to sit still, to concentrate on one stimulus, to refrain from talking and to ignore the temptation to manipulate the electrodes were all limited. Moreover, as the session wore on this behavior became pronounced and occurred more and more frequently. The type of increased activity varied from child to child. Some chose to talk to the experimenter. According to the level of functioning of the child the talking ranged from coherent statements and questions in an attempt to engage the experimenter in conversation to apparently incoherent and disconnected verbalizations. Two children chose to sing and whistle during the sessions.

Other of the hyperactive children resorted to an increase in gross motor activity, either of the entire body or of parts, such as slapping their hands against the arm rests or kicking their feet against the floor. Still others would try to manipulate objects within reach such as the door latch or the wire leading to the bulb. Additional distractions were auditory stimuli from outside of the experimental situation many of which were of such low intensity that the experimenter was not aware of them until the child would call his attention to them by asking, "What's that?" These children tended to resort to several activities, but each seemed to have his or her characteristic preferred activity which increased progressively during a given training session.

The non-hyperactive and non-distractible group of brain-damaged children provided a distinct contrast to the hyperactive and/or distractible group. Although they were not entirely at ease in the experimental situation, a small amount of restlessness was all that was exhibited. In no case did this restlessness tend to increase during the initial session or to recur in the second session when more than one training period was required.

The mongoloid group varied slightly in the amount of motor activity and distractibility exhibited. With only one of the children however, was there any excessive restlessness, talking, increase in activity, or distractibility. This one mongoloid child (L. C.) was restless and extremely distractible and required an unusually long series of reinforcements before the criterion for conditioning was reached. L. C. was perhaps the most distractible subject used in this experiment in that he would respond to all extraneous auditory stimuli (including some that were almost inaudible to the experimenter) by asking what it was. This type of behavior was very similar to that encountered in the group of hyperactive and/or distractible brain-damaged children and gives one the impression that L. C. may have been such a child.

Of the four normal patients tested, none exhibited excessive motor activity.

Extinction of the Conditioned Reflex

When the quantitative features of extinction are explored (Table 3) it is found that no significant difference in mean number of trials required to achieve extinction exists among the three retarded groups. However, a qualitative consideration of the course of events during the extinction series serves to distinguish the groups of children from each other.

Extinction in the hyperactive group was characterized by a progressive increase in extraneous activity of the children and appeared to be the result of a displacement of the conditioned reflex by external extinction through the development of adventitious movements. In the group of non-hyperactive brain-damaged children extinction pursued a classical course, with no progressive increase in restlessness occurring. In the mongoloid group and in the normal children the extinction series resulted in the progressive increase in inhibition, with four of the eight mongoloid children and two of the four normal children falling sound asleep during this session (Table 3). One of the mongoloid children slept for such a long period of time (more than three minutes) during the series that the extinction criterion was met by the sleep itself. Among the normal children, one child fell asleep for brief periods at five distinct points in the extinction sequence.

'able 3. Number of presentations of light alone necessary to reach criterion for extinction.

Brain-Damaged					Mongoloid			Normal		
Non-H and D		H and/or D								
Subj.	No. of Trials	Subj.	No. of Trials	No. of Trials to Sleep	Subj.	No. of Trials	No. of Trials to Sleep	Subj.	No. of Trials	No. of Trials to Sleep
J.J.	33	A.M.	32*	12	C.K.	35		D.T.	41*	32
J.M.	36	W.B.	20		G.H.	13*	5	S.S.	43+*	15
S.S.	8	W.W.	31		L.D.	27		B.A.	48+	
J.E.	27	V.M.	28		A.S.	14		E.R.	22	
J.S.	31+	C.C.	4		B.H.	29*	29			
B.W.	26	S.H.	20		L.L.	61+*	5			
R.A.	9	S.P.	—		E.P.	22*	21			
S.B.	12	C.H.	—		L.C.	21+				
		M.S.	—							
		L.G.	—							
lean	21.6		22.5			23.5	15.0		25.0	23.5
.D.	10.8		9.6			9.9	10.3		11.5	8.5

Indicates that sleep occurred during the extinction period.
'he scores of the subjects who did not reach the criterion for extinction are indicated by a + and e not included in the calculation of the means.

ores and corresponding probability values that the null hypothesis regarding the differences veen the mean number of presentations of light alone necessary to reach criterion for extinction can be rejected.

	H an/or D		Mongoloid	
	t Score	*p* Value	*t* Score	*p* Value
Non-H and Non-D	0.152	50%	0.160	50%
H and/or D			0.314	50%

'he p values were calculated by using Fisher's t for small samples.

When sleep occurred there was a slow, steady, increase in skin resistance which persisted until the subject awoke. Upon awakening, there was a sharp decrease, of variable magnitude, in skin resistance. This course of events was peculiar to the sleeping children. In every case the experimenter observed the subjects while they were asleep in order to further verify that sleep had occurred. In all instances the subject could be seen in the completely relaxed posture characteristic of one who is asleep, with closed eyes and head resting on his or her chest or arm.

In contrast to the pattern just described the extinction series behavior of the hyperactive and/or distractible children was unmarked by any diminution of activity levels. The pattern of restlessness and high level mobility was sustained throughout the course of the extinction series.

Discussion

The results of the present study are best understood if the acquisition and the extinction of the conditioned reflex are considered separately. This is especially true since some of the findings concerning the formation or failure of formation of the conditioned galvanic skin response are illuminated by an independent consideration of the events that occurred during the subsequent extinction series.

The formation of a conditioned reflex involves the establishment of functional equivalence between two stimuli one of which is initially neutral and the other initially effective in producing the response. In normal children the neutral stimulus rapidly becomes a focus of attention and after a variable number of presentations which overlap in time with the administration of the effective stimulus, conditioning results. This classical course of events does not occur in our hyperactive-distractible children, in 40 per cent of whom we were unable to establish a definite conditioned reflex. Attention was rarely focused and responses were made to a miscellany of situational aspects. This lack of selectivity in attention may be interpreted as a manifestation of a defective process of inhibition, with the relevant stimulus incapable of achieving dominance and so reducing the effectiveness of explicit sensory arousals. Children in the non-hyperactive brain-damaged, mongoloid, and normal groups do not exhibit this type of difficulty.

The data on the extinction of the conditioned reflex support the view that a defective equilibrium between excitatory and inhibitory relations characterizes the hyperactive and distractible brain-damaged group. A brief statement of general conditioning theory is necessary in discussing the extinction data. Pavlov has advanced two concepts to account for the disappearance of a conditioned reflex, internal inhibition and external inhibition. Internal inhibition refers to the progressive development of inhibitory activity at a cortical locus which occurs in response to the continued unreinforced presentation of the conditioned stimulus. External inhibition refers to the process whereby the presentation of extraneous stimuli may by interference function to make the conditioned stimulus ineffective. The first of these postulated mechanisms appears to be an analogue of adaption, and the second of displacement. Among the subjects in the present investigation the hyperactive-distractible group appear to lose the conditioned reflex by external inhibition or displacement, whereas, the other groups appear to achieve conditioned reflex extinction by internal inhibition. Thus the hyperactive brain-damaged group approaches the extinction of the conditioned reflex through an ever increasing degree of generalized motor activity. The children in the remaining groups appear to achieve conditioned reflex extinction through the development of internal inhibition, a process which is distinguished by a diminution of general motor activity level. In the normal children and in the mongoloid children this inhibitory phenomenon is generalized into sleep which Pavlov (3) viewed as "an inhibition which has spread over a great section of the cerebrum, over the entire hemispheres and even into the lower lying midbrain."

It is apparent that the obtained differences in both establishment of conditioning and the extinction of the conditioned reflex found are independent of the scores made on tests of intelligence, and have independent implications for the management and training of hyperactive and non-hyperactive brain-injured retarded children. Thus, the children who are in the hyperactive group may function most effectively in an environment which promotes inhibition by being repetitive and limited in the number and kinds of extraneous stimuli presented. However, such a situation would not be desirable for the non-hyperactive brain-injured group and could result in generalized inhibition.

Summary

The conditionability and rate of extinction of conditioned galvanic skin reflex of two groups of brain-injured children, a group of mongoloid, and a small group of normal children was studied. It was found that the group of brain-injured children who were characterized as being hyperactive and/or distractible required a significantly larger number of paired presentations of light and shock to reach the criterion for conditioning than did a group of brain-injured children who were not so characterized. It was found that the group of mongoloid children required a longer conditioning period than did the group of non-hyperactive and/or distractible brain-injured children.

While there was no significant difference in the number of extinction trials required by the groups studied, there were major differences in the extinction process. The most striking difference was that the hyperactive and/or distractible group of brain-injured children gave little evidence of a buildup of internal inhibition and maintained and sometimes increased their activity level as the extinction series wore on.

On the other hand half of the children in both the mongoloid and normal groups demonstrated that internal inhibition was building up by falling asleep at some point during the extinction series.

The results are discussed from the standpoint of conditioned reflex theory and suggest that the population of brain-injured children is not a homogeneous one. The various kinds of behavior displayed by brain-injured children may be understood as the result of disturbances in normal cerebral functioning which modify the effective equilibration of excitation and inhibition.

References

1. Birch, H. G.: Problems in the differential diagnosis of mental retardation. In *The Evaluation and Treatment of the Mentally Retarded Child in Clinics,* pp. 40-49. National Association for Retarded Children, New York, 1956.
2. Birch, H. G.: Theoretical aspects of psychological behavior in the brain damaged. In *Psychological Services for the Cerebral Palsied,* pp. 28-51. United Cerebral Palsy Associations, New York, 1956.
3. Pavlov, I. P.: *Conditioned Reflexes.* Oxford Univ. Press, New York, 1927.
4. Strauss, A. A.: *Psychopathology and Education of the Brain-Injured Child,* Vol. 1. Grune & Stratton, New York, 1947.
5. Strauss, A. A.: *Psychopathology and Education of the Brain-Injured Child,* Vol. 2. Grune & Stratton, New York, 1955.
6. Strauss, A. A.: Ways of thinking in brain-crippled deficient children. *Am. J. Psychiat., 100*: 639-647, 1944.
7. Strauss, A. A. and Kephart, N. C.: Behavior differences in mentally retarded children measured by a new behavior rating scale. *Am. J. Psychiat., 19*: 1117-1124, 1940.
8. Strauss, A. A. and Werner, H.: Disorders of conceptual thinking in the brain-injured child. *J. Nerv. & Ment. Dis., 96*: 153-172, 1942.
9. Strauss, A. A. and Werner, H.: Experimental analysis of the clinical symptom "perseveration" in mentally retarded children. *Am. J. Ment. Deficiency, 47*: 185-188, 1942.
10. Werner, H.: Development of visuo-motor performance on the marble-board test in mentally retarded children. *J. Genetic Psychol., 64*: 269-279, 1944.
11. Werner, H.: Abnormal and subnormal rigidity. *J. Abnorm. & Social Psychol., 41*: 15-24, 1946.
12. Werner, H. and Bowers, M.: Auditory-motor organization in two clinical types of mentally deficient children. *J. Genetic Psychol., 59*: 85-99, 1941.
13. Werner, H. and Carrison, D.: Animistic thinking in brain-injured, mentally retarded children. *J. Abnorm. & Social Psychol., 39*: 43-62, 1944.
14. Werner, H. and Strauss, A. A.: Causal factors in low performance. *Am. J. Ment. Deficiency, 45*: 213-218, 1940.
15. Werner, H. and Strauss, A. A.: Pathology of figure-background relation in the brain-injured child. *J. Abnorm. & Social Psychol., 36*: 236-248, 1941.
16. Werner, H. and Thuma, B. D.: A deficiency in the perception of apparent motion in children with brain-injury. *Am. J. Psychol., 55*: 58-67, 1942.

PART **IV**

CONDITIONED AVERSION THERAPIES

Within the past forty years diverse behavioral problems have been successfully ameliorated by use of some type of conditioned aversion technique. The usual procedure is to base the treatment on some form of classical Pavlovian conditioning model, in which the aim is to establish an aversive reaction to certain behavioral aspects of the pathology in question. This principle has been applied to such problems as transvestism, fetishism, homosexuality, compulsive masturbation, sadism, sexual exposure, obsessive actions and thoughts, writers' cramp and so forth.

Most of the early techniques achieved this aversive response by associating stimuli related to the pathology with the unpleasant effects of some nausea-inducing drug, usually apomorphine or emetine hydrochloride. This method has been most extensively applied to the treatment of alcoholism, in which alcohol is given on a number of occasions just *before* the vomiting occurs, in the hope that eventually the alcohol will take on the properties of a CS to which the CR is intense nausea at its taste, smell or even sight.

There are many problems associated with this method, including the excessive time required of the physician to provide individual attention to the patient, and practical difficulties associated with the use of an emetic as a noxious stimulus. A number of attempts have been made to cope with these problems. Miller, Dvorak and Turner's method of setting with these problems. Miller, Dvorak and Turner's method of setting up aversive therapy on a group basis provides an answer to one problem, and electric shock has been suggested as more easily applied, manipulated and controlled, and having more clear and predictable effects than chemical agents. However, electric shock aversion has its own limitations, and there is still a need for techniques utilizing aversive stimuli which are traumatic, have predictable onsets and courses of action, and, at the same time, are effective, rapid, and free of side effects. This is what Sanderson, Campbell and Laverty attempt to do by the somewhat dramatic method of temporarily suppressing respiration.

Both the group emetine technique and the method of producing a traumatic situation by the suppression of respiration have been developed primarily for the treatment of alcoholism. They could, of course, be applied to a variety of other behavioral problems. In the search for new methods of creating aversion and new areas of treatment it is important always to be aware of the fundamental principles of conditioning governing all these practices. New devices can be no substitute for scientific rigor and a knowledge of basic principles. Even when one satisfactory aversion-producing agent is discovered, it is still necessary to forestall failures or relapses by exploring such variables as intermittent versus total reinforcement, CS-UCS relationships and so forth. It is now known that, once conditioning has been established under the right circumstances, very few periodic reinforcing sessions are required in the future to maintain the aversion. Well established CR are apparently resistant to the mere passage of time, which plays little if any role in the elimination of the effects of aversive training.

The final paper in this section is perhaps the most intriguing. McGuire and Vallance have developed a remarkably simple and inexpensive, powerful yet safe technique for the use of electric shock in CR therapy based upon the method of creating an aversion. Among the cases they describe as responding favorably to treatment the most timely is probably that of the lady who was rapidly and apparently lastingly "cured" of the smoking habit. The fact that very few reinforcement sessions were required is of special importance. Despite the limitations of electric shock the future use of this ingeniously simple apparatus in the clinical development of CR aversion therapy appears warranted. Appended to this paper is a suggested modified circuit for use by North American investigators.

13

A METHOD OF CREATING AVERSION TO ALCOHOL BY REFLEX CONDITIONING IN A GROUP SETTING

by Ernest C. Miller, M.D., B. Anthony Dvorak, M.D.
and Don W. Turner, B.S.

Among the many specialized procedures which have been employed in the treatment of alcoholism is the conditioned aversion method of Kantorovich (1). A modified form of this, as popularized in the United States by Voegtlin (2) in the 1930's, consisted of a Pavlovian conditioned reflex technique with the use of emetine as an unconditioned stimulus and alcoholic beverages as a conditioned stimulus.

Voegtlin's work aroused much interest in the field of conditioning. His report of 64.3 per cent absolute arrest rate in a series of 538 patient's over a period of 4 years seemed to indicate that here was an apparently rapid, effective and reasonably safe means whereby alcoholism might be controlled by the physician. Voegtlin, apparently anticipating dissensions from therapists unable to duplicate his results, in a second paper (3) in the latter part of 1940 pointed out the necessity of scrupulous attention to Pavlovian technique to ensure success with this treatment. He emphasized the importance of proper timing when administering the alchohol, and the prerequisite of reducing extraneous stimuli; for either of these, if not carefully controlled, might inhibit the establishment of a favorable conditioned reflex.

Though the method failed to attain universal acceptance, many references appeared in the literature,* and many investigators (4-8)

* In the Classified Abstract Archive of the Alcohol Literature at Yale University, in July 1959, there were 169 references dated subsequent to 1940 to "conditioning procedures." Of the 48 therapists who reported on method and results, 26 (54 per cent) employ apomorphine rather than emetine as an unconditioned stimulus; 18 (38 per cent) follow Voegtlin's method, and 4 (8 per cent) utilize hypnosis.

Reproduced by permission from the *Quarterly Journal of Studies on Alcohol,* Vol. 21, pp. 424-431, 1960.

confirmed Voegtlin's results. As of 1947, according to Tiebout (9), claims for arrest of alcoholism with this treatment ranged from 50 to 60 per cent. It was becoming evident even to enthusiastic protagonists, however, that by itself the treatment could not be considered a panacea (10, 11, 12). Most workers began to recognize that many other factors were involved in successful arrest following conditioning. Shadel (13), in whose hospital Voegtlin developed and was carrying out the conditioned-reflex treatment, himself emphasized the importance of other supportive procedures, including pretreatment interviews, spontaneous group therapy, and follow-up for a year with occasional reinforcement of the conditioning. The personality of the patient seems important according to Wallerstein (14). Though conditioned aversion fared poorly in his recent comparative study of four treatment modalities, this therapist readily admitted that his technique might have been at fault, but also indicated that the overly depressed or guilt-ridden alcoholic responded well. Voegtlin (15) suggests that the interest and understanding of ancillary hospital personnel is perhaps an important factor. In addition, most authors advocate the use of adjuvant measures, including psychotherapy, Alcoholics Anonymous, occupational therapy, and reinforcement conditioning at regular intervals.

At the Charity Hospital of Louisiana, in New Orleans, the Voegtlin technique was first tried in the treatment of inpatient alcoholics in the latter part of 1958. Within 2 months sufficient skill in technique was acquired so that it was possible with reasonable consistency to establish a satisfactory reflex aversion to alcohol in our patients. A logistical problem developed, however, in that limitations of time (approximately 1 hour a day was available) did not permit treating even a fraction of the patients who presented themselves. At this time, a senior staff physician* suggested the possibility of attempting the procedure in a group setting.

The problem was whether such a procedure was not foredoomed to failure in that it violated a basic principle of conditioned learning, i.e., the avoidance of external inhibitory factors. Such things as noise, reflections of light, changes of temperature, and other variables of sensory value tend to dilute a conditioning stimulus and critically impede the establishment of a conditioned reflex to it. In the contemplated group situation these inhibitory factors would be manifold. There would be, first of all, many persons in the same room, some observing and directing, others retching and vomiting. This interplay could seriously divert the attention of patients from the alcohol stimulus.

Not only would the session labor under the multiple distractions common to any group situation but, in addition, conditioning might

* Dr. R. W. Buddington, Assistant Professor, Department of Psychiatry and Neurology, Tulane University School of Medicine.

be subject to interference on the individual level. In this regard the following were considered as possible sources of anxiety which might counteract the formation of the desired reflex: (*a*) feelings of degradation by vomiting before a group; (*b*) lowered self-esteem and feelings of inadequacy if the emetic response failed to compare favorably with that of the peer group. Other possible disadvantages on an individual level were that patients with considerable aggressive features in their personality might successfully resist vomiting as a covert means of expressing hostility, and those with paranoid traits might suppress their emesis as a convenient means of expressing superiority and supporting their grandiose system. Either of these effects could exert a negative effect on the other members of the group by suggestion alone.

A search of the literature revealed that two authors had mentioned group conditioning. Dubroschke (16) reported a study of 109 patients over a period of 19 months, but failed to state the number of patients in each group and did not adequately describe the procedure or qualify the effectiveness of the conditioning. Boitelle et al. (17) also reported on a series of 109 patients who were treated in groups of 2, when possible, with apomorphine conditioning. The results were quite poor, an arrest rate of 15 per cent, and the therapist doubted that conditioning by this method would last more than 2 or 3 months. It is possible that the poor results in this series reflect the choice of the conditioning drug (apomorphine) which, by its sedative action, antagonizes the formation of a conditioned reflex.

As these reports shed no appreciable light on the subject of group conditioning, we undertook to test whether or not such a procedure was possible and practical. As to the possible negative influence of a vigorously interacting group, we reasoned that if the primary attention of the patient was adequately directed toward alcohol by both verbal and physical means, as will be described later, any dissociative influence might well be mitigated by the strong element of suggestion (seeing someone else retch in the presence of alcohol).

Method

Subjects. The patients were white males who self-admittedly had a drinking problem and wished to stop. No fine distinction was attempted among psychiatric diagnostic categories except for the exclusion of obvious psychotic disorders. Physical requirements included that the patient have no history of severe gastric disturbance such as peptic ulcer, and no history of cardiac disease, and be in general good health at the time treatment started.

Physical examinations were performed on all patients, and laboratory work included an electrocardiogram before, four times during, and once on completing treatment; chest X-ray, complete blood count, urinalysis, fasting blood sugar, cephalin flocculation, alkaline phosphatase, and blood urea nitrogen. When enteropathology was suspected, a gastrointestinal X-ray survey was made.

All the patients were informed of the nature of the procedure and told that it would be unpleasant but that there was no need for undue concern. During the 2 weeks of treatment the patient was confined to the hospital and allowed all privileges but received no adjuvant psychotherapy.

Treatment Room. A sound-proofed room, 12 × 16 feet, was used. In the center of the room stood a portable table, draped with a white sheet, and upon this were placed standard one-fifth bottles of vodka, scotch, bourbon, gin, rye, rum, red wine, white wine, 95 per cent ethyl alcohol, and a liqueur. In addition, there were four to eight cans of beer, and each man was supplied with a 2-oz. jigger and a large paper cup for water. Four chairs were placed about the table so that each man could regard the others, and the table was spot-lighted from above with a large outdoor-type lamp. Chairs were placed for two physicians so that each could observe the actions of at least two patients.

Drugs. Essentially following the Voegtlin procedure, a sterile solution of emetine hydrochloride (1.25 gr. per cc.), pilocarpine hydrochloride (0.52 gr. per cc.) and ephedrine sulfate (0.60 gr. per cc.) was prepared. In addition, vials of emetine were provided so that this drug might be administered orally if deemed necessary.

Treatment Session. New groups were started on Monday mornings at 2-week intervals. For 2 weeks the patients underwent daily conditioning, Monday through Friday, skipping Saturday and Sunday and continuing through the new week until completed on Friday for a total of 10 session days. Treatment was conducted in groups of four according to the space available.

A patient previously conditioned was selected and held over to act as a "scapegoat."* This patient also helped by instructing the novices in matters of routine. Each patient was responsible for bringing a towel, a blanket and a bucket to the treatment room (these patients soon became known on the ward as the "bucket brigade"). While in the treatment room, conversation was restricted and attention was focused only on the alcoholic beverages. Each man was obliged to fill his own water glass from his individual pitcher. It is necessary that the patients consume fairly large quantities of tepid water, occasionally in the amount of 2 liters during the treatment session, as it seems to potentiate emesis and also obviates "dry heaves."

* As the study progressed, we found that in subsequent groups it was to our advantage to include a "ringer" or previously conditioned member who, owing to his low tolerance for the "sight" and "taste" and "smell" of alcohol, would invariably initiate a chain response of gagging and retching, and occasionally emesis, among the other group members very early in the treatment.

On entrance into the room, patients are requested to take places around the table. They are cautioned to refrain from conversation and to concentrate intensively upon the alcoholic beverages before them. Each patient drinks two glasses of tepid water and then receives a subdeltoid injection of 12 to 14 minims of the emetine mixture. Each therapist is provided with a data sheet upon which he records the amount of medication given his patients, the time of onset of emesis, and general behavioral observations.

Shortly after the injection is given the members of the group are requested to uncap the liquor bottles, open the beer, and pour themselves a 2-oz. glassful of the beverage of their choice. At frequent intervals each man sniffs at his glass, and only when gagging begins, or when it seems likely that the individual is about to vomit, is it suggested that he drink the liquor. Between bouts of emesis the patients are encouraged to drink copious amounts of water, and as many different beverages as possible are included in the pour-sniff-drink routine.

Sessions usually last from 30 to 45 minutes. The group is not released until all doubt is dispelled from the mind of each participant that he cannot tolerate any of the alcoholic beverages on the table.

At this point, patients are expected to wash out their glasses, cap the bottles, and repair to the ward with their impedimenta where they lie down for a period of at least 4 hours. During this period of rest, blood pressure, pulse and respiration rate are checked every 30 minutes.

Treatments are generally begun at 10:30 a.m. Patients are fasted from the previous night, as the presence of food in the stomach seems to retard the onset of emesis. Throughout the day they are encouraged to take supplemental fluids in the form of juices and chocolate milk, and they receive a diet rich in protein and carbohydrate with supplemental vitamins.

We have found individual conditionability to be quite variable. In some persons it is necessary to continue injections of Voegtlin's mixture for an entire week, and occasionally to supplement this with oral emetine (1 gr.) in water. Other patients exhibit such good response that placebo injections can be given on the second or third day with complete discontinuance of all drugs thereafter. Placebos are ultimately discontinued as the next step in the conditioning process.

Results and Discussion

Of the 20 patients who have undergone this technique, none failed to acquire an excellent conditioned aversion to all forms of alcohol which were presented to them. Our fears that the presence of many persons undergoing treatment simultaneously might exert inhibitory effects appear to have been groundless. The element of suggestion seems definitely to potentiate emesis in this situation, as there was a definite clustering of responses.

Examination of the records of each session, which include specific data on times of emesis of each patient, revealed that approximately 27 per cent of the time there was contiguous or simultaneous vomiting in three or four members of the group. About 57 per cent of the time contiguous vomiting occurred in two members of the group. Individual isolated responses occurred only in about 16 per cent of the total periods of emesis.

Early in our program we actively attempted to place all the participants in phase, that is, to have them all drinking alcohol or water, or sniffing alcohol, at the same time. It seemed, from a theoretical standpoint, that not to do so would greatly enhance stimulus generalization and possibly cause some of the subjects to develop an aversion to water. This was a matter of great concern, for frequently a mass vomiting would occur, initiated by one of the patients who was smelling or drinking alcohol but invariably joined by others who were sipping water at the time. As the experiment progressed, however, we were obliged to take a less active role in the matter of phasing. The variability of responses in each patient was such that attempts to coordinate this activity after the first 5 or 10 minutes were impractical. The excessive verbal activity required of the physicians seemed to be distractive to the patients; we thereafter adopted the less rigid manner of encouraging only the individual patient, from time to time, to "have another drink." That none of the 20 developed an aversion to water, we feel, is due to more than mere good fortune. First of all, before, during and after treatments, all physiological and psychological elements of suggestion were directed toward a favorable association of alcohol and nausea; secondly, the biological role of water favors ready extinguishment of any unfavorable reflex that might become associated with its intake.

No conclusions can be drawn from this study as to the effectiveness of the conditioned aversion treatment of alcoholism. The project is now only in its eighth month, and there is adequate follow-up on only 10 of the 20 patients treated. Of these 10, 2 have relapsed to their former pattern of drinking, and 3 have had brief lapses of from 1 to 3 days of drinking, but stopped spontaneously. The other 5 have, to this time, remained abstinent. Those who did drink were able to do so only at the expense of strenuous effort at holding down the first drink; thus, we are reasonably assured that failure to establish a satisfactory conditioned aversion was not the fault.

As a result of these studies we feel justified in concluding that adequate Pavlovian conditioning can be established in a group setting. The external and internal influences which we feared might exert negative effects on our treatment were either inoperative or, if present without our recognition, neutralized by the overwhelming element of suggestion.

The demands on the physician were not in excess of those encountered by us in our experience with the individual conditioning technique. Though two physicians were present at each session, this was largely a matter of choice and of the needs of adequate recording of the experiment. On one occasion a single physician managed the group of four patients without marked difficulty.

Something which will perhaps prove more interesting is that introduction of this conditioning variable, the interpersonal factor, contributes to these groups a feeling of solidarity, and concomitant elevation of self-esteem of the type occasionally seen in members of combat teams who have shared a common arduous experience and performed meritoriously. Though we have not attempted to utilize this phenomenon therapeutically it is conceivable that the physician employing group conditioning might find that this reaction will serve in the manner of an entree to involving these patients in group therapy subsequent to conditioning.

Summary

Conditioned-reflex treatment of alcoholism is briefly discussed. A method of establishing reflex aversion to alcohol in a group setting is presented. It is suggested that physicians employing conditioning methods might, by the use of groups, be able to expose a larger number of suitable patients to this form of treatment. It is also noted that group conditioning seems to enhance the self-esteem of the participating patients, and tends to promote strong and positive group identity, factors which might be employed advantageously in initiating group psychotherapeutic sessions.

References

1. Kantorovich, N. V.: [An attempt at associative-reflex therapy in alcoholism.] Nov. Refleksol. Fiziol. nerv. Sist. *3:* 436-447, 1929. Abst. in *Psychol. Abstr. 4*: 493, 1930.
2. Voegtlin, W. L.: The treatment of alcoholism by establishing a conditioned reflex. *Amer. J. med. Sci., 199:* 802-809, 1940.
3. Voegtlin, W. L., Lemere, F. and Broz, W. R.: Conditioned reflex therapy of alcoholic addiction. *III.* An evaluation of present results in the light of previous experience with this method. *Quart. J. Stud. Alc., 1*: 501-516, 1940.
4. Beca, M. F. and Secchi, S.: Resultado de los tratamientos anti-alcohólicos en Chile. *Rev. Psiquiat.,* Chile, *12*: 71-76, 1947.
5. Ash, W. E. and Mahoney, J. D.: The use of conditioned reflex and Antabuse in the therapy of alcoholism. *J. Iowa St. med. Soc., 41*: 456-458, 1951.
6. Kant, F.: The use of the conditioned reflex in the treatment of alcohol addicts. *Wis. med. J., 44*: 217-221, 1945.
7. Shanahan, W. M. and Hornick, E. J.: Aversion treatment of alcoholism. *Hawaii med. J., 6*: 19-21, 1946.

8. Thimann, J.: The conditioned reflex treatment of alcoholism. *R.I. med. J., 27*: 647-651, 1944.
9. Tiebout, H. M.: Alcoholism. In: Kurtz, R. H., ed., *Social Work Yearbook;* pp. 45-50. New York: Russell Sage Foundation; 1947.
10. Williams, L.: Some observations on the recent advances in the treatment of alcoholism. *Brit. J. Addict., 47*: 62-67, 1950.
11. Thimann, J.: Conditioned reflex treatment of alcoholism. *II.* The risks of its application, its indications, contraindications and psychotherapeutic aspects. *New Engl. J. Med., 241*: 406-410, 1949.
12. O'Hollaren, P. and Lemere, F.: Conditioned reflex treatment of chronic alcoholism. Results obtained in 2,323 net cases from 3,125 admissions over a period of ten and a half years. *New Engl. J. Med., 239*: 331-333, 1948.
13. Shadel, C. A.: Aversion treatment of alcohol addiction. *Quart. J. Stud. Alc., 5*: 216-228, 1944.
14. Wallerstein, R. S.: Comparative study of treatment methods for chronic alcoholism; the alcoholism research project at Winter V.A. Hospital. *Amer. J. Psychiat., 113*: 228-233, 1956.
15. Voegtlin, W. L.: Limitations and adjunctive therapies in treatment of chronic alcoholism. *Med. World,* Philad., *65*: 165-168, 1947.
16. Dubroschke, C.: Situationen in der Alkoholentzienhungskur. *Münch. med. Wschr., 95*: 242-243, 1953.
17. Boitelle, G., Boitelle-Lentulo, C. Singer, L. and Dany.: Résultats de deux ans de traitement anti-alcoolique au service libre de l'hôpital psychiatrique de Lorquin. *Ann. méd.-psychol., 110*: 348-352, 1952.

14

AN INVESTIGATION OF A NEW AVERSIVE CONDITIONING TREATMENT FOR ALCOHOLISM

by R. E. Sanderson, Ph.D., Dugal Campbell, Ph.D., and S. G. Laverty, M.R.C.P., B.Sc.

Treatment for alcoholism based upon the formation of a conditioned aversion response to alcohol appears to have enjoyed some popularity during the 1940's. Except in a few clinics, conditioning therapy is in little use today. The present communication describes a pilot investigation of a new method of producing a conditioned aversion response to alcohol which goes some way toward avoiding the difficulties met with in previous techniques.

Classically the treatment consists of an unconditioned stimulus (UCS) and a conditioned stimulus (CS). The UCS which has usually been employed is nausea and vomiting induced by emetine hydrochloride or apomorphine. The CS is alcohol. The crux of the treatment lies in the expectation that repeated administration of the alcohol just before vomiting occurs will lead to the alcohol acquiring noxious associations so that it will be avoided by the patient. Further repetition of the CS-UCS sequence should lead to the alcohol acquiring the property of initiating vomiting. Neither outcome has been rigorously demonstrated in a controlled experiment.

The theoretical expectation for most aversive conditioning procedures is extreme stability of the conditioned response in all subjects; the conditioned response should not extinguish even though repeatedly elicited by the CS with no reinforcement from the UCS (1). Tiebout (2), in reviewing the literature on avoidance therapy, concluded that, in practice, arrest of alcoholism ranged from 50 to 60 per cent. Since the spontaneous remission rate of alcoholics is believed to be about 10 per cent (3), conditioned-reflex therapy is presumably effective in about 40 to 50 per cent of the cases. It may be suspected that in many,

* This investigation was supported by a grant from the Alcoholism and Drug Addiction Research Foundation of Ontario.

Reproduced by permission from the *Quarterly Journal of Studies on Alcohol,* Vol. 24, pp. 261-275, 1963.

perhaps half, of the patients a true aversive response has not been formed. In point of fact it is impossible from the literature (4, 5, 6) to establish whether a conditioned aversion has ever been established to alcohol. The conditioning situation has rarely been described in sufficient detail, and there are no data on postconditioning behavioral responses.

The reason for failure to establish true conditioned aversion behavior could be accounted for by one or all of several factors: (*a*) The exact prediction of the time of onset of vomiting with an emetic is extremely difficult (7). Thus the presentation of the CS (in this case alcohol) in the critical time interval (which is of the order of 0 to 5 seconds) before the onset of the UCS (vomiting) must in practice present considerable problems in which only "experience" can be a guide. It has also been shown (8) that UCS which have a sudden onset are more readily conditionable than drives with a gradual onset. (*b*) Most emetics are cortical depressants; there is evidence to suggest that a drug with this characteristic inhibits the formation of conditioned responses (9). (*c*) Previous investigators of aversive conditioning in animals have employed massive physiological traumatizing stimuli—for example, high intensity electric shock as their unconditioned stimulus—in producing avoidance behavior. It is certainly not generally the case that vomiting in humans even approaches such stimuli in traumatic efficacy. A further consideration which tells against the therapy are the risks entailed by using relatively toxic emetics several times in a long treatment series. Some investigators advocate up to 30 or 40 treatment sessions, each one taking most of a day.

A new technique which has a traumatic UCS, a predictable onset, a predictable course of action, and which is relatively free of side effects would offer an opportunity for a more accurate estimate of the efficacy of conditioned aversion therapies.

One need, perhaps the basic need, for human life is the continuation of respiration. It seems axiomatic that a temporary inability to breathe, along with an inability to communicate this distress, must in the conscious human be a most terrifying experience. Succinylcholine chloride dihydrate is a curarizing drug which acts at the motor endplate of the efferent neurons serving the skeletal muscles to cause a nerve-muscle depolarization. For a short period immediately following an injection of succinylcholine the subject is totally paralyzed, unable to move or breathe. The effects of this drug on conscious humans therefore meet the criteria noted above for a therapeutically useful noxious stimulus. A pilot investigation of the use of respiratory paralysis by means of this drug in forming conditioned aversion responses to alcohol will be described below. The object of the investigation was to determine the major difficulties in planning a rigorous demonstration of the therapeutic efficacy of such treatment.

Technique and Apparatus

Each subject was placed on a stretcher in a shielded room and fitted with electrodes which were connected to a Grass Model 5 Polygraph which gave measures of four physiological variables: galvanic skin response (GSR), heart function (electrocardiogram and heart rate), respiration, and muscle tension. Changes in these four variables were used to indicate both conditioned and unconditioned responses, to predict the onset of paralysis and to predict the reestablishment of normal respiration. A hypodermic needle was put into a vein in the left arm and a saline drip was attached to the needle and left to run slowly. When the moment to give the succinylcholine* approached, a 20-mg. dose was injected into the drip behind the subject's head and then the drip was turned full on. In this way the subject was unaware that the drug had been administered.

The technique involved three experimenters; one monitored the polygraph and signaled to the other experimenters the physiological changes which characteristically mark the course of the period of apnea; another, a physician, sat behind the patient's head, administered the drug and ventilated the subject with a respirator if the period of apnea exceeded a period of about 60 to 90 sec. or if any signs of hypoxia appeared; the third experimenter presented the CS.

After the subject was connected with the polygraph he was allowed to settle down so that a constant baseline of physiological function was established. Once this had appeared he was given a bottle containing a few drops of his favorite beverage and told to grasp it, look at it, put it to his nose and sniff it, then put it to his lips and taste it, and then hand it back to the experimenter. This was repeated five times at intervals of about a minute; this routine usually took about 10 or 15 sec. After five trials, 20 mg. of succinylcholine was injected into the drip and the drip was then turned full on. As soon as the drug entered the bloodstream there was a characteristic change in GSR. This was signaled to the experimenter in the room who at once handed the bottle to the subject and at just the moment when the bottle was about to be put to the subject's lips the full effect of the drug took hold. The experimenter then held the bottle to the subject's lips and put a few drops of the drink into his mouth. As soon as any signs of regular breathing appeared the bottle was taken away. When breathing was restored and the subject's terror had subsided an attempt was made to have him repeat the grasp–look–smell–taste action a number of times to observe any changes in the physiological or behavioral responses.

* The brand used in these experiments was Scoline, manufactured by Glaxo-Allenbury.

Subjects

The subjects were selected from the Ontario Hospital, Kingston (a mental hospital maintained by the Provincial Government) and from the psychiatric ward of the Kingston General Hospital. The patients from the General Hospital were actively seeking treatment though none of them showed much anxiety about their alcoholism. The group of patients from the Ontario Hospital were not seeking treatment and, in several instances, refused treatment when it was first offered to them. Characteristically the patients who were offered the treatment had a long history of alcoholism, a poor work record and low socio-economic status; some were suspected of having brain damage; and several had been hospitalized on previous occasions as a consequence of drinking. The majority of the patients had been sent to the hospital under some legal form, e.g., hospitalization had been made a condition of remand, and many took the treatment hoping it would lead to a reduction of what they regarded as a "sentence."

The three experimenters had very little to do with the patients, who were all formally under the care of physicians on the staff of the two hospitals. The patient-experimenter interaction was minimized deliberately to exclude any possible effects that contact with the experimenters might have upon the outcome of conditioning. No alteration was made in the medical regimen prescribed for each patient; as a result the three patients in Series I, and a majority of the patients in Series II, received daily doses of one tranquilizing drug or another.

Series I

Three patients were selected from the Ontario Hospital to take part in a preliminary experiment of traumatic conditioning. This experiment had already been completed when they were asked to take part in a second therapeutic conditioning trial in which the CS would be their usual drink. Consequently the treatment was their second exposure to the respiratory paralysis.* These three patients had volunteered for the preliminary experiment when they were told it was part of an investigation into a possible therapy for alcoholism. They were told nothing beyond the fact that they would undergo a frightening but harmless experience. In all three subjects it was clear from their behavior that the second experience with succinylcholine was not so effective in traumatic effect as the first. In one case (F. V.) it is unlikely that effective conditioning took place, as alcohol was not presented during the respiratory paralysis due to a breakdown in the signaling system.

* In a further experiment, not yet published, conditioned responses have been established in subjects who were fully briefed on the exact effects of succinylcholine.

F. V., age 52, unmarried, was the second of five children. He had three alcoholic uncles. He left school after grade 9 and went to business school. A good piano player, he worked in a local music school and as organizer of musical education in county schools for 4 years. He has since worked intermittently as a salesman for many firms. He was discharged from the Army in 1941 for "drinking." He began drinking 18 months after leaving school and had six hospital admissions for alcoholism.

R. W., age 29, unmarried, was the fourth of four children, only two of whom lived. His father drank heavily and married three times. The patient was sickly as a child. He completed 1 year at high school, then held several jobs (usually truck driving) until dismissed for drunkenness. He began to drink at age 14 and was drinking heavily at 20 (claims eight bottles of wine a day). He had had four hospital admissions, including two committals, and once attempted suicide in jail.

W. J. P., age 39, divorced, with four children, was sixth in a family of six. His father drank heavily. One brother was a mental defective and father of a boy diagnosed as simple schizophrenic; another brother was an epileptic. The patient very likely was brain damaged. He left school after grade 8. He married at 21, a woman 3 months pregnant; they were separated and divorced due to his drinking. Six years ago he had entered into a common-law marriage. He began to drink at age 18, heavy drinking at 21, and was discharged from the Army because of "drinking." He was unable to keep any job. He reported drinking 3 or 4 bottles of wine a day.

Series II

Twelve patients were treated who had not had any previous experience of the induced paralysis. They were not given a detailed account of what to expect; they were told that a "chemical change" would be produced in them which might help them later if they wished to stop drinking. They were also told that the treatment was unpleasant and some of them heard accounts of the treatment from other patients. None of them seemed to have a clear idea of what might take place and several asked questions which suggested that they expected some form of electroconvulsive therapy.

R. K. McD., age 54, was married to a registered nurse and had six children. An only child, he had been brought up by a maternal aunt following his father's death (attributed to drink) when he was 6 months old; his mother was "mentally ill" from the time of his birth. He stated that he felt insecure as a child, though well cared for. He experienced the normal milestones, left school at 15 (11th grade), and held jobs in automobile service stations and as a railway baggage clerk until he joined the R.C.A.F. in 1941. He flew in bombers as air gunner and was discharged in 1945 with the rank of Flying Officer. He then worked as a machinist until laid off (not for drinking) in October 1960. He had arthritis when discharged from the Air Force and in 1957 suffered a broken back. He began drinking at age 18; his wife stated that he first showed loss of control in 1955. He had one previous hospital admission for alcoholism. Immediately before the present admission he was "drunk for 4 weeks." He usually drinks beer, then vodka.

G. W. O., age 23, unmarried, was the "weaker" of fraternal twins, "backward in everything." He was brought up at home by strict parents who "throw his behavior in his face." His physical development was retarded. He left school at 16 ("got in with a bunch of torpedoes," i.e., hooligans) and worked in hospitals as a maintenance man or in the laundry until discharged twice for "drinking;" since his last job he stayed at home and has had only casual work. He may have suffered a brain injury at birth and now has an abnormal electroencephalogram. He started drinking at high school and began to drink heavily at 19. While working, he claims, he could have a bottle of wine each morning, a dozen beers at lunch, and would stay in the beer parlor after work. He had two previous hospital admissions for alcoholism. Before the present admission he had been drinking for 4 days. He finally asked the police to help him and was committed to the hospital.

D. J., age 33, unmarried, was the youngest of a large family. His mother died when he was 17. An aunt and a brother have epilepsy. His development was normal. He left high school at 17 (5th form), enlisted in the Navy in 1947, and was discharged for poor eyesight in 1949. He worked as a production control clerk in an aeroplane factory for 2 years, then enlisted in the Army in 1953 and was discharged for "drinking" in 1956. He then worked on the DEW line for 4 months until discharged for creating a disturbance. He has since lived at home earning considerable sums of money in unknown ways. He had two "seizures" at age 17 and has a slight electroencephalographic abnormality compatible with epilepsy. He started drinking in the Navy. Since 1952 he is aggressive when drunk, though ordinarily pleasant and quiet. His violence has led to several arrests and convictions; his family pays his fines and debts. He has a confused memory of these episodes. He claims he has always felt inferior and small and unsuccessful with women, and feels guilty about having fellatio and pederasty practiced on him while drunk by army friends. He recently became less agreeable and more demanding at home, spending lavishly on cars and clothes. He had previous hospital admissions for alcoholism. Before the present admission he threatened to kill his brother with plate glass from a window he had smashed and was brought to the hospital by the police.

M. H. LaP., age 31, was married, with five children, at the time of treatment; his wife has since died. He was one of seven children brought up in fear of an exceptionally brutal mother who was a keen member of a sectarian Church. There were several alcoholics on both sides of the family. He ran away from home while in grade 6 but returned after 3 months to complete grade 8. He had many affairs with girls from an early age and goes out with other women whenever he drinks. From age 15, when his father died, he worked as a laborer and miner. He joined the Army in 1947 but was discharged after 13 weeks (drinking and delirium tremens). He first returned to laboring and then was in the Navy for 3 years. He was not promoted because of his drinking and was finally discharged and went into hospital for alcoholism. He has now worked for 5 years in one factory. He has a cataract in the right eye since the age of 5 and had an appendectomy in 1947. He started drinking at age 16 and drank heavily from the first. Since 1956 he has had a bout at least once a week, drinking beer and going off in his car, often with a woman. He comes to with no memory of how he had spent the time and often does not know where he is. Recently he has become more "twitchy" and irritable and has taken time off from work to go on a binge. He wished to get well, though he showed little emotion about it, mainly because of his wife's fatal illness.

E. J., age 41, married, with four children, was brought up by his parents. There is no family history of alcoholism. He experienced the normal milestones of childhood and completed grade 10 at age 16. He joined the Army in 1940, was discharged in 1946, worked at odd jobs until 1949 when he joined the Provincial Police until 1951, then worked for the R.C.A.F. as a radar technician until 1958. Since then he has worked as property manager in a television studio. He underwent minor surgery in 1954. He started drinking at 16 and has always maintained a schedule of 3 to 4 weeks of sobriety followed by a 2- or 3-day binge. He has made two attempts to seek help (Alcoholics Anonymous and the Addiction Research Foundation). His present concern is to reduce his indebtedness, as his pay has been garnisheed twice.

T. J. B., age 31, living in common-law marriage, with two children, was the second of three children. He was influenced mainly by his father, an alcoholic. He completed grade 10 at age 17, and was a gunner in the Navy from 1950 to 1953. He had several jobs thereafter but has worked steadily since 1958 for one firm as a driver of an oil-fuel delivery truck. He was in an automobile accident in 1954 but with no known sequels. He started drinking at 10 and drinks only beer. He has depressive mood swings. He was treated for barbiturate poisoning in 1961 and his present admission followed on overdose of "Tuinal" sleeping capsules.

J. F. M., age 38, married but separated, with one son, was one of fraternal twins, the seventh and eighth children in an intelligent family. He completed grade 10 at 16 but was not a good student. At 17 he married a girl of 17 who was pregnant. He served in the Navy during the war (1942-1945); while he was overseas his wife had two children whom he discovered on his return. He has done no regular work. He had had a partial gastrectomy following ulcers at 21, pleurisy and pneumonia at 31, and jaundice at 32. Both his ankles were broken in an automobile accident at 34. He has used alcohol since his discharge from the Navy but had not drunk for 3½ years before his current illness, which began 18 months ago. He drank following two attacks of stomach trouble and found himself in jail; as he was hemorrhaging he was sent to a hospital where he attempted to cut his wrists. He bolted from the hospital and was subsequently found by the police in possession of stolen goods. He attempted suicide again and has since remained in the hospital.

J. D. S., age 36, married with four children, was the fourth of five children; one brother committed suicide. He completed grade 10 at 15. He works as a carpenter but has had no work for 2 years as he is a known drunkard. In consistently poor general health, he has drunk heavily for 5 years, at least three bottles of wine daily. Recently he has been drinking rubbing alcohol by preference. He hears voices telling him to kill himself.

N. R., age 33, married, with two children, has no family history of alcoholism. He left school after grade 5 when his parents left for England, giving him $100 and telling him to fend for himself. He has worked as a jazz musician, Army bandsman (12 years), and salesman, but has been unemployable because of his drinking for 18 months. He began drinking at 17 when playing late at dances and now drinks a bottle of rye whisky a day. He had delirium tremens and paranoid delusions about his wife. A week prior to his admission he was jailed while drunk; on coming home he had hallucinations of insects and faces and took an overdose of sleeping pills.

L. J., age 33, a woman separated from her husband, mother of 3 children, was the fourth in a family of six children. Her father and one sister are alcoholics; another sister had a "breakdown." She left school after grade 11 and was married at 19. Her husband drank excessively and deserted the patient 6 months before her admission. The patient has been depressed, used barbiturates, and has threatened suicide. She has drunk heavily at fortnightly intervals for 4 years, was thrown out of her house by her mother, and went to the nearest hospital for help.

W. A. K., age 39, single, was the second child of six. His father drank to excess; one brother is a mental defective; his mother, maternal cousin and niece are epileptics. He reached grade 6 in school and has workd on a farm. He drank from school days, heavily since age 35. He has been drunk and depressed since his mother was hospitalized a month ago and he entered as a voluntary patient. He expresses the ambition to stay sober "possibly a year."

R. O. M., age 59, a widow, was the youngest in a family of six children. Her father was chronically ill; three siblings were hypochondriacal and the eldest is an alcoholic. The patient left school after grade 8, eloped when she was 18, and had five children. It was not a happy marriage, the parents on both sides being unforgiving. Her husband had asthma. She began to drink and use barbiturates 3 years ago, indulging in binges lasting a week during which she drinks up to 26 oz. of whisky a day. She has a recent history of depression, treated by electroconvulsotherapy, and has taken one overdose of barbiturates. She was admitted as a voluntary patient following a binge.

Experimental Results

During the five preliminary presentations of alcohol and bottle the polygraph showed a number of deflections due to the motions made by the subject in grasping the bottle, sniffing, and so forth. In only two cases was there any reaction which appeared to include anything more than movement artefact: M. H. LaP. and W. A. K. showed, throughout the preconditioning period, a consistent drop in skin resistance. This drop was arrested and momentarily reversed by handling the bottle and tasting beer. A drop in resistance is usually taken as a sign of anxiety, and in these cases the familiar stimuli of beer may have been reassuring in a situation which was anxiety-producing.

In these 15 subjects the apnea lasted for periods varying between 63 and 150 sec. with a mean of 90.4 and a standard deviation of 24 sec.

Several of the subjects made attempts to thrust the bottle away from them during the period in which they had recovered some use of their arms while the respiratory paralysis still persisted. But once fairly regular respiration had returned they stopped moving and lay very still except for unusually large respiratory motions.

Once a few minutes had passed they sought reassurance. They usually asked if "that would happen again," or would say "Don't do that again" several times over. The experimenters replied once or twice to say that the experiment was over but took no other steps to suggest that the subject had nothing to fear. Visible signs of fear or shock were seen in a number of subjects: sweating, pallor, trembling. In all the subjects the physiological record showed marked disturbances—irregular heart rate, sudden muscle twitches, fluctuation of the GSR baseline—which lasted throughout the post-conditioning sequence.

When it was thought that the subject's records were sufficiently stable the bottle was presented again. Markedly different behavior was elicited during these presentations. Four of the subjects refused to handle the bottle, pushing away the experimenter's hand and exclaiming that they would not touch it, that they had determined to give up drink. The other subjects, who went through the stipulated routine of look—smell—taste, did so in a manner which was distinctly different from their earlier performance. The movements were executed briskly or perfunctorily, in less than half the time taken before the succinylcholine shock. There were remarkable changes too in facial expression. Before the shock several among the subjects had a rather bemused expression when they tasted the drink, as of "emotion remembered in tranquility," but after conditioning they wrinkled up their faces and snorted as though an evil-tasting liquid had suddenly entered their mouths. The polygraph showed that presentation of the bottle caused marked changes in muscle tension and an immediate respiratory change; neither of these had occurred in the preshock trials.

Later, when the subjects were out of the experimental room, they were asked to describe their experience. They all agreed it was harrowing to a degree; in nearly every case they said that they had been convinced they were dying.

Follow-up

The follow-up data are not complete, as a number of the patients who had been compelled to enter the hospital have evaded attempts to obtain complete information on their present condition. Even so it is plain that a number of temporary changes in the patients' behavior had occurred which it appeared, prima facie, could be attributed to the conditioning treatment. In the ward the subjects who had been treated formed an elite group but it was fairly clear that they felt they had entered on a "trial of strength" with the experimenters.

Those subjects who left the hospital at once reported a number of curious incidents which suggested that the conditioned response to alcohol was aversive. One man, who found himself "by chance" in a pub, actually took a mouthful of beer but choked up and had to spit it out; subsequently he was overcome by anxiety when he tried to fill his car's radiator with antifreeze and had to have somebody else finish the job. Another man reported a similar incident while filling a lighter with fluid. A third was upset by advertisements for beer on television. It was evident, however, that such behavior does not, of itself, prevent a return to drinking.

The three subjects of Series I, who had been in the hospital during the winter, were sent out together to join an Army "survival" course. On their first pay day all three got drunk together and returned to the hospital to tell the other patients that the treatment did not work. The ringleader in this escapade was F. V., who explained his conduct later by saying that he was "mad" at the hospital for locking him up when they had no treatment to offer in the ordinary way so that, in effect, he had been a prisoner on an indeterminate sentence. The apparent failure of the conditioning therapy in these three cases can be accounted for by supposing that in the case of F. V. the failure to present alcohol at the appropriate moment during the conditioning trial prevented the formation of any conditioned response to alcohol. Another member of this series, W. J. P., is thought to be braindamaged due to a head injury. It has been shown (10) that brain damage, in most instances, has an adverse effect upon the formation of conditioned responses. It seems probable, therefore, that a number of factors conspired to make the therapy ineffective for these three subjects. Among these we may also include social motivation, as they expressed a desire to "beat the treatment," as well as their regular large doses of chlorpromazine, which would tend to reduce any anxiety evoked by an encounter with alcohol.

This outcome is inconclusive with respect to any assessment of succinylcholine conditioning but it suggests certain lines of investigation which should be taken into account in making an exact test of any aversion conditioning therapy. First, it appears that more than one trial with succinylcholine may have the effect of reducing the strength of the conditioned response; in animals it has been found that familiarization with a traumatic stimulus reduces the strength of a conditioned traumatic response (11). Second, it appears that subjects with brain damage may condition poorly. And thirdly, drugs and other anxiety-reducing events may militate against a conditioned response. In practical terms an experimental assessment of the therapy should include an independent test of conditioning and must involve control over all forms of therapy which may obscure the effects of conditioning.

Among the subjects of series II a number are known to have remained abstinent since they left the hospital. As the periods since treatment vary among the patients, and as the intervals between their habitual bouts of drinking also vary, it is doubtful if any estimate may reasonably be given as to the efficacy of the succinylcholine treatment. However, at present 6 out of the 12 patients are not drinking, 3 are known to be drinking, and 3 have not been found, although one of them is almost certainly drinking again. In some cases, for example M. H. LaP. and J. D. S., an overwhelming aversive response developed at once. In others, for example G. W. O., the response developed more slowly. The latter was discharged almost immediately after treatment and at once got drunk, so that he had to be readmitted. A week later he was discharged again and he has since remained abstinent. This result is of considerable interest for, in another experiment using succinylcholine as a conditioning device, it was found that the strength of the CR to the CS (which was a tone) increased during the 4 weeks following the original conditioning trial even though it was exposed to 100 extinction trials during the interval. Thus it is theoretically possible that an aversive response to alcohol may be relatively weak in the days immediately following the conditioning trials, so that it is ineffective in controlling behavior.*

Another point which emerges from the behavior of the patients who have remained abstinent is that the aversive behavior generalizes to drinks other than that used during the conditioning trial. Although each patient's favorite beverage was used, several of them ordinarily drank anything that came their way. Their later reactions, however, were to alcohol of all sorts. The basis of this generalization is apparently conceptual, as the actual taste, smell and appearance of alcoholic beverages vary considerably. Such a type of generalization is of considerable interest, as experiments on conditioned responses have demonstrated generalization along well-demarcated physical continua, such as intensity of sound or frequency of light wavelength. Conceptual or semantic generalization has hardly been demonstrated or examined.

One of the patients, R. K. McD., remained abstinent until he was involved in a motor accident in which he lost consciousness for a while and had to have treatment for the injuries he had received. As soon as he got home from the hospital he drank himself into a stupor. In this case it is tempting to explain his behavior by reference to the experiments by Brady (12, 13), who showed that electroconvulsive shock in rats (which combines cerebral insult with subsequent loss of consciousness) destroys the effect of a traumatic conditioning procedure. E. J., who was later readmitted to the general hospital for treatment of his acute anxiety, said that he had begun to drink again even

* Campbell, D., Sanderson, R. E. and Laverty, S. G. The characteristics of a conditioned response in human subjects during extinction trials following a single traumatic conditioning trial. [In preparation.]

though, whenever he drank, he suffered from a "smothering" sensation. In his case the occasion for beginning to drink again had been severe anxiety mainly owing to the fact that he had lost his job but had not yet told his wife about it.

It is plain from the observations made in this experiment that some changes in behavior have followed the conditioning trial; in the absence of a control group, it cannot be claimed either that they are a consequence of an unpleasant experience or the result of a genuine conditioned response. But the method appears to be sufficiently promising to merit further investigation. From the results which are already to hand it appears that an assessment of the treatment must take account of a number of factors: the personal and social circumstances of the patient, the efficacy of the conditioning trial, the circumstances of the patient's discharge, the number of treatments, and the use of auxiliary treatments such as sedatives and tranquilizers. Judging from the accounts of the patients used as subjects in the experiment the major difficulty which they faced on leaving the hospital was that their entire pattern of life, which had been built around drinking, was disrupted and they had nothing prepared to take the place of a routine which, in most instances, had the force of many years of practice.

From a purely experimental point of view the crucial demonstration will be to show that any change in behavior is the result of conditioning. Evidently it is necessary to develop the technique described herein in such a way that it includes a CS-CR sequence which may be evoked in patients as a test of the success of the conditioning trial. Without such an indicator it will always be possible to argue that the treatment, although aversive, is not a conditioning treatment.

The aversive stimulus to which the subjects are responding is not clearly defined. Evidently, if television advertisements and lighter fluid have aversive properties, the relevant stimuli are different from those presented during the conditioning trial. Apparently some stimulus generalization has taken place not along the lines of a physical stimulus dimension but in accordance with some conceptual scheme. This too needs more thorough investigation.

Summary

A new technique for inducing conditioned responses by means of a traumatic event is described. The trauma is a paralysis and suppression of respiration, lasting 60 to 90 seconds, induced by an intravenous injection of 20 mg. of succinylcholine chloride dihydrate. During the paralysis alcohol is presented to the patient.

The results obtained in 15 alcoholic patients indicate that a number of changes in behavior occur following the conditioning trial which are similar to the behavior found after traumatic conditioning in both animal and human subjects, e.g., longer latency of responses, and generalization. The treatment was ineffective in 3 patients who had experienced the same routine in a previous experiment without alcohol. Of 12 patients who experienced the treatment for the first time with an alcoholic beverage as the conditioned stimulus, a majority subsequently exhibited signs of aversion to all alcoholic beverages and even to suggestions of alcoholic beverages. A brief history of each patient is presented.

It is not possible to assert that the changes observed are the result of a conditioned response; nor is an experience of the respiratory trauma sufficient to produce an insuperable loathing of alcohol. Methods of investigating the therapeutic efficacy of the treatment are discussed.

References

1. Solomon, R. L. and Brush, E. S.: Experimentally derived conceptions of anxiety and aversion. In: Jones, M. R. (ed.), *Nebraska Symposium in Motivation,* Vol. 4, pp. 212-305, 1956.
2. Tiebout, H. M.: Psychology and treatment of alcoholism. *Quart. J. Stud. Alc., 7*: 214-227, 1946.
3. Cowen, J.: A six-year follow-up of a series of committed alcoholics. *Quart. J. Stud. Alc., 15*: 413-423, 1954.
4. Voegtlin, W. L.: The treatment of alcoholism by establishing a conditioned reflex. *Amer. J. med. Sci., 199*: 802-809, 1940.
5. Voegtlin, W. L. and Broz, W. R.: The conditioned reflex treatment of chronic alcoholism. X. An analysis of 3125 admissions over a period of 10½ years. *Ann. intern. Med., 30*: 580-597, 1949.
6. Lemere, F. and Voegtlin, W. L.: An evaluation of aversion treatment of alcoholism. *Quart. J. Stud. Alc., 11*: 199-204, 1950.
7. Shadel, C. A.: Aversion treatment of alcohol addiction. *Quart. J. Stud. Alc., 5*: 216-228, 1944.
8. Fromer, R.: The effect of several shock patterns on the acquisition of the secondary drive of fear. *J. comp. physiol. Psychol., 52*: 142-144, 1962.
9. Franks, C. M. and Laverty, S. G.: Sodium amytal and eyelid conditioning. *J. ment. Sci., 101*: 654-663, 1955.
10. Galambos, R. and Morgan, C. T.: The neural basis of learning. In: Field, J., ed. *Handbook of Physiology;* sec. 1, vol. III, pp. 1471-1499. Washington, D.C.; American Physiological Society; 1960.
11. Kamin, L. J.: Apparent adaptation effects in the acquisition of a conditioned emotional response. *Canad. J. Psychol., 15*: 176-188, 1962.
12. Brady, J. V.: The effect of electroconvulsive shock on a conditioned emotional response: the permanence of the effect. *J. comp. physiol. Psychol., 44*: 507-511, 1951.
13. Brady, J. V.: The effect of electroconvulsive shock on a conditioned emotional response: the significance of the interval between the emotional conditioning and the electroconvulsive shock. *J. comp. physiol. Psychol., 45*: 9-13, 1952.

15

AVERSION THERAPY BY ELECTRIC SHOCK: A SIMPLE TECHNIQUE

by Ralph J. McGuire, M.A., B.Sc., Ed.B.,
and Maelor Vallance, M.B., Ch.B., D.P.M.

Aversion therapy has been used for many years in the treatment of alcoholism (3). Apomorphine and emetine are the usual drugs used as the unconditioned stimuli for nausea and vomiting, with alcohol as the conditioned stimulus. More recently the same procedure has been used in the treatment of sexual perversions—for example, fetishism (12), transvestism (1, 5) and homosexuality (11, 7).

There are several disadvantages to the use of drugs in conditioning procedures. The time between the stimulus being presented and the nausea being produced is uncertain (2). The patient may not even feel nausea; and, further, the cerebral depressant effect of the drug may interfere with the patient's ability to form conditioned responses (4). In addition, the treatment may have to be terminated prematurely because of its dangerous side-effects.

Alternative unpleasant responses can be used to produce aversion. In experimental psychology electric shock has been widely used both in animals and in humans (13). In clinical treatment, however, it has been less often used (8; 10; 14, p. 182). The technique is simpler, more accurately controlled, and more certain in producing an unpleasant effect than drugs. This article describes a simple apparatus designed by one of us (R. J. McG.) and its use in the aversive treatment of sexual perversions, alcoholism, smoking, and neurotic symptoms.

Apparatus. The components are cheap (under £1) and fit into a box approximately 6 in. (15 cm.) square and 2 in. (5 cm.) deep (Figs. 1 and 2). It is powered by a 9-volt battery and is therefore completely portable. The shock is administered through electrodes on a cuff around the patient's forearm. To construct the apparatus requires no special skill, and the technical details are given at the end of the article.

Reprinted with permission from *British Medical Journal,* 1964, *1,* 151-153.

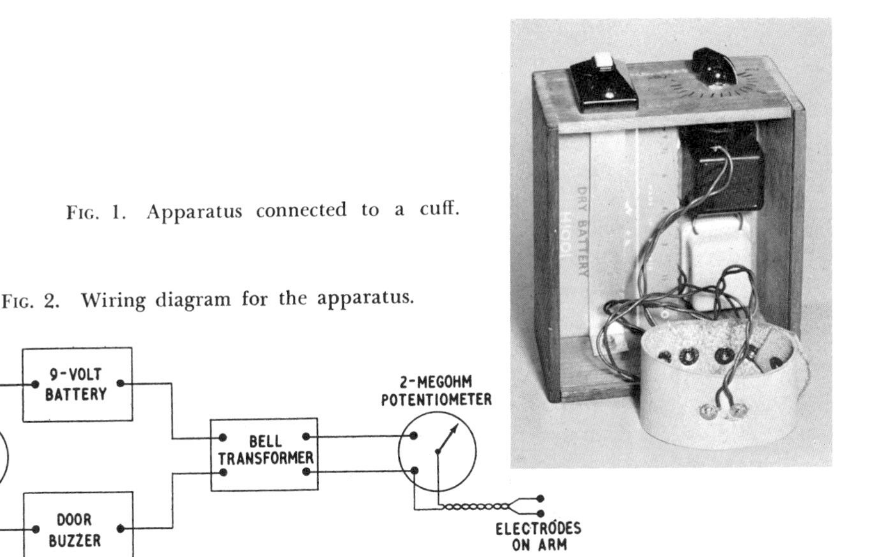

FIG. 1. Apparatus connected to a cuff.

FIG. 2. Wiring diagram for the apparatus.

Treatment Procedure. The use of the apparatus follows classical conditioning technique. The stimulus to which aversion is to be produced is presented, often by having the patient imagine the stimulus, and then a shock is administered. This procedure is repeated throughout the treatment session of 20 to 30 minutes, which can be held from six times a day to once a fortnight. The strength of the shock should be adjusted so that it is as painful as the patient can bear. Further adjustment of the voltage may be made during the session, if necessary. The patient himself decides how severe the shock should be. After initial instruction he can treat himself and may take the apparatus home to continue the treatment there. Besides saving the therapist's time and making frequent treatment possible, this arrangement is to be preferred when the symptom is one usually indulged in alone—for example, masturbation to perverse fantasies. While the patient can use the apparatus whenever he is tempted to masturbate, he should also each day deliberately carry out the treatment at a time when the desire to masturbate is not strong.

Case 1. Fetishism

A 25-year-old postgraduate student was referred after one year of analytically based psychotherapy. For 10 years he had been masturbating about three times a day to fantasies of himself dressed in blue jeans and a leather jacket, and to masochistic fantasies of being bound. Conventional psychotherapy had altered neither his behaviour nor the considerable degree of guilt that he felt. He believed, however, that he had derived benefit from it.

The theory and practice of aversion therapy were explained to him, and he was told to conjure up his usual fantasies and to give a signal by raising his hand when the image was clear. When he did so the shock was administered. This was sufficient to dispel the fantasy. The patient reported that he found it more and more difficult to conjure up the fantasy that was being treated. This was confirmed by an increased interval between shocks from 3 to 15 seconds. By the second session he was persuaded to use the apparatus himself.

At later sessions he was unable to conjure up his usual fantasies, and photographs of people dressed in his fetishist clothing were used as stimuli. At first these produced interest and excitement, but this also disappeared. By the tenth session the patient reported that he had entirely lost interest in his fetish and in his masochistic practices. From the day treatment started he had never masturbated to his fantasies, and this remained true during the one year of follow-up. At times of exceptional stress he was sometimes tempted to masturbate, but the temptation was weak enough to resist. The feelings of guilt persisted for about six weeks, and after eight weeks he masturbated to orgasm with heterosexual fantasies for the first time in his life. No positive steps had been taken in therapy to achieve this end.

Case 2. Obsessional Ruminations

A 29-year-old teacher complained of intrusive thoughts concerning his wife's character. These had started two years previously after a vague remark made by his mother about his wife. He did not believe that he had any reason to distrust his wife, but the thought continually recurred, although constantly resisted by the patient, and was accompanied by feelings of anxiety. In treatment he was asked to imagine his mother making the remark, to think of the remark and its implications, and to give a signal when he had done so, whereupon he was given an electric shock. At the second session he started giving himself the shock, and after the third took the apparatus home to use once daily. After about 10 more days he gave up using the machine as the thought no longer bothered him. It would still occasionally return accompanied by a slight tension, particularly when he was very tired. As he was a tense, anxious person he was instructed in relaxation techniques (14, p. 139) at this stage, and found this helpful. After five months he had shown no significant recurrence of the ruminations and was much less anxious in other situations.

Case 3. Smoking

A female schoolteacher of 37 who had smoked since the age of 18 was smoking 40 cigarettes a day. Despite several earnest attempts encouraged by her own doctor and aided by various "anti-smoking remedies," she had been unable to restrict her consumption of cigarettes for more than a few days at a time. She was seen several times a day and on each occasion was asked to smoke a cigarette in her usual way. She was given a shock as soon as inhalation was complete. Partial reinforcement was employed in that a shock was delivered after only three out of five inhalations. There is experimental evidence (6) that this decreases the possibility of relapse. No cigarettes were permitted outside of the treatment situations.

Treatment was continued in this way for two weeks. She then attended weekly as an out-patient, and on each occasion she had one cigarette under similar conditions. Apart from this weekly cigarette she has now had none for six months and has no difficulty in abstaining.

Case 4. Writer's Cramp

A clerical worker of 47 had developed over the preceding four years progressive symptoms of writer's cramp. These symptoms were causing so much difficulty that he was on the point of losing his job. Liversedge and Sylvester (9) had suggested an aversion treatment for this condition.

The apparatus was converted so that the circuit could be completed through a press-switch attached to a pen. The patient was asked to write a test-piece. Whenever his grip on the pen exceeded a certain pressure the switch closed and a shock went through the pen. The number of shocks delivered was recorded on a counter which was also operated by the switch. This record showed a reduction of errors per written page as treatment continued.

After attending twice a week for several weeks he was allowed to take the machine home, where he could practice each evening on work taken home from his office. His progress was assessed at the clinic monthly. In the past six months he had made excellent progress in that he writes much more quickly and his writing is now easily legible.

Case 5. Alcoholism

A business executive aged 48, whose alcoholism had reached a chronic phase with considerable social decline and repeated hospitalization, was referred for treatment of his drinking habits. After withdrawal, aversion therapy was begun. A row of 12 test-tubes was set up, nine containing whisky and three containing coloured water distributed randomly. The patient was asked to sniff each tube in turn and at the end of each inhalation from a tube containing whisky he was given a shock. After several sessions partial reinforcement was used.

In the second half of each session a similar procedure was followed, using cards, some of which bore pictures of bottles containing various types of alcohol, or carrying various symbols relating to the drinking of alcohol. Other cards had neutral stimuli such as advertisements for coffee or soft drinks.

Three sessions were held each day for three weeks. Six months after leaving hospital he was abstinent, although his condition is recognized as being very far from stable.

Another alcoholic patient who had been given whisky to drink during aversion treatment accused the therapist of adding a chemical to the whisky to give it a bad taste. The same patient went into a bar against advice during treatment, but on trying to raise a glass of whisky to his mouth he had a panic attack and returned to the hospital in an anxious state.

Preliminary Results

At the time of writing we have treated 39 cases in the Southern General Hospital by this aversive therapy. The only basis for selection had been that there appeared to be an application of the technique to the symptom. Results are given in Table I. In most cases the follow-up has been for only about one month, and therefore the cases cannot be presented as proof of the efficiency of the treatment but serve only as a guide. We and our colleagues are now undertaking controlled trials into a) sexual perversion, b) alcoholism, and c) obesity due to overeating. Objective assessment of the treatment must await the result of these trials.

Meanwhile it is hoped that others will find the preliminary results encouraging enough to test the treatment themselves. Large-scale studies are perfectly feasible with the technique here described, and the treatable conditions are such as to yield large numbers of prospective subjects.

Technical Details

Circuit. The circuit (see Fig. 2) consists of a buzzer which interrupts a circuit from the battery through a switch and transformer. In this way the D.C. voltage (9 volts) provides an A.C. current, which is then stepped up by a transformer to provide an A.C. voltage (about 70 volts).

Table 1. Immediate follow-up results on 39 cases treated by the aversion technique described.

	Smokers	Alcoholics	Sex Perv.	Others	Total
Discontinued treatment	0	3	3	0	6(15%)
None	3	2	0	1	6(15%)
Mild improvement	0	1	1	3	5(13%)
Good improvement	1	1	4	3	9(23%)
Symptom removed	6	0	6	1	13(33%)
Totals	10	7	14*	8**	39

*6 homosexuals (3 discontinued treatment); 3 compulsive masturbators; 2 transvestists; 1 sadist; 1 fetishist; and 1 who interfered with children.
**4 with obsessional ruminations; 3 writer's cramp; 1 compulsive behavior.

Components. The components required and their approximate cost are listed below.

1 push-button switch	1s. 6d.
1 4–8-volt buzzer (miniature type)	5s. 0d.
1 small transformer, about 50 : 1 ratio	7s. 6d.
(The above three items are such as are used for a house door-bell)	
1 grid-bias battery, 9 volts	1s. 9d.
1 potentiometer, 2 megohms, log. track	2s. 6d.
1 knob for above	9d.
1 box (cigar-box ideal)	—
1 armband with electrodes	—
	19s. 0d.

The electrodes need only be metal studs about ⅜ in. (1 cm.) in diameter, placed about 1 in. (2.5 cm.) apart. The most effective arrangement is to make a simple cuff of soft leather or elastic webbing. A snap-fastener with three or four alternative positions allows adjustment and two snap-fastener studs can be used as electrodes. Electrode jelly is unnecessary unless the patient has an extremely sensitive skin.

Adjustment. If the circuit has been wired correctly the buzzer should sound when the button is pressed. No subject need be in the circuit at this stage. If this does not happen, check first that the transformer is correctly connected; secondly, increase the voltage from the battery, or, thirdly, change the low-voltage tappings on the transformer if a choice is provided. Start with the 5-volt tapping, but if the buzzing or the shock is too weak change to the 3-volt position. At its minimum the shock should be almost imperceptible and at its maximum it should be unbearable.

The drain on the battery is about 300 mA as measured on a D.C. meter. This should allow several hours' operation, and as the buzzer is actually in operation for only about 30 seconds per session, battery wastage is no great problem.

Summary

A simple apparatus which can deliver a painful electric shock to the subject for aversion therapy is described. It has advantages over nausea-producing drugs, particularly in allowing the patient to treat himself even at home. The use of the apparatus is illustrated by cases of fetishism, obsessional ruminations, smoking, writer's cramp, and alcoholism. Technical details are given of the components and their assembly which requires only the most rudimentary knowledge of electricity.

We thank Professor T. Ferguson Rodger, in whose department the work was carried out, for his encouragement, and Drs. J. M. Carlisle and B. G. Young for allowing us to include their results in our figures.

References

1. Barker, J. C., Thorpe, J. G., Blakemore, C. B., Lavin, N. I., and Conway, C. G. (1961). *Lancet, 1*: 510.
2. Eysenck, H. J. (1963). *Brit. J. Psychiat., 109*: 12.
3. Franks, C. M., (1960a). In *Behavior Therapy and the Neuroses,* edited by H. J. Eysenck, p. 278. Pergamon Press, London.
4. ——— (1960b). In *Handbook of Abnormal Psychology,* edited by H. J. Eysenck, p. 479. Pitman, London.
5. Glynn, J. D., and Harper, P. (1961). *Lancet, 1*: 619.
6. Hilgard, E. R., and Marquis, D. C. (1961). *Conditioning and Learning,* p. 286. Methuen, London.
7. James, B. (1962). *Brit. med. J., 1*: 768.
8. Kantorovich, M. V. (1929). *Nov. Refl. Fiziol. Nerv. Sist., 3*: 436.
9. Liversedge, L. A., and Sylvester, J. D. (1955). *Lancet, 1*: 1147.
10. Max, L. W. (1935). *Psychol. Bull., 32:* 734.
11. Oswald, I. (1962). *J. ment. Sci., 108:* 196.
12. Raymond, M. J. (1956). *Brit. med. J., 2*: 854.
13. Solomon, R. L., and Brush, E. S. (1956). *Nebraska Symposium on Motivation,* vol. 4, p. 212. Univ. Nebraska Press, Lincoln.
14. Wolpe, J. (1958). *Psychotherapy by Reciprocal Inhibition.* Stanford Univ. Press, Stanford, California.

NORTH AMERICAN MODIFICATION

by Robert Fried, Ph.D., and Cyril M. Franks, Ph.D.

The original unit can be modified to meet the needs of investigators in the U.S.A. and Canada. The components employed in the following circuit diagram are inexpensive and readily available in the United States. The modified unit is portable, easily assembled and has the advantage of being battery operated yet comparable to standard laboratory equipment utilizing American line voltage (110 VAC, 60 cps). It is also possible to vary the duration of the shock stimulus as well as its intensity.

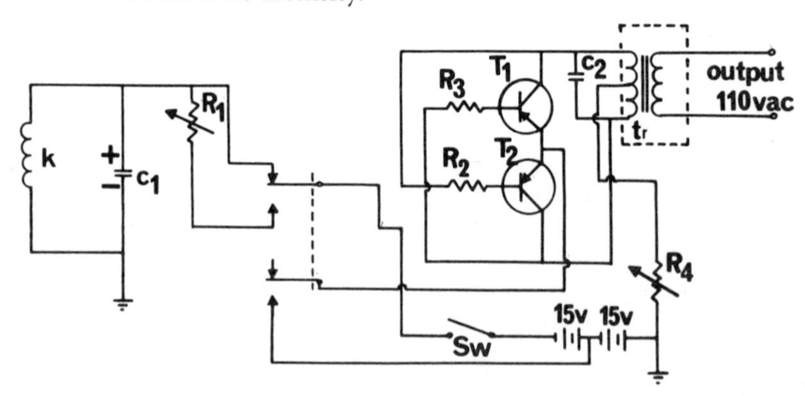

The unit consists essentially of two modules, a D.C. to A.C. converter and a time-delay relay. For an output of approximately 110 VAC, and an approximate current of 50 milliamps (assuming 50 K-ohms to be representative skin impedance) R_2 and R_3 should be each 3 K-ohms. If desired, the frequency characteristics of the circuit may be altered by changing the value of the capacitor connected across the input ends of the transformer (tr). The duration of the shock stimulus may be altered by varying the setting of R_1. With the given component values this duration can be made to vary from zero to 1.5 sec. To increase this time range it is merely necessary to increase the value of the potentiometer R_1. The shock intensity (output voltage) may be adjusted by changing the setting of R_4.

A momentary depression of the switch (Sw) turns on the current which is then turned off when the relay returns to its normal state.

Further details of the circuit diagram or the use of the actual unit may be obtained either from the authors of this Modification: Dr. Robert Fried of the Department of Psychology, Hunter College, New York, N.Y. or from Dr. Cyril Franks at the Neuro-Psychiatric Institute, Princeton, N. J.

Components	Manufacturer	Price
R_1-R_4: 10 K-ohms potentiometer 2 watt, linear taper.	International Resistance Co. 401 North Broad St. Philadelphia, Pa.	1.00 ea.
R_2-R_3: 3 K-ohms resistors, 1 watt	I. R. C.	.20 ea.
C_1: 100 mfd capacitor, 25 VDC.	Sprague Products Co. 481 Marshall St. North Adams, Mass.	.81
C_2: 0.1 mfd capacitor, 200 VDC	Sprague	.20
T_1-T_2: 2N255A transistors	Delco Radio Division General Motors 700 East Firmin St. Kokomo, Ind.	.90 ea.
tr: filament transformer 115-6.3 VAC	United Transformer Corp. 150 Varick St. New York, N. Y.	3.38
Utility Cabinet (3 x 4 x 5 inches)	Bud Radio Co. distr. by Atlas Electronics 775 Pfeiffer Blvd. Perth Amboy, N. J.	1.38
Insulated tip jacks	H. H. Smith Co. distr. by Atlas Electronics.	.18 ea.
k: relay (DP/DT. 24.0 VDC; 750 ohms, series T-154 CC).	Allied Controls, Inc. 2 East End Ave. New York, N. Y.	3.50
15 volt batteries	Eveready	1.50 ea.
Switch, pushbutton, momentary.	Lafayette Electronics (#SW 70) 100 6th Ave. New York, N. Y.	.20

PART V

NON-AVERSIVE CONDITIONING THERAPIES

The differentiation between aversive and non-aversive conditioning techniques is sometimes difficult to establish and there is often doubt as to whether any specific conditioning procedure does or does not follow the usual classical conditioning situation. Lovibond,* for example, carefully analyses the treatment of enuresis in these terms and arrives at the conclusion that the conditioning treatment process for this disorder, as formulated by Mowrer and others, follows the avoidance rather than the non-aversive model. Such distinctions are far from academic since their resolution would strongly influence the procedural details of the treatment. For example, one implication of accepting an avoidance paradigm is that the treatment should be so set up that a response to a noxious stimulus provides escape from this stimulus and thus facilitates the development of the required avoidance response. Certainly the appreciable relapse rate following initial arrest of bed wetting suggests that further attention be given to this problem in setting up future procedures.

Geppert, although little concerned with such matters, demonstrates that it is possible for the clinician to achieve a successful management of the enuretic patient by the careful use of a more or less classical conditioning technique. It is important to note that, despite special interest in this possibility, no one has produced any evidence of "symptom substitution." On the contrary, the reverse is commonly reported, the cessation of the troublesome condition being followed by favorable changes in personality and attitude. The need now is for further research of a clinical nature. Little is yet known about the nature of the differences between those enuretics who respond to this form of treatment and those who fail.

The next paper, by White, also demonstrates that certain forms of disordered behavior in children can be effectively treated in accordance with established principles of conditioning without any recourse to psychodynamic concepts. And, again, it is noteworthy that CR treat-

* Lovibond, S. H. The mechanism of conditioning treatment of enuresis. *Behav. Res. Therap.*, 1963, *1*, 17-21.

ment of the symptom was followed by neither remission nor symptom substitution.

Many theorists have attempted to understand problems of addiction to alcohol in terms of some conditioning or learning theory model. Wikler has formulated a theory of drug addiction whereby the actual drug experience serves as the UCS and the associated environmental factors as the CS. There are some recent experimental data available which provide impressive evidence in favor of his theory.* If the etiology of narcotic drug addictions can be described in such terms, one might expect a conditioning method to be likewise applicable to their treatment. Over three decades ago Rubenstein showed how such a model might be successfully applied to the treatment of morphine addiction. It is not suggested that his paper, reprinted here, is an example of sophisticated clinical research or that the procedures are above reproach. What is important is that Rubenstein has succeeded in demonstrating the feasibility of using such procedures.

At the present time the most extensively used method of drugless analgesia in childbirth is that of psychoprophylaxis, as described by the Soviet physicians Velvovsky, Platonov, Ploticher and Shugom (translated into English). There is also Vellay's book in English and Chertok's in French.** There is, in addition, an active International and an American Society for Psycho-Prophylaxis in Obstetrics.

The method has provoked much theoretical dispute both within and outside the Soviet Union, and it is far from certain that the terminology of Pavlovian physiology and the conditioned reflex provide adequate explanations. Nevertheless, practical results appear to speak in favor of the method and, whether the emphasis is upon prophylaxis or therapy, the approach is worth serious attention. To illustrate the method and its possibilities we offer part of Bonstein's book.

The final paper, by Quarti and Renaud, is of interest because it demonstrates in a striking manner how conditioning techniques may be effectively applied to disorders not ordinarily treated by the psychiatrist. The possibility that irregularities of body function other than constipation may profitably be investigated by similar procedures merits serious consideration.

* Wikler, A. Studies on conditioning of physical dependence and reinforcement of opiate drinking behaviour in morphine addicted rats. First Annual Meeting of the Amer. College of Neuropsychopharmacology, Washington, D.C., Jan. 24-27, 1963.

** Chertok, L. *Les methodes psychosomatiques d'accouchement sans douleur.* Paris: L'Expansion Scientifique Francaise, 1957; Vellay, P. *Childbirth without pain.* Dutton: London, 1960; Velvovsky, I., Platonov, K., Ploticher, V., & Shugom, E. *Painless childbirth through psychoprophylaxis.* (transl. D. A. Myshne) Moscow: Foreign Languages Publ. House, 1960.

16

MANAGEMENT OF NOCTURNAL ENURESIS BY CONDITIONED RESPONSE

by Thomas V. Geppert, M.D.

Treatment of chronic nocturnal enuresis often poses a vexing problem, and even prolonged programs employing the conventional therapeutic methods are frequently fruitless. That this is a major problem, especially in pediatrics, is attested to by estimates of up to 16% incidence in the child population (1) and also by the profuse literature on the subject. Although the incidence is smaller in higher age brackets, enuresis presents the adult patient with a serious problem that often has a pronounced effect on his social adjustment. A few cases of enuresis, variously estimated at from 3 to 10% (2) of the total, arise from definite anatomic or physiological anomalies for which specific surgical or medical procedures are indicated. The majority of cases appear, however, in children who simply have never been able to respond to the stimulation of a full bladder by awakening. After the age of 3 or 3½ years, when the average child becomes a deep sleeper, self-training becomes even more difficult.

I shall not attempt to establish the causes of enuresis, since I feel that there is a wide variety of causes, from "laziness" to deep psychic disturbance (3). Rather, it is my purpose to encourage more general use of conditioned response therapy. I feel that the response to such therapy is rapid, complete in most instances, and relatively simple. In my experience, it not only has been harmless to patients with an emotional disturbance, but in every case has resulted in an apparent feeling of accomplishment that aided in subsequent psychiatric adjustment. As to the necessity for satisfactory treatment, one need only listen to the mother of a 10-year-old enuretic child or to the embarrassed plea of the boy about to go to scout camp.

Considerable success has already been reported in controlling enuresis by conditioning a patient to awaken in response to bladder tension

---

Reprinted from *The Journal of the American Medical Association*, May 30, 1953. Vol. 152, pp. 381-383.

rather than yielding to the urge to urinate (4). The cases in the present report were all managed by this conditioned response method, with about 91% successful results. It must be emphasized that all the children in this group had previously unsucessfully tried the usual procedures, such as restricting fluids or earning awards. This report is based on the study of 42 case histories. Every case was managed in the patient's home under the guidance and supervision of the prescribing physician. Cases were unselected, except that no patient was treated by this method without a previous physical examination and routine urine test.

Method of Treatment

The object of this treatment is to teach the enuretic to respond to nocturnal bladder tension by awakening rather than by urinating. This conditioned response is established with the aid of an automatic electric alarm device, which awakens the patient immediately each time micturition begins. Once this response pattern has been established, the patient tends to sleep for increasingly longer periods before awakening and eventually sleeps through the entire night. The apparatus used operates on small, self-contained batteries, with no danger of electrical shock to the patient. The alarm is contained in a small cabinet placed on a night stand near the head of the patient's bed. The patient sleeps directly on a moisture-sensitive bed pad, which is connected to the alarm cabinet by an electric cord and plug. Whenever micturition begins, the first few drops of urine moistening the pad render it sufficiently conductive to permit the passage of an electric current, which, though feeble, is capable of setting off the alarm. Awakening in response to the alarm bell, the patient ceases voiding (the wet spot on the pad is seldom larger than a silver dollar), silences the alarm by means of a switch, and goes to the bathroom to complete urination. Before the patient returns to bed, the alarm is conditioned for reuse by replacing the wet pad with a dry one.

Since every treatment was carried out in the home and the majority of the subjects were young children, close supervision and cooperation of the parents was required. In addition to simple instructions for proper use of the apparatus, parents were briefed on the psychological aspects of the therapy. The classical principle of Pavlov was explained. They were impressed with the fact that the alarm device is not a treatment in itself but rather an effective tool to be used in developing a conditioned response and that, like all tools, it must be used properly to obtain the most satisfactory results. Parents were given the following specific instructions: 1. The patient must awaken immediately when the alarm sounds. If he sleeps too soundly, someone must sleep nearby to awaken him. (It was found that even the heaviest sleepers learn to respond to the alarm bell alone after being assisted in this manner.) 2. After being aroused by the alarm, the patient must be thoroughly awakened before he goes to the bathroom. Sleepwalking to the bathroom may actually reinforce the habit of urinating while sleeping and thus defeat the purpose. The alarm bell should be allowed to ring until the patient is sufficiently aroused to turn it off himself. 3. The patient must never be allowed merely to turn off the alarm and go back to sleep. 4. An attitude of sympathetic assistance and cooperation is of primary importance. 5. Use of a night light is recommended, especially for sound sleepers. The patient awakens more easily and with less confusion. 6. It is best for the patient to sleep naked from the waist down to insure urine reaching the pad promptly, but the wearing of pajamas should be resumed during the last week that the alarm is in use in order to return as nearly as possible to normal conditions before the alarm is removed. 7. Ingestion of liquids should not be restricted. In fact, if the patient normally wets the bed sporadically, copious drinking in the evening, especially of mildly diuretic soft drinks, may be helpful in giving the patient more frequent experience with alarms. 8. The patient (or parent) must report to the physician weekly, describing exactly how the alarm is being used and how the patient reacts. (Each patient or parent was given a progress record chart on which to record the times he was awakened by the alarm and the times he awoke in response to bladder tension alone.)

During the weekly conferences, the physician has an opportunity to visualize the patient's reaction pattern and correct any procedures and practices being used by the patient or parent that may be incompatible with the establishment of the desired conditioned response. In each case, the alarm was used for at least one week after the last wetting incident occurred. In doubtful cases, such as those of sporadic wetters who might normally experience a week or more of dry nights or cases in which progress had been slow and uncertain, a longer "dry" period was employed, depending on the circumstances.

Results

In 38 (90.48%) of the 42 patients managed in this manner, enuresis was arrested. Five in whom treatment was successful reverted to the old habit, but four of these promptly responded to a repetition of the treatment, and the fifth is being treated similarly at this writing. Seventy-four per cent of the patients treated successfully were eventually able to sleep through the entire night (many of them had achieved this by the time the alarm was removed), and 85% showed noticeable improvement in emotional stability and personality adjustment. Duration of therapy varied from 1 to 15 weeks, the average being 4½ weeks. In one of the patients in whom this treatment failed enuresis was later arrested by psychiatric management, and, conversely, four of the patients in whom it was successful had previously resisted psychiatric efforts.

In seven patients enuresis had begun at the age of 3 or 4 years, but in all others it had persisted since birth. Corrective measures previously employed included use of drugs in 30% of the patients, systems of rewards in 54%, punishment in 24%, restriction of liquids in 80%, psychiatric treatment in 8%, hospitalization in one case, and arousing at regular intervals in 60%. It is significant that in the system of taking the child to the bathroom at regular intervals during the night, all but two of the children were reported to have been not thoroughly awake when this was done. All but two of the patients were sound sleepers. Forty-three per cent of the patients had a history of one or more cases of enuresis in the father's or mother's family, usually including the father or mother. Seventy per cent of the patients were males, and 74% were in the 5 to 10 year age group.

Examination of the record charts for all patients reveals a rather typical progress pattern, consisting of four distinct stages; however, the duration of each stage varied considerably with different patients, and certain stages were omitted entirely in some cases. Typical treatment in a patient who wets every night progresses as follows:

Stage 1. In the first stage, the patient wets with the same frequency, usually two or three times nightly, as has been his habit before beginning the treatment. At each wetting the alarm bell awakens him and he goes to the bathroom to complete urination. Duration of this stage is usually less than one week, and the frequency of alarms decreases toward the close of this stage.

Stage 2. In the second stage, the patient begins to awaken in response to the stimulus of bladder pressure alone on some occasions, but he still wets and sets off the alarm on other occasions. The desired conditioned response is beginning to appear but is not yet firmly established. During this stage, alarms decrease and dry nights increase in frequency.

Stage 3. When the patient no longer wets the bed, the third stage has begun. He awakens once or twice a night to go to the bathroom, or he may sleep through some or all of the nights. The alarm does not operate, but the patient is aware of its presence. When this stage has continued for 7 to 10 days, the fourth stage is considered to have begun, and the alarm is removed.

Stage 4. The patient is on his own in the fourth stage. He may arise from time to time to go to the bathroom at night, but he tends to sleep for increasingly longer periods and, eventually, to sleep through the entire night.

Patients commonly develop sufficient confidence by the end of the third stage to request removal of the alarm, but, if the patient seems uncertain or if his progress has been slow and irregular, use of the alarm is continued for an additional week or more. Some patients sleep through the night after the third stage, while others may prolong the fourth stage for weeks or months, but the nuisance and embarrassment of bed wetting have ceased. The patient's progress chart usually reveals these stages clearly and aids the physician in deciding when to remove the alarm. Sporadic wetters were the slowest to respond, and the stages of progress were sometimes difficult to recognize in such cases.

Comment

The chief cause of failures unquestionably was poor parental cooperation. In a number of patients, enuresis was arrested despite poor or no parental cooperation, but progress in these cases would probably have been more rapid with more intelligent home management. Some parents regard the alarm as a complete mechanical treatment in itself and shun the responsibilities of seeing to it that the subject awakens immediately, is wide awake, and is never allowed to merely turn off the alarm and go back to sleep. In several cases the parents became discouraged if the child was not cured after three weeks and discontinued the treatment prematurely. Some parents could not force themselves to "unduly disturb" their children by thoroughly awakening them after they were aroused by the alarm, and in one patient ephedrine was clearly indicated and prescribed, but the parents declined its use because of their antipathy to the use of drugs in general. These same parents failed to contact the physician regularly for fear of incurring a fee that they thought unnecessary and were frequently too "tired" to get up with the boy when the alarm sounded. Failure in this case was not surprising.

The auxiliary use of ephedrine or a similar agent is beneficial in cases in which the subject sleeps so soundly that the alarm bell alone cannot arouse him. Many of the patients were very sound sleepers, and it was occasionally necessary for a parent to sleep nearby and awaken the child at each alarm. In the majority of cases, the patient learned to respond alone after being assisted in this manner for the first few nights, but if he did not do so after 7 to 10 nights, ephedrine was prescribed. The dose was decreased by a factor of one-half each succeeding week after the patient began to respond.

While this conditioned response method seems to have been used more extensively in Europe and Australia than in this country, the method recently has been gaining in popularity here. Several versions of the apparatus have appeared on the market. Whatever mechanical merits these respective devices may or may not have, it is regrettable that the majority of them are offered directly to the public without the prescription or supervision of a practicing physician. Over-the-counter marketing is, of course, conducive to self-diagnosis and treatment and may result in indefinite postponement of needed medical or surgical treatment in patients with organic disease. Probably, it is possible to establish the conditioned response in a patient with organic disease, which then persists and develops undiscovered in the "cured" patient. Although the incidence of organic lesions is low, they must always be suspected until proved absent (1). It is also desirable for the treatment to be under the physician's guidance because the majority of parents cannot be expected to be sufficiently acquainted with the psychological principles involved to diligently follow the most effective procedures and avoid those that may be incompatible with the establishment of a conditioned response.

The use of this method in cases of possible psychiatric origin has been questioned on the ground that it is symptomatic treatment. In discussing this point in their report of cases treated in this manner, Davidson and Douglass conclude, ". . . we feel that in a good many cases personality difficulties are the effect rather than the cause of the enuresis (4b). Again, Hubble writes, "The disorder [enuresis] persists long after the precipitating situation has disappeared and been forgotten."

Summary and Conclusions

Treatment of a group of 42 patients with chronic nocturnal enuresis by development of a conditioned response is described. All patients, after examination to rule out organic lesions as a cause, were treated by being awakened immediately after the commencement of nocturnal urination by an automatic electric alarm. The purpose of this procedure was to condition them to awaken instead of urinate in response to bladder tension. All patients had resisted a variety of treatment methods previously. Enuresis was arrested in 38 (90.5%) of 42 patients, and the majority of these patients eventually learned to sleep through the entire night; five required a second treatment after reversion, and in four the treatment was unsuccessful. Parental cooperation is of primary importance for success in the case of young children, and lack of it is the commonest cause of failure; hence, professional supervision is an important feature of the treatment. Personality difficulties improved considerably in the majority of patients, indicating that such maladjustments may often be the effect, rather than the cause of enuresis. The conditioned response management of enuresis appears to offer a positive method of attack on a common and stubborn affliction and its attendant personality difficulties.

References

1. Robb, E. F.: Enuresis, *Minnesota Med., 30*: 91-96 (Jan.) 1947.
2. Hubble, D.: Enuresis, *Brit. M. J., 2*: 1108-1111 (Nov. 11) 1950.

3. Kriegman, G., and Wright, H. B.: Brief Psychotherapy with Enuretics in the Army, *Am. J. Psychiat., 104*: 254-258 (Oct.) 1947.
4. (*a*) Mowrer, O. H., and Mowrer, W. M.: Enuresis—Method for Its Study and Treatment, *Am. J. Orthopsychiat., 8*: 436-459 (July) 1938. (*b*) Davidson, J. R., and Douglass, E.: Nocturnal Enuresis: A Special Approach to Treatment, *Brit. M. J., 1*: 1345-1347 (June 10) 1950. (*c*) Seiger, H. W.: Treatment of Essential Nocturnal Enuresis, *J. Pediat., 40*: 738-749 (June) 1952.

17

THE USE OF LEARNING THEORY IN THE PSYCHOLOGICAL TREATMENT OF CHILDREN

by John Graham White, Ed.M.

Introduction

For some years there has been growing dissatisfaction among British clinical psychologists with psychoanalytically oriented psychotherapies. On the other hand, there has been an increasing desire to derive treatment procedures from the body of general psychological theory, in particular learning theory, which will allow of more precise formulations of problem and predictions of outcome according to the specific theoretical postulate chosen. The application of conditioning and other learning techniques in the treatment of both children and adults was, of course, described thirty years ago by M. C. Jones (5); twenty years ago, by Mowrers (8); and more recently by H. G. Jones (3, 4), Eysenck (2), Walton (11, 12) and Walton and Black (13, 14). The accommodation of theory and practice has been most fully attempted so far by Mowrer (6, 7), Dollard and Miller (1), and Shoben (9, 10).

The following case study demonstrates that some forms of disordered behavior in children can be explained and treated according to well-established principles of learning,* without any recourse to "psychodynamic" concepts and without any attempt to produce "insight" in the patient by means of verbal "interpretations" of behavior.

Case Study

Several years ago a child of five and a half was admitted to hospital in consequence of her refusal to eat and also because she was suffering from what appeared at the time to be rheumatic pains.

* The phrase *learning theory* in the context of this paper is used to cover both of Mowrer's (7) two factors, solution learning and sign learning.

Reprinted with permission from *Journal of Clinical Psychology,* 1959, *15,* 227-229.

Relevant History

The patient was the second of two girls, the only children in the family. The older child had been born during the war; for the first four years of her life the father had been with the Army abroad, and she became the "mother's baby." By the time the younger child was born the father was back home, and she became his baby. He gave her lavish attention, played with her, and almost from the time she was born fed her (she was breast-fed for only a "few weeks"). Apart from the manner in which it was carried out the history of feeding was uneventful. The child was enuretic at night until admission to hospital. From infancy, when her father was nursing her, the patient "used to hold on to and play with his collar. She would never go to bed without his collar. . . . If she lost hold of the collar in the night she would call out and mother would find it for her."

Between the ages of 3 and 4 years the child's appetite became capricious. She insisted on having her main meal at 6 o'clock, when the father came in from work. She would sit on his knee throughout the meal and he would often feed her. When the father was present the mother was rejected; this younger child was the self-avowed rival of both her mother and her sister.

Father was the kind of person who would do anything to avoid "disagreeableness," such as violent scenes of any kind, and could easily be influenced by threat of this. Thus, going up to bed at night and settling for sleep were, for a long time before the child came to hospital, occasions for crises and emotional tension. Mother would put her to bed, the patient would scream, and then father would go up and read to her until she fell asleep. This went so far at times that not one, but several, books were read until the parents were exhausted.

A month before this child's fifth birthday the father spent seven weeks in hospital with an illness which was to prove fatal. The patient could not see him during this time but clung to his collar at night. When he returned home—to die—the child wanted to spend all her time in his bedroom. About two months after his discharge the father died; and the mother told the patient that he had gone to "God's hospital." The child expected that he would come back.

In September of that year the mother started to go out to work, and an aunt used to give the patient her meals. Quite fantastic antics were resorted to by her adult relatives to induce her to eat her mid-day dinner. For example, one of the relatives would put on a dance or some other performance while the grandmother tried to feed her with a spoon. Her appetite deteriorated gradually. In October she became ill with what was later diagnosed as acute rheumatism. She was confined to bed for six weeks; and during this time her appetite deteriorated to the point where she was refusing all solid foods and took only milk and fruit drinks. The family doctor himself tried to feed her with a spoon but with no success. Once the child commented to her mother, "Dr. B says if I don't eat I'll never be a big girl. If I grow into a big girl my daddy won't recognize me, will he?" By mid-December the doctor, getting worried, called in a pediatrician who took both mother and child to a hospital. There the nurses tried forced feeding; but this was quite unsuccessful and was in any case stopped by the pediatrician.

Treatment

The most urgent task now was to revive appetite. The case was discussed in the Psychiatric Department. The immediate problem was formulated in terms of simple conditioning with father as the conditioned stimulus, upon which the conditioned response of eating had come to depend, reinforcement being supplied both by satisfaction of hunger, as well as by anxiety-reduction through sitting on the father's knee and being fed by him. The first step, therefore, was to provide a substitute for the father and to arrange a series of experiences that might gradually approximate those obtaining before the father's death. In other words, principles were to be used that involved both stimulus-substitution and the generalization continuum. The attempt was to be made to replace the father as conditioned stimulus, first by the psychologist and, later, by members of the child's own family, such as uncles, the father's sister, and finally her mother. It was decided that the psychologist, a man, should undertake this part of the treatment, and in accordance with the theoretical formulation no "interpretations" were to be given to the child.

For the first week the psychologist saw the child every day for an hour and arranged a series of play sessions and tea-parties in a large play house which was equipped with miniature furniture and paraphernalia such as cooking utensils, plates and tea sets.

During the first session the child and psychologist attended to the various needs of dolls and only the dolls were fed. The mother was present on this occasion but was excluded from all subsequent sessions. On the next afternoon, while worrying considerably about "supper on the ward" the child nevertheless ate a number of miniature biscuits and drank dolls' cups full of milk laced with stout, a beverage to which her father had been partial. Play with dolls and tea parties continued every day that week with the child still refusing all meals on the ward, except once when she accepted a sausage from an uncle who was visiting her in the evening. At the weekend it was decided that the child should return home and in future attend as an out-patient.

The weekend was spent partly at home and partly at the house of a paternal aunt and uncle. (This paternal aunt was later to prove an excellent mother-surrogate, in bridging the gap between the dead father and the mother.) On Monday mother reported that the patient had eaten a little solid food both at her aunt's and at home; and while the psychologist was having his coffee the child asked for a cup, too. During the subsequent play sessions that week larger cups were substituted for the dolls' cups and full sized biscuits introduced.

In the middle of the second week the mother reported an "embarrassing" experience. They were at the grandmother's house the previous day when suddenly a neighbor, an elderly Irish woman, came in with the patient and said to the mother, shaking her finger disapprovingly in her face, "Don't you tell me this child won't eat; she has just eaten two plates of spare-ribs and cabbage." That evening the mother suffered a further "embarrassment" when another neighbor, a man, called and the child told him, "I don't eat in this house. I won't eat for my mummy." By the end of the second week, although the child still refused to eat with her relatives, she had eaten fruit and nuts at this neighbor's house.

The Christmas holiday and a head cold now intervened, and the psychologist did not see either mother or child for six days. However, after a further week the patient was prepared to sit down to meals with her mother and sister but did not regularly eat anything with them. A month after referral the mother reported that the child had for the first time inquired what there was for lunch and had eaten something of everything that was available.

During this period the play sessions had continued, never less frequently than four times a week, with the patient often preparing the meals she and the psychologist ate together and determining their other activities. The psychologist played the role of submissive father and pampered to her whims, until one day, six weeks after beginning treatment, when the child had him skipping for his tea while she beat time on a hammer-peg board, he made a note to introduce at an opportune moment a little more "reality" and a little less "pleasure" into the father-child relationship.

The opportunity came in a day or two when the patient refused to stay in the playroom while the psychologist had a talk with her mother. He therefore terminated the interview and sent her home without the cup of coffee that had been promised her by the clinic secretary. Interestingly, the mother was very upset at this, fearing that the child would refuse to attend again. She attended, however, and a period of retraining was started in which a different set of responses began to be rewarded, i.e., responses other than those of exploiting the relationship with the therapist. She began to do little useful jobs about the clinic, such as mending books, as well as playing. The child continued to eat better, now taking a regular breakfast, and even to say she was hungry; but after three months of treatment she suffered a set-back when the mother had to return to work. Her diet was again reduced to fluids; and she insisted on having a collar, this time an uncle's to go to sleep with. The relapse lasted, however, only three or four days.

For the next six weeks she was unable to attend the hospital because of measles and then chicken-pox. Five months after her initial referral to the Psychiatric Department the child was showing an interest in food and developing special tastes; and a month later her eating was no longer a cause for anxiety to her relatives. By this time the psychologist had managed to transfer a large part of the father's mantle on to two uncles, one of whom (the husband of the paternal aunt already mentioned) the patient described as her "No. 1 uncle," saying that she loved him "nearly as much as Daddy." Nevertheless, it was learned from the aunt that the psychologist still possessed almost divine qualities for this child.

After seven months this phase of the treatment was concluded. For three years now the child has remained free of her symptoms, the nocturnal enursesis having cleared up twelve months after the feeding difficulty had been disposed of. She has been healthy and fairly well-adjusted at home, at school, and with her play friends, despite the death of a grandmother, of whom she was very fond, two years ago, and more recently, of her No. 1 uncle.

Summary

In spite of the fact that for more than thirty years psychologists have been interested in applying principles of behavior discovered in general psychology, especially those of learning, to the understanding of behavior disorders and neuroses in children, these principles have been largely neglected in treatment. In order to demonstrate that this failure of transfer need not necessarily be perpetuated, the history and treatment were described of a five and a half year old girl who for three months had resisted all attempts by her relatives, by the family doctor, and by hospital nurses to get her to take solid foods.

References

1. Dollard, J. and Miller, N. E.: *Personality and Psychotherapy*. New York: McGraw-Hill, 1950.
2. Eysenck, H. J.: *The Dynamics of Anxiety and Hysteria*. London: Routledge & Kegan Paul, 1957.
3. Jones, H. G.: The application of conditioning and learning techniques to the treatment of a psychiatric patient. *J. abnorm. soc. Psychol.*, 1956, *52*: 414-419.
4. Jones, H. G.: Neurosis and experimental psychology. *J. ment. Sci.*, 1958, *104*: 55-62.
5. Jones, M. C.: A laboratory study of fear: the case of Peter. *Pedag. Sem.*, 1924, *31*: 308-315.

6. Mowrer, O. H.: *Learning Theory and Personality Dynamics.* New York: Ronald Press, 1950.
7. Mowrer, O. H.: *Psychotherapy. Theory and Research.* New York: Ronald Press, 1953.
8. Mowrer, O. H. and Mowrer, W. M.: Enuresis: A method for its study and treatment. *Amer. J. Orthopsychiat.,* 1938, *8*: 436.
9. Shoben, E. J.: Psychotherapy as a problem in learning theory. *Psychol. Bull.,* 1949, *46*: 366-392.
10. Shoben, E. J.: Some observations on psychotherapy and the learning process. In O. H. Mowrer, *Psychotherapy. Theory and Research.* New York: Ronald Press, 1953.
11. Walton, D.: Reciprocal inhibition, sedation threshold, practice and the treatment of compulsions and schizophrenic slowness. *Bull. Brit. Psychol. Soc.,* 1958, No. 36.
12. Walton, D.: Learning theory, personality, drug-action, and the treatment of stammering. *Bull. Brit. Psychol. Soc.,* 1958, No. 36.
13. Walton, D. and Black, D. A.: The application of learning theory to the treatment of stammering. *J. psychosomatic Res.,* 1958, in press.
14. Walton, D. and Black, D. A.: The application of modern learning theory to the treatment of chronic hysterical aphonia. *J. psychosomatic. Res.,* 1958, in press.

18

THE TREATMENT OF MORPHINE ADDICTION IN TUBERCULOSIS BY PAVLOV'S CONDITIONING METHOD

by Charles Rubenstein, M.D.

In a previous article (1) we indicated the value of Pavlov's conditioning methods as an aid in the treatment of certain phases of pulmonary tuberculosis. We suggested that his work might be applied to good effect in dealing with the varied symptom-complex so frequently met with in this disease—the depression, poor appetite, nervous indigestion, headaches, insomnia, excessive perspiration, etc. It was pointed out that Pavlov had demonstrated by his experiments that the above conditions may be modified by the establishment of properly selected conditioned reflexes. We now consider another phase of the conditioned reflex's potential usefulness in the field of pulmonary tuberculosis.

Not infrequently we are confronted with the problem of treating narcotic addiction. By reason of their proneness to aggravate the chest condition the usual withdrawal methods have proved far from satisfactory in their application to the tuberculous patient. The writer has successfully applied the conditioning method at the Los Angeles Sanatorium to two pulmonary cases addicted to the morphine habit. In both cases it was found that the treatment was rapid and effective, and did not produce the so called withdrawal symptoms. We are citing these two cases at some length.

Case F

Male, white, 38 years of age, single, no occupation. Entered the Los Angeles Sanatorium April 19, 1929. Complained of shortness of breath, cough with profuse expectoration, palpitation of the heart, loss of weight, malaise, fever, and occasional pain in the chest without definite location. *Diagnosis:* Far-advanced pulmonary tuberculosis; also addicted to the morphine habit. *Family History:* Father suspected of

---

Reprinted with permission from the *American Review of Tuberculosis,* 1931, *24,* 682-685.

being tuberculous but never definitely diagnosed as such. Remainder of family history negative. *Personal History:* Had no children's diseases and did well at school. Began to smoke at age of ten. Left home at age 15. Led dissipated life. At age of 28 quite suddenly began to cough, lose weight, and have night-sweats. A diagnosis of pulmonary tuberculosis was made and from then (1921) to the time he entered the Los Angeles Sanatorium patient was an inmate of sanatoria in various parts of the United States. In 1926 suffered from heart attacks and insomnia, and then began to use morphine. On April 28, 1929, two weeks after patient entered Los Angeles Sanatorium, attempt made at inducing artificial pneumothorax of left lung, without success. On June 18, 1929, left phrenicotomy performed but without improvement in patient's condition. On the contrary, he showed increased cough and expectoration, rise of fever and other symptoms of toxemia. The heart attacks (fibrillation and tachycardia) became more frequent, and morphine was resorted to more often and in constantly increasing doses.

Patient came under our care July 1, 1930, at which time he weighed 105, about 35 pounds below his normal weight. Then suffered from chronic constipation, and tongue thickly coated. Was markedly dyspnoeic and cyanotic, and afflicted with great mental depression and anxiety. Physical examination, X-ray and laboratory findings showed widespread involvement of both lungs, with cavity-formation in left. *Neurological Findings:* No nystagmus or ataxia. Babinski absent. Pupils equal, but irregular and react to light. Romberg absent. Deep reflexes diminished. Abdominal reflexes not elicited. Halting speech and difficulty in pronouncing certain words. Patient moody. Periods of euphoria when under influence of morphine, followed by depression when effects wore off. It should be added that just prior to the institution of the conditioned-reflex treatment patient had been receiving about 8.5 grains of morphine per day, administered half-hourly in doses as high as 0.5 grain.

Conditioned-reflex treatment instituted July 2, 1930, and following method used: At the start each hypodermic injection was accompanied by the ringing of a bell. Due to the fact, however, that this form of external stimulus could not be conveniently used during sanatorium rest hours and at night, it was abandoned after a few days, and massage of the dorsal surface of the forearm for one minute after each hypodermic injection was substituted. We were able gradually to diminish the daily amounts of morphine by substituting sterile injections, and after four weeks the morphine was entirely replaced by physiological salt hypodermics, every injection still being accompanied by massage. The total amount of morphine the patient received for the first week was 32.4 grains; for the second it was 13, the third, 7, and the fourth 2.5. Six weeks after commencing the treatment, on the initiative of the patient, who with diminished doses of the narcotic grew very sensitive to the needle, the sterile injections were discontinued entirely. It is interesting to note that on one occasion during the third week of the treatment, when the morphine injection was administered unaccompanied by massage, patient complained that no morphine had been given him. The sterile hypo followed by massage seemed always to satisfy him however. It was also noted that the treatment did not provoke the usual withdrawal symptoms. On the contrary, the characteristic restlessness, weakness, and loss of weight were absent. The patient felt well and comfortable, gained 32 pounds in the five months following the institution of the treatment, and his lung and general condition showed remarkable improvement. The patient's sole complaint related to a steady pain in the lower extremities. This pain became more pronounced as the morphine dosage was diminished. This may be explained however by the fact that the patient, having acquired a general hypoaesthesia from the prolonged use of morphine, was insensible to the peculiarly constricted position in which he invariably kept his legs while in bed. With the return then of aesthesia to those parts some pain for a time was inevitable. After 3½ months of total abstinence from morphine, patient was discharged.

Case L

Female, white, 38 years, married, housewife. Entered Los Angeles Sanatorium June 19, 1930. Complained of cough, rapid respiration, poor appetite, loss of weight, night-sweats, insomnia, restlessness and frequent headaches. *Diagnosis:* Far-advanced pulmonary tuberculosis and syphilis; also addicted to the morphine habit. *Family History*: Negative. *Past History:* In August, 1928, patient had hemorrhage, about 10 ounces, followed by dry, hacking cough, slight malaise, loss of appetite and weight. Six months later had another hemorrhage of approximately same size as first; also raised small quantity of blood two weeks before entering Los Angeles Sanatorium. Physical examination, X-ray and laboratory findings showed bilateral pulmonary involvement. Wassermann 4 plus. Since first pulmonary hemorrhage patient had been repeatedly given hypodermic injections of morphine, the doses being rapidly increased to the point where in June, 1930 she was getting two grains per day.

The conditioned-reflex treatment was instituted June 4, 1930. In this case a tuning-fork, held close to the ear until the vibration ceased, was used as the conditioning stimulus. Patient was also instructed to count until the sound died out. At the start of the treatment the patient was getting four hypodermic injections of 0.5 grain of morphine daily. After three days, the reflex having been established, we began gradually to replace morphine with sterile water. Ten days later we were able, without exciting any withdrawal symptoms, to replace all morphine hypodermics by sterile water. It was observed that the best effects were marked by the patient when the vibrations were more prolonged than usual. The presence of visceral syphilis however, complicating and interfering with our observations, constituted a serious obstacle to our study and treatment of the case. In view of the advanced pulmonary condition of the patient, antisyphilitic treatment was not vigorously pursued, and finally, on August 2, 1930, patient was discharged at her own request so that she might seek specific treatment at home.

Summary

1. A practical field for the application of Pavlov's work on the conditioned reflex is presented for use on patients with tuberculosis.
2. Two cases of morphine addiction, successfully treated by this method, are reported.
3. This form of treatment is safe and rapid, and does not, in our experience, provoke the usual withdrawal symptoms.

Reference

1. Rubenstein, Charles: Pavlov's Work and Its Clinical Possibilities, *California & Western Medicine,* January, 1930.

19

CONDITIONING TECHNIQUE OF PSYCHOPROPHYLACTIC PREPARATION OF THE PREGNANT WOMAN

by Isidore Bonstein, M.D.

Pain

The study of pain should be conducted in respect to its production, transmission and finally its perception.

It is known that sensation is due to the peripheral irritation of the corpuscles of Vater and Paccini and free nerve-endings.

From there, the impulses follow the nerve fiber which, by way of the posterior roots of the spinal cord, penetrate the posterior horn of the grey medullary substance, cross the median line by way of the grey commissure, and reach the lateral fasciculus of the opposite side of the cord to get the thalamus. From there, after synapsing with other fibers, transmission is projected upon the cerebral cortex.

We are mostly concerned with the problem of pain perception. There are two theories: the first postulated by Head, considers the thalamus as being the center of pain. The second describes the thalamus as being a relay station, and attributes pain perception to the cerebral cortex. This second conception has been convincingly defended by Pavlov.

By experimentally defunctionalizing the cerebral cortex, either by anesthesia or by excision, he demonstrated that pain stimuli can be related to two different types of phenomena: the unconditioned reflexes, subcortical, unconscious; and the conditioned reflexes, cortical, conscious, which are the only ones manifesting the *subjective* phenomenon of pain.

In man, it was evident that anesthesia suppressed both consciousness and memory of pain. This thereby showed that these phenomena were cortical. In anesthesia, only in conditioned reactions, motor and vegetative, with subcortical circuits persisted.

Reprinted with permission from *Psychoprophylactic Preparation for Painless Childbirth,* London, William Heinemann Medical Books Ltd., 1958, pp. 26-44.

The great variability of pain intensity, according to the surrounding conditions constitutes a valuable argument.

Everyone knows what great modifications painful sensation can undergo, depending upon various activities.

A distraction or a captivating task can erase a violent headache or toothache. It is known that a soldier in combat can be wounded without realizing it.

Several authors had already noted, without appreciating all the possible consequences, the attenuation and even disappearance of pain phenomena by concentration of the attention, or by muscular effort.

It is to the school of Pavlov that merit is due for the proof of the cortical character of pain sensation, and the mechanism of its transformation.

The famous experiment reported in his *Lectures on Conditioned Reflexes* and accomplished by Dr. Erofeeva is a brilliant demonstration of this fact:

We take a dog with a chronic salivary fistula—our usual laboratory animal for these experiments—and let a strong electric current act on his skin. This, according to the subjective terminology, is *a pain stimulus;* but according to the objective term is a *destructive stimulus.* It is obvious that the answer to such a stimulus is a usual reflex, a defensive reaction of the animal; he protects himself with all his might against the stimulus. He tries to break loose from the stand, he bites the stimulating apparatus, etc. The stimulation passes into the center of the defense reaction; it is expressed in defense movements. If you repeat this experiment for several successive days, the irritability of the animal increases with each repetition, and the defense reflex becomes reinforced.

But let us perform this experiment in another way. If you give the dog food during the action of the destructive stimulus (he will not eat the food, forcibly introduced into his mouth in order to stimulate the taste cells), you will notice that the defense reaction becomes weaker and weaker, and in the course of time may vanish. This means that you have before you a fact from the first category—an inhibition.

The stimulation of the food center leads to inhibition of the center for pain reflexes

If feeding is often repeated simultaneously with the pain stimulus, finally *you will not only fail to have the defensive reaction,* but, on the contrary, with the application of the electric current, you will see that the dog develops the food reaction; he turns toward you, looks toward the place from which the food is brought, and saliva flows. The stimulation which entered into the center for defense reaction, now passes over the food center—i.e., the center which governs the movements and secretions relating to food. This is an illustration of the second group of reflexes; it is a conditioned reflex.

From this example, you witness how one phenomenon passes inevitably over into another; and thus their relationship is clearly established. First, as you have seen, the pain center was inhibited, and then the stimulation was transferred to the food center. Hence follows the logical conclusion that the processes are essentially one and the same, that there is merely a transference, an alteration of direction, an attraction of energy from one center to another. And if the new center is the stronger, as in the given case, all the energy of the first center passes over to his stronger center, and the previously active center becomes entirely quiescent.

(The foregoing experiments taken from *Lectures on Conditioned Reflexes* by I. P. Pavlov, Vol. I, p. 187, translated and edited by Horsley Gantt, M.D., Internat. Publ., New York.)

The famous English physiologist, Sherrington, witnessing such an experiment, exclaimed, "Now I understand the psyche of the martyrs."

Another experiment, no less interesting, done by Dr. Rogov, should be mentioned. It concerns a human subject and utilizes the second system of signalization, speech, whose formidable force appears evident.

On the skin of a subject is placed a circular tube, permitting, by the circulation of hot water, thermal stimulation of exactly determined intensity.

The vaso-motor modifications are studied with plethismograph.

First a stimulation of 43° Centigrade is applied, which produces an unconditioned reflex of vaso-dilatation and a subjective sensation of painless heat.

A bell is used as the conditioning stimulus, and after twenty to fifty associations (according to the subject) this bell provokes the vaso-dilatation.

If the experimenter says, "I ring the bell!" that is to say, substitutes the verbal stimulus for the direct stimulus, the vaso-dilatory conditioned reflex is produced in the same fashion.

A stimulation of 65° Centigrade is then applied. It provokes, in contrast to the stimulation of 43°, an unconditioned vaso-constriction. At the same time, there is a subjective sensation of pain.

The subject is then told "I am applying the heat" at the same time that the 65° thermal stimulus is actually given. In other words, that which provokes the sensation of pain, and not of heat.

We then observe a vaso-dilatation instead of the unconditioned vaso-constriction, while the patient declares a subjective sensation of heat, *but no sensation of pain.*

The subject has presented the vaso-motor conditioned reflex corresponding to the verbal signal and the subjective sensation allied with the same signal, instead of the vaso-motor reaction and the subjective sensation linked with the unconditioned stimulus, applied at the same time as the verbal conditioned stimulus.

The effect of the verbal stimulus, although conditioned, has superseded the effect of the direct stimulus, though "unconditioned."

These experiments throw a new light on the mechanism of certain types of pain, which we simply designate as "psychic."

Besides conditioned connections, *the functional status* of the cortex directly influences pain sensation. After we observe an exhaustion of cortical activity, either following prolonged work (overwork), or after intense activity (emotion), we notice a diminution in the strength of cortical processes, and, consequently, of inhibition.

Thus the points of excitation created at the level of the cerebral cortex by the sensitive stimuli diffuse with greater ease and assume a new quality. Exteroceptions can become painful (hyperalgesic) and interoceptions are no longer inhibited and acquire the character of visceral pain.

Pain sensation is neither a simple mechanical phenomenon, nor a mysterious psychic one. It is the result of cortical processes in which the two fundamental antagonistic processes, excitation and inhibition, are seen in a constant struggle. It depends upon the general functional state of the cerebral cortex. It can be created, facilitated (lowering of the pain threshold) or, on the contrary, inhibited, increased (elevation of the threshold) by conditioned links.

Pain in Childbirth

Throughout the entire pregnancy, and often long before pregnancy, in the minds of women, ties have been established between the words "pain" and "uterine contraction." We have here an example of the creation of a strong-conditioned connection by the medium of the second system of signalization. The future mother learns from other women that they have perceived uterine contractions in the form of pain. She learns that it is an extremely unpleasant pain of which she shall long retain a disagreeable memory, but a pain that is necessary to experience the joy of motherhood.

She is told by her obstetrician that the pain will not only be necessary, but useful, because it is that pain which will announce the onset of her labor.

The unconditioned reflex to pain, with all its objective and subjective manifestations, is linked in the pregnant woman, through the medium of the second system of signalization, to uterine contraction. *Uterine contraction will, for the woman, be the signal of pain.*

A conditioned reflex can only be developed and maintained as long as it is not inhibited by other reflexes. The absence of conditioned associations (on the bases of the second system of signalization) capable of inhibiting reflex pain is due to the woman's ignorance of the exact physiologic process of childbirth for the association between pain and uterine contraction is practically the only thing the woman learns about her forthcoming confinement.

This ignorance nourishes an entire series of emotional manifestations, going from apprehension to fear, and connected with the voluntary dramatic, exaggerated tales, which are generously presented to the woman during her pregnancy.

This emotional state, prolonged, if not violent, exhausts and upsets the equilibrium of the cerebral cortex.

The onset of labor increases this exhaustion by way of new emotions. The painful manifestations weaken her yet more. The woman is incapable of re-establishing the tone of her cortical activity, because she cannot act. *She knows of no other action but to submit passively to her confinement.*

This cortical disturbance and the functional derangement which it brings about, produce a vicious circle. The biological regulations of the organism (vascular and hormonal) are upset. The uterus works under poor conditions, suffers, and the enteroceptions originating in it become more and more violent.

To sum up: the pain of childbirth results from particular qualities which the enteroceptions, linked to the various phenomena of uterine contraction, assume at the level of the cortex.

The purpose of preparing the woman for painless childbirth will be to reorganize her cortical activity. This will be done by suppressing the conditioned pain reflexes, and by creating new useful conditioned reflexes capable of associating uterine contraction with a strong, positive, and painless activity. It will suppress, by inhibition, uterine enteroceptions.

In order to suppress a conditioned reflex, two prerequisites are necessary:

1. The suppression of the link, existing objectively outside of the woman's brain and reproduced in the brain by conditioning, between pain and uterine contraction.

2. The creation of new conditioned reflexes, uniting in a general way childbirth with the pleasant prospects of the birth of a baby. Or more precisely, the creation of conditioned reflexes associating uterine contractions with practical actions on the woman's part, permitting her to adapt her body and to participate actively in her confinement.

For this purpose, a certain procedure has proven to be very useful. In the course of the lectures we advise the future mothers to learn how to feel their painless Braxton-Hicks contractions, during the last weeks of pregnancy. They are told to notice them and to perform shallow and fast breathing, while feeling the hardening of their uterus.

This correlation between painless uterine contraction and the new type of respiration to be used later, during labor, builds a favorable conditioned reflex, excluding the feeling of pain.

The preparation must remove the former obnoxious acquirements of the brain and replace them with new, positive and beneficial conditioned reflexes.

The first point consists of teaching the women the true physiological processes of pregnancy, labor and delivery. They will thus overcome the elementary and false connection between labor and pain.

The second point consists of a simple, but clear explanation of the cortical activity. Many examples must corroborate the demonstration. They will understand the importance of an active participation in their childbirth.

The third point includes teaching women the different activities which they will have to practice during their labor and delivery. The links between these activities and the various enteroceptions (especially uterine contractions) must be stressed and repeated.

A persistent activity of thought must be maintained during the different stages of confinement. Consciousness and thinking create potent, positive cortical foci, with great power of inhibition.

A special type of breathing will reinforce this permanent active pattern, especially during the arrival of maximum uterine enteroceptions, during dilatation and delivery.

Normal breathing is an unconditioned reflex, non-cortical. The modification of the respiratory rhythm, advocated during the uterine contractions, is a cortical conditioned reflex.

During the educative period, this type of breathing has been correlated to Braxton-Hicks painless uterine contractions. So, a new conditioned reflex has been created, linking three elements: the special type of breathing, the uterine contraction and the subjective fact that the hardening of the uterus is *painless.*

The reflex of bearing down, at the end of dilatation, is an unconditioned one, due to the enteroceptions originating from the pelvic floor on which the presentation presses. But learning to bear down correctly, willingly, and in the right direction, is a conditioned reflex, cortical, grafted on the unconditioned one.

The neuro-muscular education taught in the course is another acquirement in the same direction. Muscular decontraction corresponds in the brain to a state of inhibition, which is an active phenomenon, able to be conditioned. It is used, also, in order to reinforce favorably the cortical activity.

When the patient starts her labor, all these conditionings must be strengthened. This is done by the attending doctor or the nurse, simply by repeating shortly the different elements taught.

To sum up: preparation for painless childbirth consists in creating conditioned dynamic stereotypes in the woman's brain. These stereotypes are reinforced when labor begins.

Psychoprophylactic Preparation of the Pregnant Woman

At the first examination, in the beginning of pregnancy, the future mother should be told briefly about the method of painless childbirth. If she is interested in the idea, a short summary of the principle, the training and its results, must be given by the obstetrician. It is very important, from the beginning, to warn her against tales and gossip likely to condition her brain to the idea of painful labor and delivery.

If told by friends or neighbors about the suffering and pain of their deliveries, she must simply answer: "My case is *different,* I am going to practice a new method—the psychoprophylactic preparation for painless childbirth which has proved to be effective in thousands of deliveries and makes all the difference!"

It is important from the first interview to associate in the woman's mind the idea of childbirth with the certitude of a successful labor, with the absence of fear of pain and anxiety about her own and her baby's life and with the pleasant atmosphere of the maternity hospital, where doctors and nurses will be ready to help and support her.

The fact must be stressed that labor and delivery are physiological events. If she follows the teaching and behaves correctly she will experience no pain and no discomfort.

From the beginning, besides general somatic and obstetrical examinations, a thorough case history is important, stressing the psychological dispositions and tendencies. If disturbances of some consequence are noticed in this field, they should be corrected by suitable psychotherapy.

Clinical determination of the nervous type is advisable. Best results are obtained with women of strong and well-balanced character. Nervously weak and feeble women display their fear of pain, sometimes up to phobia. In these cases failures are more frequent. Their preparation must be specially extended and thoroughly done.

From the thirtieth week on, the pregnant woman follows the course of eight lectures; one every week. Experience has proven that group teaching is the best; from five to ten patients in each class. It is very important to find speakers with didactic talent and really able to reach their listeners. We have noticed that, as a rule, pregnant women interested in the preparation are very receptive and attentive. The room must be pleasant and quiet. Comfortable seats, a couch and a few pillows are necessary.

We do not need to insist upon the importance of regular attendance at the lectures, which should be illustrated by pictures and diagrams. The future mothers must be encouraged to ask questions.

For most women eight lectures of forty-five minutes to one hour are enough. It is important not to allow more than eight to ten days between the last lecture and term. After this lapse of time a supplementary refresher session must be added.

Here is the program of the course of eight lectures as given at Dr. Lamaze's Maternity Hospital in Paris:

1. *Introduction*

From its interest will depend the assiduity of the future mothers. Starting with very simple notions on the central nervous system and the autonomic nervous system, the text explains Pavlov's ideas about fundamental and conditioned reflexes. Details on the functioning of the brain cortex are given, explaining why some stimuli are noticed whereas some others are not. Examples from daily life illustrate the importance of the emotional state in given situations and their repercussions on perception. The story of a confinement, from beginning to end, as it happened formerly, is told. The errors of the past are stressed. Childbirth was a passive event, a kind of disease that women had to undergo without any defense. They had no possibility of reaction. Ignoring everything about childbirth there was no useful or valuable behavior to which they could adapt themselves.

Parturition is not a *passive* phenomenon. It is an active event belonging to a woman's life.

When a woman arrives at the maternity hospital to deliver her baby, after having followed the course of instruction, she comes to perform an action. She has been educated for this action. She understands it, she is able to analyze, to control, to direct it. Therefore she will be an impelling element.

Our role is essentially to educate the patient. We know that ignorance is the main reason causing the conditioned reflex for pain. Our duty is to eliminate ignorance.

We know that some activities built into conditioned reflexes prevent the perception in the brain cortex of uterine contractions as unpleasant or painful stimuli. Our duty is to teach these activities.

Our future mother will be able to face her parturition knowing in advance its successive phases and their use. She will follow and live the entire evolution. In full conscience, she will accomplish an action to which she was formerly submissive.

From a resigned and passive woman who, by ignorance, had admitted pain in childbirth as an inevitable fact, she will become the conscious actor in the most beautiful fight in life, the fight for giving life.

2. *Physiology of Respiration*

The connections between breathing, pregnancy and parturition are stressed. After explaining the importance of oxygen in life, in muscular and nervous metabolism, the elimination of CO_2 is described. A good oxygenation is important for the pregnant woman because:

(*a*) her own metabolism is increased;

(*b*) her fetus gets its oxygen through the maternal blood. During labor and delivery a perfect oxygenation must be obtained because the maternal organism is submitted to an intense activity, hence the need for a large amount of oxygen.

It is important to insist on the deleterious consequences of hypoxia for the mother and especially for the baby.

The idea is to place before the woman her responsibilities, showing her, however, that she will not be alone. A well-trained staff will support her.

If she practices, regularly, the breathing exercises taught during pregnancy she will be at ease during labor and delivery.

After describing carefully the mechanics of breathing and the anatomical connections of the different organs involved, we shall teach an exercise to be used as a link between our theoretical description and physical reality. This breathing exercise has no direct relation with parturition. Its use is to make the pregnant woman conscious of the connections between her organs and the muscles most concerned during confinement.

3. *Neuro-Muscular Education—Study of Muscular Relaxation*

The future mother must know the situation of the important muscles concerned and their actions. She must be able to differentiate between the useful ones and those which, if tense, would obstruct the normal progress of her labor. This, in order to neutralize the latter.

Training is the only way to reach this target. Women must acquire during pregnancy new and useful reflexes. They correspond in the brain cortex to new connections and to new centers of stimulation. Knowing in advance the necessary activities which permit proper adaptation to be maintained, the parturient is protected against the feeling of fear and anxiety.

Technically speaking, neuro-muscular education and muscular relaxation are very easy to realize. The patients are told to sensitize their muscles by performing a movement. It is important to perform this movement with more force than usual.

After having felt and accurately located a muscle or a muscular group, the patients are requested to relax them to the utmost. This inhibition of motivity is an active effort able to become a conditioned reflex.

Muscular relaxation corresponds to a relative cortical activation, helping to maintain a favorable nervous balance and saving oxygen.

4. *Mechanism of Labor*

This should be given by the obstetrician himself and illustrated by numerous diagrams and pictures. Starting from fertilization, the evolution of pregnancy is described. The importance of amniotic fluid is stressed. Braxton-Hicks contractions are explained. Having mentioned that often well-prepared mothers do not notice the first regular contractions at all, it is indicated that the symptoms of labor should be described. The first, the second and the third stages should be explained with details and illustrations showing particularly the flexion, rotation and deflection of the baby's head along the birth canal.

A new exercise is introduced in order to render the pregnant woman conscious of her painless Braxton-Hicks contractions.

5. *The First Stage of Labor—Dilatation—How to Behave during its Phases*

Experience has shown that in order to remember something, the average person needs five repetitions.

After a quick review of the anatomical data, the process of dilatation of the cervix is described and divided into two periods: from the beginning to 5 cm. and from 5 cm. to full dilatation. The second stage is explained and contractions carefully analyzed.

A complete, actively controlled muscular relaxation is prescribed for the duration of the contractions. A special type of breathing must be adapted to the different features of the contractions. Shallow and fast respiration seems the best. Pure oxygen may be administered towards the end of the first stage, during or between contractions.

The exercise described is very simple: shallow and fast breathing during one minute or more, while relaxing all the muscles of the body.

At home, morning and evening this type of respiration must be practiced synchronous with the Braxton-Hicks contractions. A new conditioned reflex, combining a painless contraction with shallow and fast breathing, will be formed and contribute greatly to prevent any feeling of discomfort during labor.

6. *Expulsion—How to Behave during the Second Stage according to its Physiology*

A feeling like "bearing down" indicates the second stage. Women were usually told, "Bear down like moving your bowels." This suggestion is contrary to the real physiological effort of expulsion, as it contracts the muscles of the pelvic floor, precisely those which we know it is very important should be relaxed.

The woman is told exactly how to bear down during contractions. She must learn how to fill her chest, to hold her breath and to use her upper abdominal muscles while willingly relaxing her perineum and her thighs. It is a matter of training and must become, through repetition, a perfect reflex. An exercise of dissociation is shown.

Another important reflex must be created. When the head is crowning, an order will be given to the mother so as to permit a very slow and progressive extension—"Don't bear down any more and get completely relaxed." For this, shallow and fast breathing must be practiced.

These two exercises are rehearsed in the class.

7. *Function of the Brain*

This lecture is given at Dr. Lamaze's Maternity Hospital by Dr. R. Angelergues, a neuro-psychiatrist, who begins with a quick summary of the anatomo-physiology of the brain and the spinal cord.

When an impulse reaches the brain cortex, a definite area is stimulated. All around this point the brain reacts by creating a state of inhibition. This dampening is very important as it prevents the excitation from spreading and producing uncontrolled phenomena.

The brain may have a variable power of action. If one's brain receives a weak stimulation, it will react around the weak point of stimution by a weak area of reaction, of dampening.

If, on the contrary, one's brain has a strong activity of thought, like for instance when one concentrates on a subject, there is, around the active area, a vast and intense inhibition, preventing the perception of other impulses.

When a person is exhausted, anxious or frightened, the strength of the brain is markedly decreased; one cannot concentrate and any stimulus is felt unpleasantly.

Up to now most mothers have had their babies as though they were in a highly emotional state.

The teaching received recently by the prepared mothers, has built in their brains areas of activities, each one corresponding to possibilities of action.

When labor starts, these possibilities of action will, in turn, produce a strong cerebral activity able to prevent unpleasant impulses from being felt. The acquired conditioned reflexes play the role of a barrier, obstructing the perception of uterine contractions as painful stimuli.

8. *Review of the Theory and the Exercises of Muscular Relaxation—Presentation of the Film on Painless Childbirth*

The signs and symptoms indicating labor are mentioned once again. The pregnant woman must know when she has to come to the maternity hospital.

The different activities for the first and second stages are repeated in the classroom, followed by a visit to the delivery room. There, on the very delivery table, the future parturient will rehearse the three exercises.

Every woman must be individually tested. Any mistake should be corrected carefully. Lastly, the film showing a successful delivery is presented. Always ask for questions.

As already mentioned, no more than eight to ten days must be allowed between the last lecture and term. If it happens, the pregnant woman should attend the eighth lecture again.

Painless Childbirth as Team-work

To be successful, painless childbirth needs team-work. We face here a normal trend in modern medicine. Specialization calls for skilled and trained co-operation. Everyone must play his part and play it well. The obstetrician is the chief, and every member of the staff must endeavor to help maintain the good conditioning of the parturient. This requires understanding of the method and a special training.

The psychoprophylactic method totally changes the old approach to obstetrics. Formerly the principle was—"Knock out your patient as much as possible, within safe limits of course, in order to suppress her feelings and her memory."

The contrary is requested in our new technique. Keep the patient psychically as active as possible, in order to maintain a high degree of brain power, hence of conditioning. She must be aware of the phases of her labor. She must follow the evolution in her mind and feel the progress of her baby's head in her birth canal.

Through the course of lectures she has acquired a good education and knows what her action must be in the different stages of childbirth. She knows many facts and has acquired conditioned reflexes ready to play their role.

What she needs is moral support and someone always ready to coach her. When necessary, she must be reminded what to do. Imperfect behavior or activity should be immediately corrected in order to keep up a good conditioning.

Except in the very beginning of labor, she must not fall asleep because sleep decreases cortical activity and consequently diminishes the conditioning.

Positive-minded nurses or midwives are the best. They should be understanding and able to acquire the parturient's confidence. No sign of nervousness must ever be allowed to appear. Even if very busy, the nurse must have the art of giving the impression that she has plenty of time. Nervousness is catching and, let us repeat once again, conditioning against pain can be easily destroyed.

In comparing childbirth to the performance of a symphonic orchestra, we may say that the obstetrician is the conductor and the parturient the "soloist" supported by all the other performers. One poor musician may ruin all the value of a group.

Mistakes are not permitted in the realization of painless childbirth. Everyone, from the porter of the maternity hospital to the chief nurse must follow the rules. Education is necessary. One cannot imagine how complicated it is to prevent the unaware night porter from asking with sympathy to new-comers—"Are your pains very bad, my dear?"

All the personnel must understand the importance of a psychohygienic atmosphere, of a correct and suitable vocabulary, and of positive attitudes. *Any person likely to meet parturients should have followed the course and be informed of the details of psychoprophylactic preparation.*

Four qualities are essential, namely: amiability, comprehension, calmness and kindness. No patient must ever be made to feel "a stranger."

The doctor, when he comes, will bring a feeling of authority and of safety. He will decide if an obstetrical reason necessitates changes in the course of labor or delivery.

20

A NEW TREATMENT OF CONSTIPATION BY CONDITIONING: A PRELIMINARY REPORT

by C. Quarti, M.D., and J. Renaud, M.D.

Translated and adapted by Moneim A. El-Meligi, Ph.D.

Introduction

Today, constipation is one of the most widespread functional disorders. Its varied causes include irregularity of alimentary habits, functional disorders of the gallbladder or—more often—the psychosomatic correlates of certain modes of contemporary living, as in the case of city dwellers who lead lives which are physically sedentary yet subject to continual stress. Whatever its cause, constipation is basically a disorder of intestinal motility, presenting in a variety of forms: spastic, paretic, or as an irregularity in the alternation of the phases of contraction and relaxation in the intestinal muscle.

The consequences of constipation are as different as their causes and all are to be deplored. The "maladie des laxatifs" may be considered as the least serious. It occurs following a long period, during which the patient exhausts the pharmacopoeia, passing from one group of laxatives to another. As laxatives are substituted and doses are increased, the process of elimination becomes progressively artificial, deviating more and more from the normal physiologic pattern, due to exhaustion of the liver cells, irritation of the gall bladder or interference with the reflex system of interestinal motility.

It is a pleasure to acknowledge the many clarifications of the medical aspects of this paper provided by my colleagues at the New Jersey Neuro-Psychiatric Institute, Drs. McMillan, de Bernard and Kanther. Dr. Habiba Wassef was particularly helpful in the translation of the paper with respect to medical terminology. My gratitude goes to Dr. Franks for drawing my attention to the potential importance of this paper and for his editing of the final manuscript. We are grateful to the authors of the article and the editor of La Clinique (Paris) for permission to translate and reproduce this paper. The original reference is as follows "Note préliminaire sur un nouveau traitement des constipations par réflexe conditionnel" La Clinique (Paris), 57, 1962, 577-583.

Treatment of constipation therefore calls for a therapy aimed at the cause rather than the symptom. It should make use of the natural resources of the organism, avoiding the use of any medication which, because of the complexity of the mechanism of defecation in its temporal sequence, may exert an untimely pharmacological action. The goal of treatment should be to restore the normal physiological functioning of the mechanism of defecation, not by artificially stimulating defecation, but by re-educating the intestinal motility and helping it regain its own harmony.

Physiological Basis of Defecation

To facilitate the presentation of the techniques to be utilized in our method of re-education, a brief physiological account seems to be in order.

Movements of the alimentary canal, responsible for the transfer of the contents from the esophagus through the stomach, small intestines, and finally to the anus, are under the co-ordinated control of the nervous system. The prerequisites for a normal passage are:

(a) Adequate food intake, both quantitatively and qualitatively. This food intake is, in itself, an important stimulant for intestinal motility. The rate of passage also depends on the state of fluidity and viscosity of the intestinal contents, which in turn depend on the type of foods consumed (bringing us to the psychological implications of alimentary habits), the intestinal juices and bile (the flow of the latter being under the reflex control of the nervous system).

(b) Well co-ordinated intestinal movements. Three types of intestinal movements are responsible for the progression of the intestinal contents, namely: segmentary, pendular and peristaltic. The first two are attributed to intrinsic nervous reflexes and are modified by extrinsic sympathetic and vagal activity. Peristalsis is produced by extrinsic nervous impulses; it is a mass reflex response that may encompass the entire length of the intestines, and is dependent upon the co-ordinated action of certain medullary centers and abdomino-pelvic autonomic pathways.

The average time for the passage of chyme from the stomach to the anus is about 24 hours. Serious irritation of the gastric mucosa produces a "mass reflex" represented by an active peristaltic wave which reduces the duration to a few minutes. The stimulus for this reflex is the entry of food into the stomach, which explains the healthy habit of having the first bowel movement in the morning after breakfast, thereby evacuating the digestive products of the previous day.

(c) The act of defecation begins with the passage of feces across the pelvirectal flexure where local sphincter-like thickening of the circular muscle fibres exists. The sphincter presumably relaxes and feces enter the rectum, whose lumen immediately reacts by slight constriction or dilatation, depending on the size of the fecal mass, so as to produce an active resistance which will now be the stimulus for the final explusive movements. Distention of the rectum by sudden entry of feces gives rise to a perineal sensation, often agreeable, and a conscious desire to defecate. If this desire is acceded to, a co-ordinated reflex is set up, emptying every part of the bowel from the middle of the transverse colon to the anus; the diaphragm descends, the glottis is closed, the abdominal muscles and levator ani contract, waves of peristalsis pass over the distal part of the colon, the sphincter ani are relaxed and the feces are evacuated through the narrow anal canal. The reflex centers for defecation are situated in the medulla and in the spinal cord corresponding to the sacral segments 2, 3, and 4.

Neurophysiological Changes in Constipation

The rectum initially presents the physiological phenomenon of adaptation, which is also the ultimate end of all physiopathological changes in constipation. It ceases to respond to the presence of the fecal mass in its lumen, either due to paretic relaxation of the rectal wall instead of maintaining an active resistance to the pressure exerted by the feces, or to failure of the pressure and stretch receptors to respond to their specific stimulus. On the other hand, the phenomenon of adaptation may take place normally in instances of refrain from defecation, when circumstances are unfavorable at the moment the desire is experienced. In this way, certain modes of existence, serving only to increase these unfavorable conditions, become a common cause of constipation. The resulting rectal stasis sets up the colo-colic reflex producing reflex inhibition of intestinal motility and peristalsis. The vicious circle, characteristic of chronic constipation, is thereby established.

Restoration of Normal Physiological Rhythm to the Intestinal Passage

The physiological rhythm of the bowel motions should first be obtained, at which point the vicious circle will be interrupted. Laxatives may succeed in overcoming rectal inertia, once in a while, by strong stimulation reaching above the threshold of its wall receptors.

The afferent component of the defecation reflex is associated with a special conscious sensation, "the desire to defecate." This characteristic indicates the exact moment at which the reflex commences, and aids in the physiologic timing of any therapeutic procedure.

According to the laws of conditioning of the nervous system, it is possible to establish almost any reflex at will, including that of defecation. Conditioning consists of subordinating acts and signals. In other words, if a neutral stimulus or signal is repeatedly applied a few seconds before the basic unconditioned stimulus which elicits a precise organic reaction, the initially neutral stimulus will finally replace the unconditioned stimulus and will *of itself* elicit the reaction. The reaction becomes conditioned to the neutral stimulus which will therefore be called a conditioned stimulus. Almost any stimulus, suitably employed, may become a conditioned stimulus, viz. internal or external afferent impulses, the conscious or physiological notion of time or even the disappearance of a stimulus.

Conditioned reflexes may be simple or chain-like, with overlapping of one reflex with the other, since the acquired conditional quality may be transferred from one stimulus to the next, giving rise to conditioning of the 1st, 2nd, 3rd order and so forth. This process is known by Soviet scientists as summation.

The conditioned reflex depends for its appearance on the formation of new functional connections in the central nervous system in accordance with precise laws, of which the following are of interest to us:

(a) For a conditioned stimulus to retain its new properties, it should be reinforced periodically by following it with the basic unconditioned stimulus.

(b) A conditioned stimulus repeated without reinforcement will, after a variable interval of time, lead to weakening and, finally, extinction of the conditioned reflex. However, extinction is never complete because the pathway will always remain.

(c) Under similar experimental conditions, visceral conditioned responses develop more rapidly and are more lasting than responses conditioned within other systems. This phenomenon is attributed to the functional differences existing between the corresponding visceral or cortical sensory areas of the brain. Recording the action potentials evoked by sensory stimulation of both areas shows that, in the former, the potential persists much longer even after cessation of the stimulation.

(d) Though all sensory stimuli reach the cerebral cortex few are retained, the rest are ignored. It can therefore be assumed that, in the same manner, selection is made from different stimuli sharing the same sensory field. This capacity to make a selection is a function of the affect, and the process which leads to it is called motivation. The totality of motivations ranges in intensity from the very instinctive act to the highest intellectual activity. Instinctive behavior is produced by an essential "primitive" affective stimulus; and the more behavior becomes emotionally-free, i.e., intellectualized, the less pronounced becomes the participation of the affective quality. Nevertheless, all mental acts comprise an affective component; the more marked this component is, viz. motivation, the more rapid and lasting the conditioning will be. In other words, the more emotionally charged is the material to be learned, the more the learning process is effective.

The neurophysiological basis for the above is as follows:

It is known that the same association areas and fibres in the frontal lobes permit the transmission and spread of the emotional charge to the corresponding areas in the brain with which they are functionally synergistic. Therefore, the frontal lobes produce a certain "quantum" of energy comprising an intellectual and an affective component, the ratio of which will depend on the functional associations engaged at the moment of production of this energy.

There exist two pathways for the reflexion of the cortico-subcortical afferents. The first is essentially cortico-thalamic; a given sensory stimulation takes place through intra-cortical associations, produced by the impulses received through the diffuse thalamic system. This implies very little, if any, of a vegetative, affective or "primitive" type of response. The second is more complex; in addition to the preceding pattern we have the regions that play a paramount role in the emotional life, namely, the limbic system. This system, apart from the functional characteristics mentioned above, is closely related to the hypothalamus and, through it, to the neurovegetative expressions of affectivity, its primitive or instinctive aspects. This implies also the participation of the reticular alerting system which brings about the massive intervention of *cortical activity*. When stimulated, the activating effect of both the hypothalamus and the reticular formation is so great that the reappearance of the extinguished conditioned reflexes could be brought about without further reinforcement and sometimes could even be sustained several months.

(e) Finally, there is the role played by electric stimulation in methods of training. According to certain authors, the most minor electric shock serves as a necessary reinforcement for obtaining rapid and durable associations. The mechanism by which this phenomenon is produced is yet unknown. It may be due either to the emotional charge contained in the defense reflex provoked by the shock, or to an inherent power in the electricity itself. The only evidence available in this respect is from the experiments of Vinogradova and Sokolov who demonstrated that the response evoked by a new stimulus differs from that produced by the same stimulus associated with an electric shock.

Re-education of the Mechanism of Defecation Using the Laws of Conditioning

Because of an awareness of the act of defecation, the subject is conscious of the moment at which the defecation reflex is set up. The stimulus that elicits this reflex is the passage of the fecal mass through the pelvi-rectal flexure or, in the case of chronically constipated subjects, the stimulation of the wall of the rectum. We are going to designate this stimulation the absolute or unconditioned stimulus and we will associate with it a signal or conditioned stimulus.

Since defecation is accompanied by a mass reflex in the colon, associating the conditioned stimulus with the sensation of defecation will also mean associating the colic reflex with the conditioned stimulus. Repetition of the conditioned stimulus in association with the unconditioned stimulus would make it possible, after a certain period of time, for the former alone to elicit not only the defecation mechanism but also the accompanying reflex colonic contractions.

The conditioned stimulus should have a slight affective quality and, if possible, be of a pleasant nature lest sympathetic reactions interfere with the elicited processes. It is also thought useful to utilize electrical means of stimulation because of the empirical importance of this modality in conditioning.

The apparatus used (Fig. 1) is transistorized and generates a current modifiable so as to provoke a sensation which is almost pleasant. The subject is stimulated by two electrodes which are applied on each side of the lumbar spine and secured on the abdomen by a strap (Fig. 2). The apparatus is visible to the subject and has a switch which permits him to change the intensity of stimulation at will. In practice, individual differences in sensitivity and resistance of the skin are very wide.

The subject to be re-educated continues to take his usual laxatives so as to produce one bowel movement per day. As he goes to the toilet he puts on the apparatus, starts operating it prior to defecation and stops the electric stimulation as soon as his evacuation is terminated. Should the desire continue, and should evacuation reoccur while still on the toilet, stimulation should be resumed each time. Since the characteristics of the stimulation maintain an affective state that we may call "pre-emotional awakening," it is very important that the subject thinks of the association taking place within him. An association is thus facilitated between the conditioned stimulus and the evacuation reflex.

Gradually the subject should reduce the quantity of laxatives until eventually he will no longer take any and will go to the toilet even without having the desire to defecate. Once conditioning has been established, which generally happens after 20 to 30 applications, the electrical stimulation alone produces defecation according to the individual rhythm of digestion.

The second step is for the subject to utilize the principle of vertical synthesis, going to the toilet every day at a given hour (preferably after breakfast in order to benefit from the morning gastro-colic response). Thus, one gets conditioning of the second order, the chosen hour becomes the conditioned stimulus and finally the patient can dispense with the apparatus altogether.

It is advisable in periods of nervous or physical stress to reinforce the reflex by resuming the use of the apparatus for a few days. In principle, a normally developed subject can practice his own re-education with-

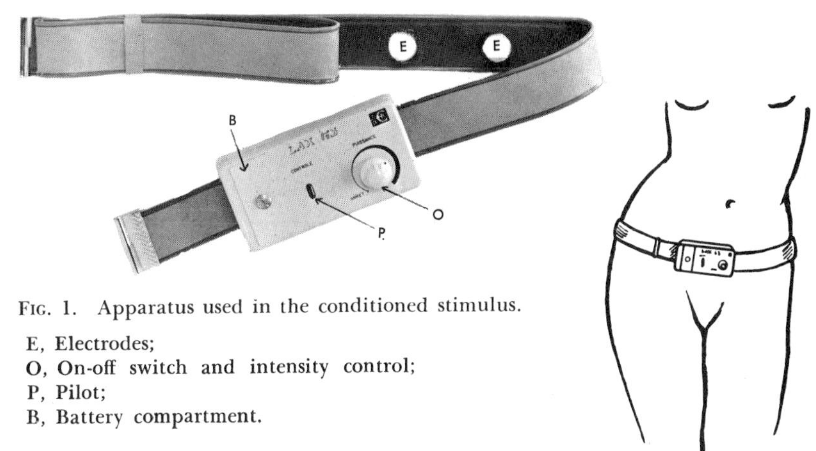

FIG. 1. Apparatus used in the conditioned stimulus.

E, Electrodes;
O, On-off switch and intensity control;
P, Pilot;
B, Battery compartment.

FIG. 2. Position of the apparatus in use.

out special guidance; in practice it is preferable that the overall management be the responsibility of the treating physician. The physician is best able to assess progress, supervise the tapering off of laxatives and determine the moment when re-education has been accomplished.

The following are three illustrative case reports:

Case 1

An unconstipated subject used as a control. The object of this experiment is to demonstrate the instigation of defecation by electric stimulation in a healthy woman of 38 years. Her intestinal passage was normal apart from ordinary irregularities and transitory periods of constipation which had never necessitated the use of laxatives. During the first ten applications daily evacuations took place at all times, though never in the morning. On the morning of the eleventh day, as the subject was manipulating the apparatus to prepare the electrodes, she was suddenly seized by quite intense tenesmus and straining. The feeling was not distinct enough to lead her to the toilet, but a feeling of heaviness and of intestinal movements persisted until her attention was diverted by another activity.

From the 20th day the subject decided to try one application without having any desire to defecate, in the morning and on an empty stomach. The preliminary operations (preparation of the saline solution to moisten the electrodes, fixing the belt, and so forth) were sufficient to trigger a pressing need, followed by normal defecation. After twelve days the subject had conditioned herself to evacuate at a fixed hour. A few days later, the process of vertical synthesis having been extended, seeing the apparatus, or even hearing or pronouncing its name, would be sufficient to elicit the sensation of the need to defecate. Naturally, her voluntary inhibition could control these phenomena, which we point out here only for their physiological importance. It should be noted that the technique was also effective during her periods of transitory constipation.

Case 2

M.M., a young woman of 34 years, suffering from dysmenorrhea and migraine, of a nervous temperament but otherwise quite balanced. Occasional periods of constipation appeared to be principally related to her mode of living, her menstrual cycle and her emotional state. She did not go spontaneously to the toilet except when her daily life imposed on her a physical and nervous hyperactivity. This occurred at a regular rate of three to four times per week.

During this period of conditioning she could, thanks to nightly laxatives, evacuate, on the average, of once every two days. After a week, a sort of "reverse" conditioning took place, the apparatus becoming indispensable to her. On the one hand, in spite of her absent-mindedness, she would never leave it at home when she went out all day; on the other hand, should she feel the need to go to the toilet under circumstances that made it impossible to use the apparatus, this circumstance would immediately cut off the need.

After 21 days, either seeing the instrument or just talking about it would make her feel some intestinal movements, but without distinctive need. On the 26th day, following a bulky movement on the previous day, we advised her to try the method without feeling the need to defecate. She had some mild abdominal pains, passed a great deal of flatus and experienced a sensation of "evacuation" but no bowel movement.

The following day a very positive result ensued without any desire to defecate. She described the event as follows: . . . "after about thirty seconds of electric stimulation, without any effort on my behalf, and without preliminary sensations of any sort, defecation happened precipitously." Since then positive results were obtained each day.

Case 3

M.R., a woman of 36 years, suffering since she was 30 from hepatic insufficiency which severely restricted her diet and intake of laxatives and certain other medicines. Moreover, she had megacolon. She managed to go to the toilet about twice per week through the effects of mucilages. Being a simple-minded woman, she could not relate to us precise physical or psychic phenomena other than the fact that, after only eight days, she had already cut down by half the dose of laxatives necessary for a normal evacuation. To avoid irregularity in the progress of the treatment we waited 30 days before encouraging her to go to the toilet and administer the stimulation without a desire to defecate. She had had her mucilage the previous evening. The result was very positive.

Later, among the trials with or without laxative, some failed and some succeeded. The ultimate result of all these more or less successful trials was that the patient was able to go regularly to the toilet three or four times per week, without laxatives but always with the apparatus. For reasons which could not be readily ascertained it was not possible to establish second order conditioning in her case.

Conclusion

We have thus demonstrated that the principles of conditioning may be practically applied in the treatment of constipation. Bowel evacuation represents but one among the many activities of the human organism which can be conditioned. In man, such conditioning is easily brought about without a complicated apparatus. The present method is of significance for several reasons: it is convenient, easy and simple; the principle of "visceral re-education" may be extended to a wide variety of other diseases of a largely functional nature; it helps us to understand some of the mechanisms which govern our physiological existence. Finally, it is suggested that the general approach represents a most important medical attitude: confidence in the mechanisms of re-adaptation and in the fundamental tendency to revert to normal functioning that is inherent in every living organism.

PART VI

OPERANT TECHNIQUES

It is only during the past decade or so that the vast body of accumulated knowledge about the operant behavior of animals has been applied systematically to the study of man. Unquestionably the most recognized technique is Skinner's *free operant conditioning* and it is this method, along with its various elaborations and applications, which is the subject of this section. Free operant conditioning provides a continuous, precise, objective and sensitive way of obtaining data which are readily amenable to quantification and analysis. The method can be easily adapted to the needs of the particular subject; with children or mental defectives the incentive can be pennies or candy, with certain adults tobacco or credit-chips may be preferable.

Because free operant conditioning closely approximates the free and adjustive behavior of individuals in their natural habits, the method is of special value in the investigation of human social behavior, but more sophisticated rewards need to be offered in this case. Some social reinforcers, such as music, lose much of their reinforcing value if broken up into segments or reward units. The sight of a hungry kitten drinking milk was therefore introduced by Lindsley as an effective reward for desirable response on the part of the experimental subject.

The range of clinical problems that have been studied by the method of free operant conditioning is remarkable. These include: the experimental investigation and operant control of stuttering; the provision of a valid record and indicator of the duration and pattern of behavioral recovery from electroshock therapy and from surgical anesthesia; the production and study of organized behavior during sleep; and the study of vegetative human organisms at the idiot level. This technique is ideal for the measurement of psychopharmacological responses or the study of drug effects in animals and man. Specially developed cribs and units are available for the study of exploratory and other forms of behavior in babies and small children. The free operant method has even been applied to the measurement and prediction of consumer response to advertising as reflected in the subject's viewing and other behavior.

In the first two papers Lindsley and Ferster show how the technique may be applied to the study and modification of behavior in chronic psychotics and children respectively. Ferster develops Skinner's notions about the use of generalized reinforcers and applies them in an analysis of the effects of positive reinforcements upon autistic children. In the third paper Ayllon and Michael present a bold plan whereby the psychiatric nurse can be trained to apply these behavioral principles.

These techniques are increasingly being applied to the therapeutic modification of behavior. In one study, Ayllon and Haughton* showed how their method of behavioral engineering might be successfully applied to the therapeutic control of schizophrenic patients, using food as the reinforcing agent. There are many such examples in the literature of chronic psychotic patients being retrained by some form of operant conditioning. The earlier studies tended to focus on motor operant procedures; the more recent emphasis has been upon the use of verbal operant procedures. It is hoped that, by reinstating or strengthening the desired behavior, the disturbed patient will be brought into more constructive contact with reality.

Just as the differences between the approaches of the behavior therapist and the psychodynamic psychotherapist should not be regarded merely as a matter of semantics, so it is important to recognize that verbal conditioning studies which attempt to modify behavior in some systematic manner are not to be regarded as mere analogues of psychotherapy. The recent emphasis upon psychotherapy as an exercise in reinforcement schedules is of value only if this distinction is kept in mind.

In the final two papers Brady and Lind show how it is possible to analyze hysterical blindness experimentally by means of operant techniques, and Barrett applies a similar method to the therapeutic control of severe multiple tics in a patient who had been unable to obtain relief for this distressing symptom by psychotherapy or medication.

* Ayllon, T., and Haughton, E. Control of the behavior of schizophrenic patients by food. *J. exper. Anal. Behav.,* 1962, *5:* 343-352.

21

CHARACTERISTICS OF THE BEHAVIOR OF CHRONIC PSYCHOTICS AS REVEALED BY FREE-OPERANT CONDITIONING METHODS

by Ogden R. Lindsley, Ph.D.

During the last sixty years experimental psychology has made great progress in objective behavioral measurement. The most sensitive, objective, and sophisticated of these methodological developments are those of B. F. Skinner and his associates (3, 12, 15). These methods are generally described under the term "free-operant conditioning." The purpose of this research is to attempt to modify and make clinically relevant the methods of free-operant conditioning in order to produce medically useful, objective laboratory measures of the psychoses.

Behavioristic Approach to Psychosis

The general approach to the analysis of psychosis that we are using is behavioristic. Naturalistic or behavioristic approaches to mental illness are rare in psychiatry today, even though the word "behavioral" occurs in many titles and programs. The behaviorist uses behavior as the final criterion of behavior and does not resort to mentalism or physiologism as his final criterion of knowledge or relevance.

At earlier times, naturalistic approaches (2) were briefly tried by men like Kraepelin (5), Pavlov (10), and even earlier by our own Benjamin Rush (11). It is my conviction that early attempts at a behavioristic approach to psychiatry suffered from a lack of popular appeal and sound laboratory techniques of behavioral measurement. I am also convinced that today, even though the approach still suffers from popular appeal, methods which demonstrate its superiority over introspective approaches are available.

Skinner (13, 14) and Ferster (4) have discussed some of the implications of a behavioral approach to psychiatric problems. However, with-

---

Reprinted with permission from *Diseases of the Nervous System,* Monograph Supplement, Vol. XXI, No. 2, Feb. 1960.

out objective data such discussions are at best scientific extrapolations, plans or philosophies. The proof of the pudding is not the logical nature of the plans, but the knowledge and control of behavioral deviation produced by research based upon such plans.

To a behaviorist a psychotic is a person in a mental hospital. If psychosis is what makes, or has made this person psychotic, then psychosis is the behavioral deviation that caused this person to be hospitalized, or that is keeping him hospitalized. Looked at from this point of view, very few psychotics are at this moment behaving psychotically. Neither is there any assurance that they will behave psychotically when we wish to evaluate or to sample their behavior in a brief test conducted at irregular intervals. In fact psychosis, defined in terms of the behavior that hospitalizes a person, is most often highly infrequent.

Most patients are hospitalized because the time of occurrence of their infrequent psychotic episodes cannot be predicted. Since the occurrence of these episodes cannot be predicted, the patient must be continuously hospitalized to insure that such episodes do not occur outside of the hospital. Also, many currently hospitalized patients behave psychotically only when they go home. Even though relatively normal in the hospital, they continue to be hospitalized because there is no safe place to send them. There are other patients who once behaved psychotically, but have become institutionalized and do not wish to leave the hospital, and still others who have no home to return to. For these reasons we should not expect all the patients in a mental hospital to exhibit psychotic behavior at any given moment.

Therefore, a few patients should behave relatively normally on all behavioral tasks. In fact, any behavioral measure that clearly separates all hospitalized psychotics from all unhospitalized individuals is merely a correlate of hospitalization and no better a measure of psychosis than the absence of hospital keys, neckties, or some other side effect of the way we care for psychotics.

If we wish to maximize our chances of measuring psychosis, we should evaluate the behavior of patients at the time they are actually doing what they are hospitalized for occasionally doing. This means that we should study our patients long enough to capture a psychotic episode in one of our experimental observation sessions. For, at that moment we would be surely measuring the behavior of a psychotic at the time he is behaving psychotically. This demands that our experimental rooms and recording devices must be indestructible, so that they will not be rendered inoperative by the bizarre behavior of any patient when he has a psychotic episode. Very few of the previously used measurement devices are capable of measuring the behavior of patients while they are behaving maximally psychotic. In this sense the earlier devices are extremely limited.

Selection of Patients and Habitat

If we wish to investigate a new phenomenon we should select the ideal conditions for observing it. We should maximize its amplitude and frequency of occurrence and minimize any changes in these properties, whether spontaneous or caused by agents other than those we can manipulate for investigational purposes. This means that the acutely ill psychotic is a poor research risk. For there is a high probability that his psychosis will change in degree or type while we are endeavoring to analyze it. Also, the natural habitat of the acute psychotic is a dynamic environment in which therapy is maximized and research design usually destroyed. The admissions unit is a model of confounded, rather than isolated and controlled behavioral variables.

However, the chronic psychotic has a maximized form of psychosis and the lowest probability of spontaneously changing during the course of study. Also, the chronic psychotic's natural habitat (the back wards of large state hospitals), although far from the research ideal of full experimental control, more closely approximates this research ideal of full control than does an admissions ward. Moving chronic patients to admissions units or research wards, takes them from their natural habitat which reduces the probability that their psychosis will remain stable, and places them in an environment full of uncontrolled behavioral variables.

Therefore, in order to maximize our phenomenon and its stability we select a group of approximately 50 chronic psychotics for intensive investigation, who would continue to live on the back wards in their natural habitat. They were hospitalized a median of 18 years, insuring that their behavioral deviations were maximum and stable. Males were selected to eliminate any behavioral fluctuations that might be correlated with menstrual cycles. Patients were selected independently of psychiatric diagnosis in order to eliminate any theoretical bias, and to approach our subject matter with a maximized degree of freedom, limited only by our methods of observation and creative ability in adopting the methods to the measurement of clinically relevant behaviors. The clinical relevance was sought in clinical practice and experience, rather than in formal theory or diagnosis.

Research Design

The research design is frankly Darwinian rather than Newtonian. It is our feeling that there is not enough experimental data on the behavior of psychotics in finely controlled situations to draw exact and meaningful generalizations at this time. Since the behavioral properties of psychosis are highly individual, each experiment must be conducted in such a fashion that each patient serves as his own control. We must not have to resort to the behavior of any other individual in order to determine the significance of the effects of any agent upon the behavior of our experimental subject.

The experimental observations are conducted in continuous experimental sessions of one or more hours duration each week-day, until we have exhausted our ability to obtain further important experimental information concerning the behavioral abilities and symptoms in a given patient. Although psychosis is clinically known as an oscillating, dynamic process, and patients are clinically known to be timid, afraid and nervous in novel situations, the majority of previous experimental studies of psychosis have investigated psychotics in novel situations. It is important to remember that we often evaluate a psychotic in 15 minutes, a secretary in one month, and an executive in one year. It seems to me that we might do better by reversing this order—at least until we develop reliable and exact methods of evaluation.

In our own research, we have found that the behavior of many psychotics is modifiable by manipulating properties of the immediate physical environment. However, their behavior is so slowly modified that experimental manipulation and observation must be continued over a period of years in order to disclose such slowly developing laws of psychotic behavior. Shorter periods of observation would show no lawful modification in the patient's behavior, and lead us to conclude that it was not modifiable, and the law of psychotic behavior would remain hidden.

Intensive investigation of single psychotics is the only way that a number of different behavioral deficits may be catalogued with respect to individual psychotics in attempts to locate and define syndromes of behavioral deficits which could define sub-types of psychosis.

Then again the currently used therapeutic variables (tranquilizing drugs, insulin, and psychotherapy) appear to take weeks, months and even years to reach their maximum effect. Experiments must be conducted over a period of years in order to provide a continuous measure of the effects of such variables on the behavior of individual patients. This intensive and continuous study of single individuals also permits a comparison of the effects of several different therapeutic agents upon the same individual as the experimental case history grows. I know of no other way to adequately control for placebo effects without confounding the results with individual variability in reaction.

Apparatus and Techniques

The theoretical and historical background and the modifications of the method of free-operant conditioning for use with chronic psychotics, including its advantages and disadvantages have been discussed elsewhere (6, 16). In brief, a volunteer patient is conducted, or conditioned to approach a small six-foot square experimental room. Such a room is shown in Fig. 1. In this room there is only a chair and a manipulandum panel on one wall. On the panel is a plunger that can be pulled and a small aperture through which small objects can be automatically presented. Such a controlled environment can be used to measure the simplest operant or "volitional" behavior known—pulling a plunger for an unconditioned reinforcement or reward.

However, by manipulating the objects or events used as reinforcers, a wide variety of different motivations or "interests" can be studied (7). By manipulating the contingencies of these reinforcers upon the plunger-pulling responses, a wide variety of discriminations and other behavioral processes can be studied. For example, with such a simple experimental environment, motivations ranging from food to social altruism, and discriminations ranging from simple visual to time estimation and complicated concept formation can be studied (8).

By permitting visual communication between such rooms (opening windows as shown at the sides of the room in Fig. 1), social interaction from the most primitive facilitation and imitation to complicated leader-follower relationships in cooperation and competition teams can be controlled and objectively measured (1).

By changing the form of the manipulandum or plunger, a wide variety of different response topographies ranging from simple manual to complex vocal responses can be studied. If the manipulandum is carefully designed, peripheral response properties (fatigue, frequency limitation, etc.) can be overcome and will not confound the interpretation of the data.

By making intelligent and creative changes of the types described above, and making these one at a time so that variables are not confounded, the method of free-operant conditioning can be modified to the objective and exact measurement of behaviors as clinically relevant as vocal hallucinatory symptoms in chronic psychotics.

Behavioral Records

Since the response recorded by the operation of the manipulandum is free to occur at any moment during the experimental session, maximum information is obtained if responses are recorded as they occur in time. Graphs of the distribution of the responses in time are automatically made on cumulative response recorders. The operation of such a recorder is schematically shown in Fig. 2. The paper is driven under the pen at a constant rate. The pen makes one small movement up the paper when each response is made. In this way a graph of cumulated responses plotted against time is automatically produced. The slope of the pen tracing gives an index of the rate of response. If the slope is almost vertical, the rate is high and even. If the slope is horizontal, no responses were made. Events, such as the presentation of reinforcements can be marked on the record by a downward deflection of the pen. After 500 responses have been made, the pen is auto-

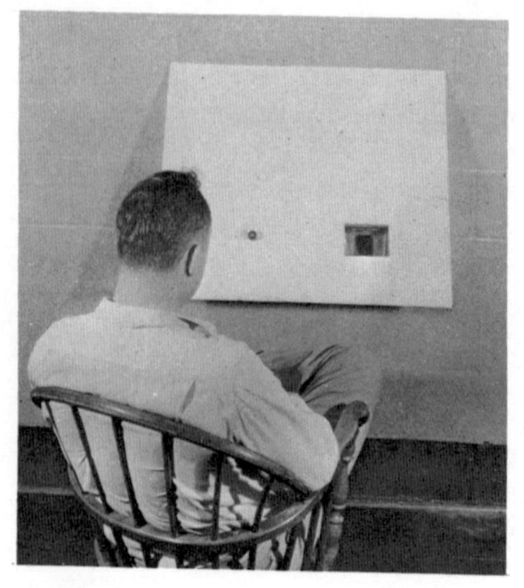

FIG. 1. An experimental enclosure for the free-operant conditioning of chronic psychotics. The room is indestructible and designed to measure the behavior of even extremely disturbed patients while they are engaging in psychotic episodes. Any small physical object can be automatically presented through the aperture on the right as a reinforcement for pulling the carefully designed plunger on the left. The windows at the side can be made transparent for the study of social interaction with patients in adjoining rooms.

matically reset from the top to the bottom of the paper where it is ready to draw another segment of a cumulative response record.

Clinical records of the patients' behavior on the wards and in psychiatric and psychological evaluations are periodically made in the usual manner. Also, the patients can be observed within the experimental rooms through a hidden periscopic system. Important changes in their symptoms and other demeanor are written down and used for correlation with the operant response records. The non-operant records are useful in making plans for developing new manipulanda to bring clinically relevant response topographies out on an electrical switch for automatic recording and programming. The non-operant records are also useful for correlation with the operant records in demonstrations of the validity and meaning of the operant data.

Characteristics of the Operant Behavior of Chronic Psychotics

The first and most striking characteristic of the free-operant behavior of chronic psychotics is the extreme degree of behavioral debilitation found in the majority of patients. For example, approximately 90% of the patients are unable to respond normally in the simple situation shown in Fig. 1. Also surprising is the unpredictability of the patients' operant ability from observations of the patients' ward behavior and general appearance. Remember, that we are talking here of dynamic behavioral ability—the ability to develop and to maintain new behavioral repertories, as distinguished from the behavioral repertoire that a patient may have acquired before he became ill.

For example, Patient No. 48, shown in Fig. 3 has a much greater current behavioral repertoire, but a much lower current behavioral modifiability than Patient No. 46, shown in Fig. 4. The first patient was an acute depressive and now is a chronic schizophrenic with an

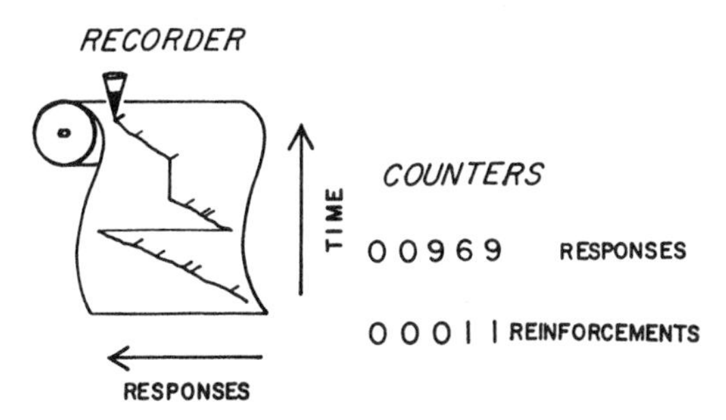

FIG. 2. Schematic diagram of operation of a cumulative response recorder. Described in text.

operant response rate (candy reinforcement on a 1'VI schedule) of zero responses per hour. The second patient has always been a psychotic idiot, but he now has an operant response rate of over 1,000 responses per hour and he can form primitive counting discriminations. Both patients are currently untestable by psychometric procedures.

Low, Erratic Operant Response Rates

Normal humans and lower organisms respond at moderately high (above 800 responses per hour) and remarkably even rates of response on variable-interval schedules of reinforcement. Fig. 5 shows six records of normal humans responding on that schedule for five-cent coins as reinforcers. Note that although reliable individual differences in rate of response exist, all the rates are above 800 responses per hour and are relatively even. These reliable individual differences in rate of response have not been extensively studied, and could probably be related to personality differences in preferences for certain work tempos. Perhaps they might even be related to accident proneness, with the high rate person going through doors before he opened them, and the low rate person going through doors after he had closed them.

Fig. 6 shows six records of chronic psychotics responding on the variable-interval schedule for candy reinforcement. Note that the majority of the patients respond intermittently. Approximately 50% of those patients with a normally high number of responses per hour show an abnormally high number of pauses in responding greater than ten seconds. During these pauses patients that have readily observable psychotic symptoms can be observed displaying these symptoms.

Summarizing the debilities in simple operant responding on a one-minute variable interval schedule of intermittent reinforcement with candy, we find that only 20% of our unselected group of 50 chronic psychotics are capable of responding at the normal rates above 800 responses per hour; 50% of these, or only 10% of the total group of patients responded at normally high and even rates of response, with no pauses in their responding greater than 10 seconds in duration.

FIG. 3. Patient No. 48, an acute depressive, who has recently been rediagnosed schizophrenic. He has been hospitalized during the last six of his 42 years and is currently untestable by psychometric techniques. His operant response rate is zero, but his repertoire of personal and social behavior is relatively high.

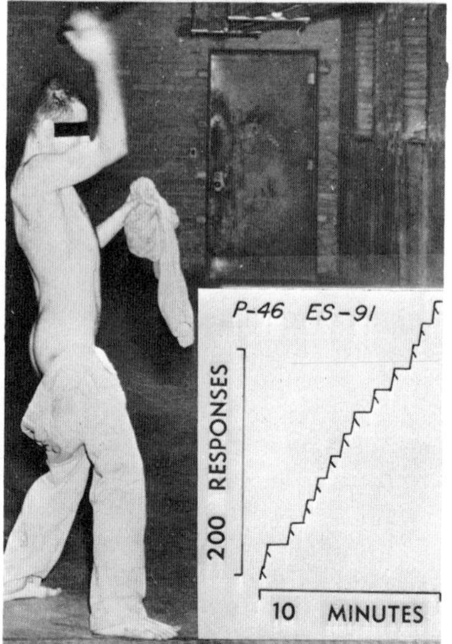

FIG. 4. Patient No. 46, a psychotic idiot, who has been hospitalized for 24 of his 29 years. He is currently untestable by psychometric methods, but has an operant response rate of 1,000 responses per hour and primitive ability to form simple discriminations. He has almost no socially appropriate behavior.

Psychotic Incidents

We have termed these small pauses in responding on a schedule of reinforcement which produces even responding in normals, "psychotic incidents." They have been successfully quantified by using, 1) automatic counters which record the total number of inter-response times

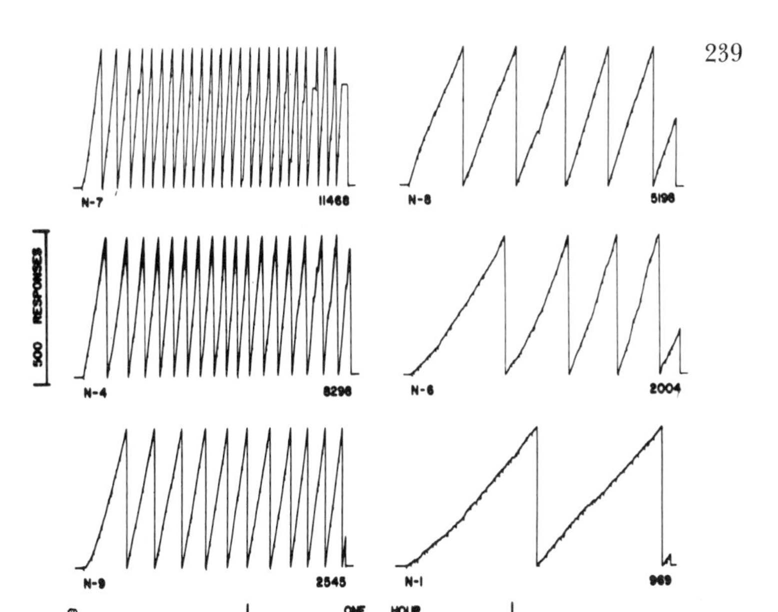

Fig. 5. Cumulative response records for six unhospitalized normal adults, responding on a one-minute variable-interval schedule of intermittent reinforcement with five-cent coins. Each record is of the fifth hour of responding on this schedule. Under each record is printed the number of the subject on the left, and on the right the number of responses made during the hour.

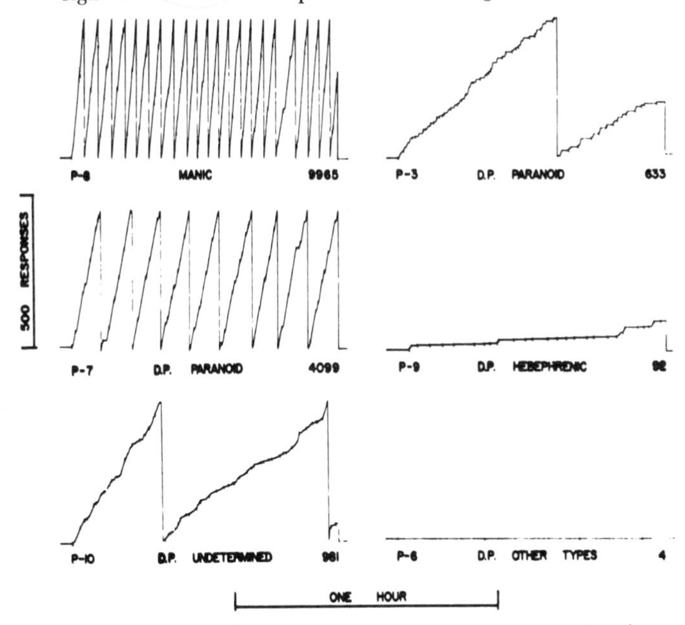

Fig. 6. Cumulative response records for six hospitalized adult chronic psychotics, responding on a one-minute variable-interval schedule of intermittent reinforcement for small assorted pieces of candy. Each record is of the fifth hour of responding on this schedule. Under each record is printed the number of each patient to the left, the most recent psychiatric diagnosis, and to the right the number of responses made during the hour.

greater than ten seconds that occur in each experimental session, and 2) automatic time indicators which record the total amount of time spent in inter-response times greater than ten seconds. These two quantities give a record of the number and total duration of psychotic incidents within a given experimental session. The average duration can be computed from the two. These measures correlate highly with clinical measures of ward behavior, and ward assignment, and with the ability to work in hospital industry (9). However, they do not correlate with psychiatric diagnosis nor with years of hospitalization. Therefore they indicate the general degree of psychosis or psychotic debilitation rather than the presence of a particular form of psychosis from which a given patient suffers. In other words, these measures have the disadvantage of being non-specific measures of the different types of psychosis, but the distinct advantage of permitting a direct comparison of the effects of a given therapy on the severity of psychosis in several different patients with different types of psychosis. Therefore, the measures are useful in the evaluation of therapies on patients with different types of psychosis, once non-psychotic causes of intermittent responding have been ruled out.

Since low, erratic rates of response on variable-interval schedules occur in non-psychotic individuals under certain unusual conditions, erratic response rates do not indicate psychosis unless these other potential causes are ruled out. Low, erratic response rates occur in normal individuals when: 1) inappropriate reinforcement is used, 2) before the response is fully acquired and the experimental situation is still novel, 3) when a competing response system is present, and 4) in acute physiological illness or under the action of certain drugs. These are a difficult, but not impossible, set of variables to rule out in order to make our measures specific to the psychoses.

In order to further investigate and to rule out the *possibility of inappropriate reinforcement,* several different reinforcing stimuli were tried with a large number of patients (7). Reinforcers used were: money, food, candy, cigarettes, male and female nude pictures, bursts of music, tokens, escape from loud noise, and escape from a dark room. Although significant differences in rate response for these different reinforcers were found in most of the patients, no patient was restored to a normal rate of responding by any of these reinforcers. The different reinforcers could be used to develop motivation profiles for diagnostic use, but were not useful in providing high, even rates of response for the maintenance of behavior for further investigation. Therefore, the low rates of response did not appear to be due to inappropriate reinforcement.

To investigate the *possibility of slow acquisition* causing the low, erratic rates of response, patients with extremely low rates were held on the variable-interval schedule with candy reinforcement for over a year of one hour experimental sessions each week-day. Only three of these patients (approximately 10%) showed a gradual increase in rate of response. The experimental history of one of these patients is shown in Fig. 7. Responses per hour are plotted in thousands (10-day medians) against experimental sessions on the abscissa. The rate of response gradually increased from less than 10 responses per hour to over 6,000 responses per hour in 260 hours, or 14 months. When the response was no longer reinforced (extinguished), it slowly declined in rate to less than 10 responses per hour within 140 experimental hours, or 8 months of calendar time. This decrease in rate during extinction shows that the rate increase during reinforcement was produced and maintained by the candy reinforcement, and not by the patient's activation, visits to the laboratory, or personal attention in the waiting room and during the daily physical examination. When the responses were again reinforced, the rate immediately increased to over 4,000 responses per hour. This immediate re-acquisition showed that a permanent change had been made in the patients' behavior, and that he did not have to go through another long drawn-out re-acquisition process.

However, the patients that showed this slow acquisition did not develop completely normal rates of response. Even though their rates of response were well above the lowest normal rate of 800 responses per hour, their responding was still erratic with an abnormally high number of pauses greater than ten seconds in duration. These three patients differed from the majority of the patients that did not show slow acquisition because the manual plunger-pulling response mechanically competed with their psychotic symptoms which were primarily manual in nature. In other words, these data suggest that slow acquisition of a high rate of response is possible in some patients with candy reinforcement, if a non-symptomatic response is reinforced which *mechanically* competes with the patient's most characteristic motor symptom.

Since slow acquisition only occurs with a very small number of patients, it is more probably a form of restricted occupational therapy, rather than a general property of the behavior of chronic psychotics. Therefore, the possibility that the low rates of response of the majority of the patients were due to slow acquisition was ruled out.

Since each patient was in a finely controlled environment during each experimental session, the *possibility of a competing response system* as normally conceived can be ruled out as a cause of the pauses in responding or psychotic incidents. The records of the non-psychotic individuals shown in Fig. 5, attest to the fact that no stimuli were present in the rooms which would produce competing responses in non-psychotic individuals. However, our more recent analyses strongly suggest that many forms of psychosis act as a competing response system does on the free-operant behavior of non-psychotics. In other words,

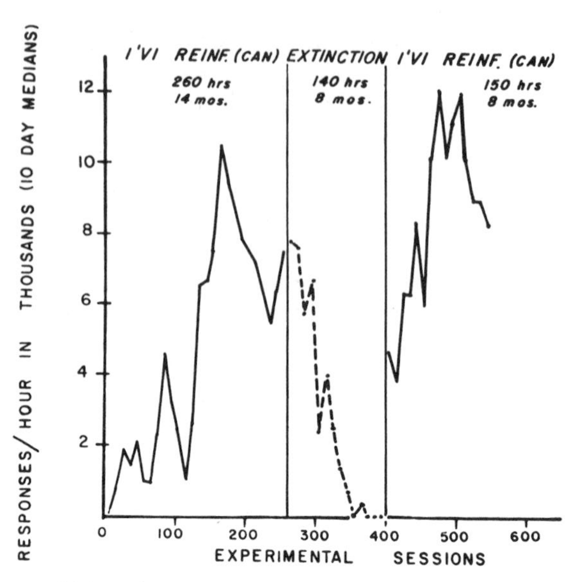

FIG. 7. Slow acquisition, slow extinction, and immediate re-acquisition of a high rate of plunger-pulling reinforced with candy on a 1' VI schedule in a chronic psychotic. Patient No. 36.

many psychotics behave similarly to non-psychotics who are being intermittently bombarded with behavioral stimuli.

Our physiological controls (the daily physical and weekly laboratory examinations) and therapeutic controls adequately rule out the *possibility that acute physiological illness and drug action* caused the pauses in responding. It is important to note that in careful behavioral investigation such physiological controls are absolutely necessary in order to attribute any recorded behavioral deviations to other causes.

Psychotic Episodes

Occasionally certain patients who usually respond at higher, more even rates of response, will have a period of very low, erratic responding which lasts for a period of 20 or 30 minutes up to several hours. During these periods of lowered response rate, they can be observed displaying hallucinatory, disturbed, destructive, or other more extremely psychotic symptoms than they usually display. Psychiatric aides usually say a patient "went high" when such episodes occur on the wards. It is the unpredictable occurrence of such episodes that keeps many chronic patients in the hospital, off parole, or on the disturbed ward.

Such periods of temporarily lowered response rate, and increased duration and/or frequency of psychotic incidents, we have termed *psychotic episodes.* Cumulative response records of a single psychotic incident, and a psychotic episode in the behavior of patient No. 7 are shown in Fig. 8. This figure will be described in more detail in a later section of this paper. Here, we wish only to point out that such psychotic episodes occur, and that they are the truly psychotic behavior which keeps many patients hospitalized, and that they can be automatically and objectively recorded. Some drugs, for example Benactyzine at high dosages, increase the frequency and duration of psychotic incidents and produce one of these psychotic episodes in many patients.

Psychotic Phases

In the intensive, longitudinal studies several of the patients showed marked rhythms in their rate of response. These rhythms characteristically occur over relatively long periods of time. For a few weeks the rate of response will be consistently high. Then, for a few weeks or months the rate will be consistently low. Then the rhythm will repeat. We have called these periods of low response rate *psychotic phases.* They are not related to temperature, humidity, phases of the moon, home visits, or changes in ward assignments or hospital social environment. They are related to ratings of the patients' ward behavior until the behavior rating scales lose their sensitivity as a result of repeated administration.

An example of these psychotic phases is shown in Fig. 9. At the start of the experiment the patient was hospitalized for 20 years and was 52 years old. He was first hospitalized at the age of 18 and diagnosed as a manic-depressive. The diagnosis at admission for his current period of hospitalization was dementia praecox, hebephrenic type. His last hospital diagnosis (in 1951) was schizophrenia, paranoid type. A current "blind" diagnosis was organic psychosis.

It is easy to see how long-term hospitalization and the loss of social reinforcement could suppress the socially observable behavior of a patient to such a low level that such behavioral rhythms, which were originally easily observed without instrumentation and used to diagnose a manic-depressive psychosis, could later only be recorded by sensitive, and highly quantified behavioral recording devices.

It is important to note the havoc that can be wrought by including such a patient in a drug evaluation study of the type that would run a 30-day placebo control while the patient happened to be in a psychotic phase, and a 30-day drug run when the patient was in his following more normal phase. The drug would be interpreted as therapeutic. It is also important to note that such patients could be of great value in attempts to show physiological or biochemical correlates of psychosis. For, here in a single physiological system we have a naturally oscillating

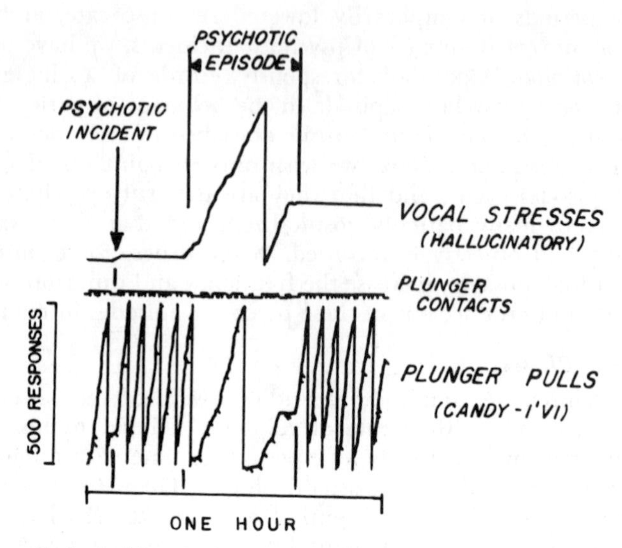

FIG. 8. A psychotic incident and episode appearing in simultaneous cumulative response records of vocal stresses with psychotic or hallucinatory origin and manual plunger-pulls reinforced with candy on a 1' VI schedule. Manual contacts with the plunger are recorded on the event marker between the cumulative records.

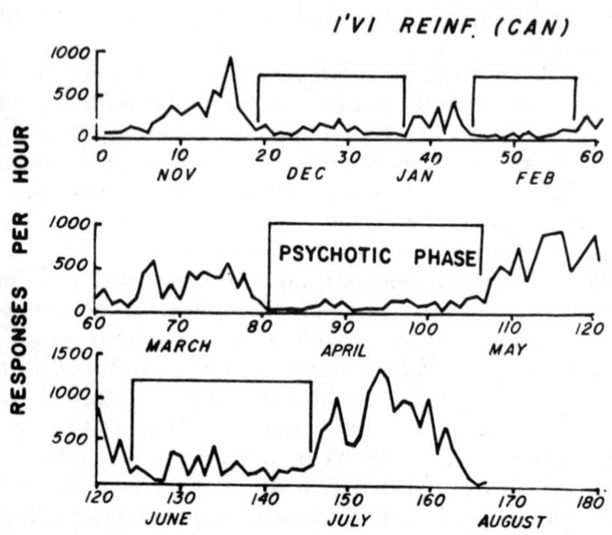

FIG. 9. Psychotic phases or rhythms in rate of response of a chronic psychotic responding on a 1' VI schedule of candy reinforcement. Each experimental session lasted one hour and was conducted on successive week-days. The months of the year are printed below the experimental session closest to the first of each month to indicate calendar time. Patient No. 52.

amount of psychosis, which could be correlated with samples of biochemical materials in order to determine correlations without confounding the data with inter-patient differences in behavior or chemical quantity.

Practical Use of Free-Operant Rate of Response in Therapeutic Evaluations

Although the simple free-operant rate of response on a variable-interval schedule is a non-specific laboratory measure of the degree of psychotic disability, nevertheless, it is more reliable and more sensitive to most therapeutic variables than other existing evaluative techniques. Here I shall present only a few examples of therapeutic evaluation. We have collected a large number of similar evaluations, which clearly demonstrate the practical utility of the method in its current form in this application.

Since we are methodologists, we will continue to refine and to develop more complicated and more exact measures of the psychoses. It is more efficient if large scale therapeutic evaluations using our currently available measures are undertaken by those trained and equipped for therapeutic evaluation. Like the lens maker in microscopy, we wish to hand our latest lens over to the histologist, and get back to our business of designing and polishing more powerful lenses.

Electroshock and Insulin Coma

In Fig. 10, the rates of response on a one-minute variable-interval schedule of reinforcement with candy (solid line) and feeding a kitten, or succor (dashed line) reinforcement are plotted against experimental sessions. The patient was in an acute psychotic depression and undergoing electroshock and insulin coma therapy. At the top of the graph the crosses mark the days in which EST was given in the morning before the afternoon experimental session. Note that the extremely low rate of response was not increased during the EST series.

At the vertical line, on the 32nd experimental session, the insulin treatment was begun. The number of units of crystalline insulin that were injected each day are plotted in the black curve at the top of the graph. Note that there was no increase in the operant response rate until the first coma occurred when the therapist levelled off the dosage of insulin. Note also, that the rate of response reinforced by feeding the kitten was increased much more than the rate reinforced with candy. This shows that the rate increase was not caused by a need for sugar increased by hypoglycemia, unless succor is also increased by hypoglycemia. The major therapeutic effect was produced by the first coma. The rate was also increased after the next ten insulin comas, but returned to the pretherapy level for the remainder of the treatment.

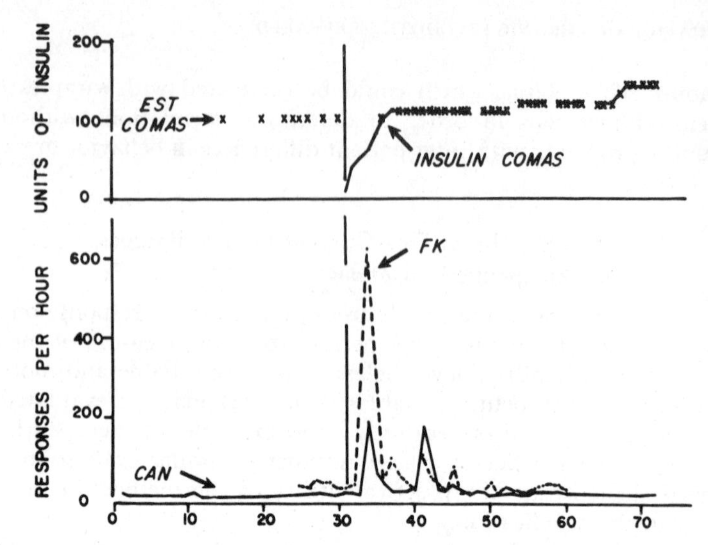

FIG. 10. Effect of electroshock and insulin comas on rate of response of an acute psychotic responding on a variable-interval schedule for candy (solid line) and for succor (feeding milk to a hungry kitten—dashed line). The electroshocks had no effect, and the insulin produced increases in the rate of response at the time of the first insulin reactions and comas. Patient No. PF-3.

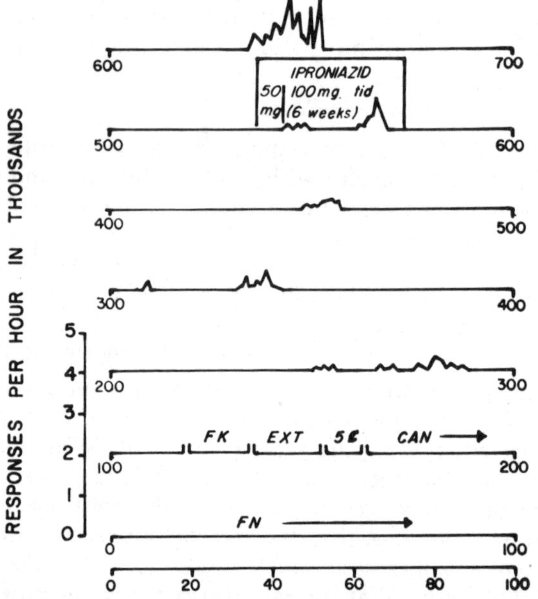

FIG. 11. Experimental history of a chronic psychotic responding on a variabl interval schedule for various reinforcers (FN—Female Nude Pictures, FK—Feedi a Hungry Kitten, EXT—Extinction, 5c—five cent coins, and CAN—penny pieces candy). The history covers a period of five years and seven months of almost dai experimentation and reveals severely depressed operant behavior with sever "spontaneous" recovery phases of extremely low magnitude in addition to an initi but not sustained, therapeutic effect of iproniazid medication. Patient No. P-

Monitoring courses of insulin therapy with operant response rates might prove to be useful in individualizing insulin treatment by providing an exact measure of the degree of therapy produced by each coma. The therapist would then have the information necessary to give the comas at intervals designed to produce the maximum therapeutic effect in each patient.

Iproniazid

In Fig. 11, the rates of response on a one-minute variable-interval schedule of reinforcement are plotted against experimental sessions for a regressed chronic psychotic, patient No. 4; 700 daily hour-long experimental sessions are shown in the graph. During the first 200 sessions, female nude pictures, feeding a kitten, five-cent coins and candy were used in attempts to determine the most appropriate reinforcer for this patient. From the 200th session on, candy was used as the reinforcer. Note periods of "spontaneous" increases in rate of response around the 250th, 280th, 310th, 340th, and 460th sessions.

On the 535th session 50 mg. t.i.d. of iproniazid (Marsilid) was administered for four weeks with no therapeutic effect. On the 545th session, the dosage was increased to 100 mg. t.i.d. and a slight rate increase was produced and sustained for a few days. However this increase was of no greater amplitude than the previously recorded "spontaneous" increases. About three weeks after the rate had declined, there was another temporary rate increase of a much greater magnitude than was found in any previous "spontaneous" increase. After six weeks of 100 mg. t.i.d. iproniazid administration liver damage began to develop and the medication was terminated.

From about the 640th through the 660th session another "spontaneous" rate increase occurred in which the rate went up to 1,500 responses per hour.

In summary, the iproniazid given in the heaviest dosages that were medically feasible, appeared to produce only two "recovery cycles" in this chronic patient. The recovery cycles are only significant because of their timing with respect to the change in dosage of the drug. In terms of therapeutic significance, the "recovery" is not significant, for it was not maintained during or after the drug administration, and it was of no greater magnitude than the several "spontaneous" improvement periods in the patient's experimental history.

Student-Nurse Psychotherapy

In Fig. 12, the experimental case history of patient No. 4 is continued. At the first arrow, psychotherapy sessions with a student nurse were begun. Psychotherapy sessions lasted one hour and they were held on Mondays, Wednesdays and Fridays. At the second arrow, the patient stopped swearing during the therapy sessions. The nurse became a

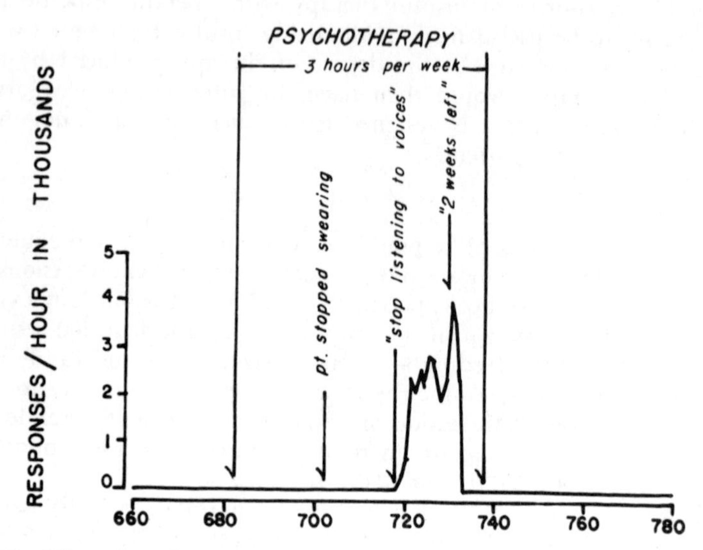

FIG. 12. Effect of psychotherapy sessions on operant rate of response of a chronic psychotic. The graph is a continuation of experimental history shown in Figure 11, using same size ordinate and abscissa scales. A student nurse conducted the one-hour therapy sessions three times a week. The effect of the psychotherapy was six times greater than that produced by 100 mg. t.i.d. iproniazid given for six weeks, and three times greater than the highest "spontaneous" improvement cycle in the patient's six-year experimental history. Patient No. P-4.

little irritated because the patient was inattentive and mumbled a lot during the therapy sessions. At the third arrow she told the patient to stop listening to his voices. "They are only part of your illness and you should not pay attention to them." By the third experimental session immediately following this therapeutic session the rate of response had climbed to over 2,000 responses per hour. Responding was maintained at this high rate, even on the two days of each week that the nurse did not see the patient.

At the fourth arrow, the nurse told the patient that after two weeks she could no longer see him. The rate of response jumped up about another 2,000 responses per hour immediately after this information was given the patient, and then abruptly fell to zero responses per hour. At the fifth arrow the nurse left the hospital and the therapy was terminated.

The rate increase which occurred during the psychotherapy was abrupt in onset and termination, in contrast to the gradually onsetting rate increases which were "spontaneously" and drug produced. This fact taken together with the close timing of the recovery with relevant psychotherapeutic variables, leaves little doubt that the recovery was produced by the nurse's visits. This was the highest rate of response emitted by the patient in over four years of daily experimental observation. Therefore, the effect has high statistical significance and cannot be attributed to chance. However, since the patient was by no means "normalized," and since the recovery was not maintained after termination of the therapy, the psychotherapeutic sessions had only a relatively weak and supportive effect. In this respect their therapeutic significance was relatively low, even though greater than that produced by iproniazid.

Nevertheless, quantified, objective measures of the effect of single psychotherapeutic sessions on the behavior of chronic psychotics are scarce, and this effect is highly significant from that point of view. In cooperation with Dr. Jack R. Ewalt we have plans to continue the investigations of psychotherapeutic effects using more highly trained therapists. The method shows promise as a device for accurately calibrating the effect of single therapeutic sessions. Such sensitive calibrations of the effects of single therapeutic sessions will permit the therapist to determine, by single manipulation which variables in the sessions were active. In this way a true experimental analysis of psychotherapy can be undertaken, and the functional aspects of psychotherapy can be proven by the methods of natural science in the laboratory.

In summary, three hours per week of psychotherapy conducted by a student nurse produced an increase in the rate of operant responding of this chronic psychotic that was three times that of any "spontaneous" improvement recorded in over three years of daily behavioral measurement, and that was six times the improvement produced by 100 mg. t.i.d. of iproniazid administered for six weeks.

Specific Characteristics of Psychotic Behavior

More complicated behavioral processes are debilitated by fewer agents than the rate of a simple operant response. For this reason debilities in these more complicated behaviors more specifically indicate the presence of psychosis and the type of psychosis than do debilities in the simple rate of response. However, in order to determine debilities in more complicated behavior, the scientist needs enough behavior to study. Only about 50% of the chronic patients have useful rates of response above 100 responses per hour, so specific debilities cannot be determined in the other 50% of the patients who are extremely debilitated.

Due to our lack of time, I will only briefly summarize the more complicated, and hence more specific behavioral characteristics of the psychoses that we have located to date. The majority of the patients have extremely slow extinction processes. We have located one patient in which there appears to be a complete lack of extinction. In counting discriminations as measured on fixed-ratio schedules of reinforcement, approximately 50% of the patients have deficits. In more complicated discriminations based upon differential responding to two manipulanda and two lights, 90% of the patients show deficits. These discriminatory deficits have diagnostic utility in separating seniles and true mental defectives from the social mental defectives.

Simultaneous Recording of Vocal Symptoms and Non-Symptomatic Responses

Visual observation of patients through the hidden periscopic viewing system has shown that most patients with abnormally long pauses in their operant responding engage in their particular individualistic symptoms during these pauses. The development of keys or switches to automatically and electrically record the occurrence of these symptoms would facilitate their further analysis.

Simultaneously recorded cumulative records of both the psychotic symptoms and the reinforced operant responses would permit an exact and objective analysis of their competition. Such simultaneous records would also permit an objective search for sympto-specific drugs which should decrease the frequency of symptoms without decreasing the frequency of reinforced operant, normal, or non-symptomatic behavior.

Also, the symptom key could be used to automatically schedule the presentation of environmental stimuli contingent upon the psychotic symptoms. The differential reinforcement of symptomatic responses would show whether they are or are not affected by environmental changes in the same way as are non-symptomatic responses.

In Fig. 8 simultaneously recorded cumulative records of vocal stresses and manual plunger-pulls are shown from the 747th experimental session with a chronic psychotic patient. The vocal responses were never experimentally reinforced and can be considered to have a psychotic origin. Their content was identical with that in the vocal behavior of the patient whenever he "went high" on the wards.

Patient No. 7 is male, 58 years old and he has been continuously hospitalized for 29 years. His experimental behavior has been under study for five years. Admitted in 1930 at the age of 29 he was diagnosed dementia praecox, paranoid type. The recent "blind" diagnoses were simple schizophrenia (by the clinical psychologist), and schizophrenia, mixed (by the psychiatrist). His recent Wechsler-Bellevue I.Q. was 60 and he scored in the 3rd percentile on the Hospital Adjustment Scale and lives on a locked ward. His personality picture is "that of a withdrawn, colorless patient who shows little evidence of acting-out and whose general defense is that of compulsivity in terms of wanting a fixed routine, his own things, and to be left alone." He is very untidy, but not incontinent. He collects worthless objects and eats cigarette butts. He cleans the hospital basement floors but needs almost constant supervision. He is a good worker unless provoked, when he has tantrums and runs about, yelling, biting his fists, and pounding the walls. He behaved in this fashion during the psychotic episode shown in Fig. 8, and it is this behavior which keeps him on a locked ward.

Consider Fig. 8 and note the exact nature of the functional competition between the patient's vocal symptoms and his manual operant responses. The manual responses were reinforced on a 1'VI schedule with candy. The rate of reinforced manual non-symptomatic responses was reduced about 75% for two periods by competition from a moderate rate of never-reinforced vocal symptomatic responses.

The first period of symptom display and reduced rate of normal or non-symptomatic behavior lasted only about one minute and might be properly called a "psychotic incident." The second period lasted about 20 minutes and appears to be composed of a long series of psychotic incidents. Such sustained periods of psychotic display are often called "psychotic episodes."

Note that in the psychotic episode the vocal symptoms began about two minutes before the manual response rate dropped. This delay in the reduction of the non-symptomatic responding by the symptomatic responding shows that the competitive effect of the symptoms takes a minute or two to build up. The delay also demonstrates the physical independence of the two responses and their recording systems.

Note also that at the end of the episode there was a period of about two minutes with no vocal responding before the non-symptomatic responses returned to their pre-incident rate. This delay in the recovery of the non-symptomatic responding shows that the competitive effect of the symptoms lasts longer than their display. These delays in onset and recovery of the competitive effect of the symptoms suggest that the competition is a higher-order behavioral effect than the symptom. The delays also show that symptoms can occur without the competition.

Note also that a relatively even rate of vocal symptoms and manual responses was maintained throughout the episode. These even episodic rates indicated that the severity of the psychotic episode and its competition with the normal behavior was maintained at about the same intensity throughout.

Also shown in Fig. 8 is a record of the time that the patient's hand was in contact with the manipulandum (plunger contacts). The contacts were recorded by a capacitative relay circuit. The event pen on one recorder was in the "up" position whenever the patient's hand was on the manipulandum. Note that the patient usually took his hand off the manipulandum when a reinforcement was delivered. At this time he placed the candy in a paper bag that he carried. But also note that his hand was off the manipulandum during the psychotic incident and much of the time during the psychotic episode. This record of contacts shows that the symptomatic vocalizations not only compete with the recorded manual responding, but also compete with non-recorded responses necessary to the performance of the recorded responses.

In summary, a voice key to automatically record the competition between symptomatic vocalizations and the normal non-symptomatic behavior of patients within an experimental setting was developed. Its use has clearly shown that the pauses in the operant responding of patients with vocal hallucinatory symptoms are due to functional competition from these symptoms. The opportunity to record the exact nature of this competition will be useful in further research into the basic nature of psychosis. Objective recording of these vocal symptoms and their competitive effect will also be useful in the evaluation of therapeutic agents. Such a high degree of exactitude in the observation of the competition between the psychotic symptoms and normal behavior of a patient can be obtained by no other currently available psychiatric research device.

Functional Definition of a Psychosis

In order to show that Darwinian, naturalistic observations can lead to what might be called theories, lastly I shall present a way of defining a certain type of psychosis. This definition is functional because it describes the psychosis in terms of its effects on and interaction with non-psychotic behavior.

This notion is a direct outgrowth of the simultaneous measurement of symptomatic and non-symptomatic behavior described in the last section. When normal individuals are placed in this two-channel recording situation the only vocal responses they emit, when alone and being reinforced for their manual responses, are occasional bursts of singing and whistling. This singing and whistling can be readily separated from most psychotic hallucinating by the pattern of response emission which is regular for singing and whistling, and irregular for one-sided conversations with no one. Also, the singing and whistling does not compete with, but rather seems to "pace" along with the plunger-pulling responses.

However, if non-psychotic individuals are given an hallucinogenic drug (i.e., Benactyzine in high dosages) and their name is called over a hidden microphone, they will carry on a "psychotic-like" one sided conversation with no one. When questioned afterwards they report having had auditory hallucinations. The interesting fact is that the drug-induced vocal hallucinatory symptoms in the non-psychotics do not compete with their plunger-pulling responses. The non-psychotics pull the plunger for nickels without reduction in rate through their hallucinatory episode.

Also, the non-psychotics do not hallucinate for as long a period after their name is called over the hidden speaker as do the psychotics. The after-discharge of the drug-induced and experimentally stimulated hallucinatory episodes in the non-psychotic is much shorter than the after-discharge of the "spontaneous," or experimentally stimulated hallucinatory episodes in the psychotic.

To date we have run very few psychotic and non-psychotic subjects under these conditions, but the data collected are amazingly uniform. Therefore we tentatively venture the hypothesis that one property of one form of psychosis is that its symptoms have an abnormally long after-discharge and an abnormally high degree of competition with strongly reinforced non-symptomatic behavior. In other words, it is not the symptom (talking to no one) that defines this form of psychosis. Neither is it the stimulus that produced the symptom ("hearing" your name called when no one is there) that defines the psychosis. Rather, it is having the symptomatic response (talking to no one) last long after a non-psychotic would stop, and more importantly being unable to do anything else demanded of him while this talking is going on, that defines the psychotic.

I think this definition of psychotic symptoms has a lot of clinical relevance. We are all familiar with the old lady walking down the street, obeying traffic signals, nodding and occasionally speaking to friends along the way. She is not hospitalized as a psychotic, because she is walking down the street and only talks to no one when there is nothing else to do with her mouth. She just "talks to herself."

And again, if a person goes to a psychiatrist and says, "I worry all the time, I think I am going to die, please help me." The psychiatrist will probably ask, "Do you sleep well? Do you eat well? Are you getting your work done?" If the answers to all of these questions are honestly in the affirmative, the patient is not diagnosed as psychotic and hospitalized. Rather he is classified as an interesting and compensated neurotic. On the other hand, if a man is located who has been talking to no one in a closet for three days, and has done nothing else, he stands a high probability of being immediately hospitalized if he won't even stop talking to his "friend" for the police.

Summary

Much of what we have learned from our carefully controlled experiments appears in retrospect to be composed of things that skilled, experienced clinicians "knew" all the time. But, that is as it should be, for the business of science is to separate the wisdom of casual and field observation from its superstition, and then to quantify and to make this wisdom practically useful. For the first time we have brought a few facts of psychosis into the body of natural science. In so doing much of what we have brought in looks just as the clinicians always said it did. But remember that we now have the advantage of measuring these things automatically in the laboratory. And also remember that we have left many things that clinicians say in the clinic.

References

1. Azrin, N. H., and Lindsley, O. R.: *J. Abn. Soc. Psychol.*, 1956, *52*: 100-102.
2. Bernard, C.: *An Introduction to the Study of Experimental Medicine*, 1865; Reprinted, Henry Schuman, 1949.

3. Ferster, C. B., and Skinner, B. F.: *Schedules of Reinforcement.* New York: Appleton-Century-Crofts, 1957.
4. Ferster, C. B.: *Psychiat. Res. Reports,* 1958, *10*: 101-118.
5. Kraepelin, E.: *The Psychological Experiment in Psychiatry, Psychol. Arbeit.* Leipzig: Engelmann, 1896.
6. Lindsley, O. R.: *Psych. Res. Repts.,* 1956, *5*: 118-193, 140-153.
7. Lindsley, Ogden R., Skinner, B. F., and Solomon, H. C.: *Periodic Project Reports,* Metropolitan State Hospital, Waltham, Mass. June 1953-August 1956. Microcard No. FO-57-524-527, L. C. No. MicP 57-30.
8. Lindsley, O. R.: *Symposium on Cerebral Dysfunction and Mental Disturbance,* Chicago, Ill., June 6, 1959. To be published in *Amer. Psychiat. Assoc. Monogr.,* 1959.
9. Mednick, M. T., and Lindsley, O. R.: *J. Abn. Soc. Psychol.,* 1958, *57*: 13-16.
10. Pavlov, I. P.: *Lectures on Conditioned Reflexes,* Volume Two, *Conditioned Reflexes and Psychiatry.* Translated by W. Horsley Gantt. New York: International, 1941.
11. Rush, B.: *Medical Inquiries and Observations on the Diseases of the Mind,* 1835.
12. Skinner, B. F.: *The Behavior of Organisms.* New York: Appleton-Century, 1938.
13. Skinner, B. F.: *Science and Human Behavior.* New York: Macmillan, 1953.
14. Skinner, B. F.: *Theory and Treatment of the Psychoses.* St. Louis: Washington University Studies, 1956.
15. Skinner, B. F.: *Amer. Scientist,* 1957, *45*: 343-371.
16. Skinner, B. F., Solomon, H. C., and Lindsley, O. R.: *J. Nerv. Ment. Dis.,* 1954, *120*: 403-406.

The work described in this paper was accomplished under contracts N5-ori-07662 and Nonr-1866 (18) sponsored by the Group Psychology Branch, Office of Naval Research, and Research Grant MH-977 from the National Institute of Mental Health, U.S. Public Health Service. It could not have been performed without the cooperation of the Staff of Metropolitan State Hospital (Dr. William F. McGlaughlin, Superintendent), the Harvard Medical School, Department of Psychiatry (Directed by Drs. Harry C. Solomon and Jack R. Ewalt), my own execellent Laboratory Staff, and last but not least, the patients.

The initial help and guidance of Dr. B. F. Skinner speaks for itself in the nature of the method and the content of the reference list.

The insulin was administered by Dr. Karl Dussik, of the Active Treatment Staff, Metropolitan State Hospital.

The iproniazid medication was directed by Dr. Samuel Bogoch, of the Mass. Mental Health Center. This part of the study was supported by Hoffmann-LaRoche Laboratories.

The Student-nurse psychotherapy was directed by Father William P. Sullivan, Chaplain, Metropolitan State Hospital, and administered by Miss Marion Donahue, Student, Boston College School of Nursing.

The Benactyzine research was supported by Merck, Sharpe, and Dohme Laboratories.

22

POSITIVE REINFORCEMENT AND BEHAVIORAL DEFICITS OF AUTISTIC CHILDREN

by Charles B. Ferster, Ph.D.

Infantile autism, first described by Kanner (6), is a very severe psychotic disturbance occurring in children as young as 2 years. At least outwardly, the childhood schizophrenia is a model of adult schizophrenia. Speech and control by the social environment are limited or absent; tantrums and atavistic behaviors are frequent and of high intensity; and most activities are of a simple sort, such as smearing, lying about, rubbing a surface, playing with a finger, and so forth. Infantile autism is a relatively rare form of schizophrenia and is not important from an epidemiological point of view. The analysis of the autistic child may be of theoretical use, however, since his psychosis may be a prototype of the adult's; but the causal factors could not be so complicated, because of the briefer environmental history. In this paper, I should like to analyze how the basic variables determining the child's behavior might operate to produce the particular kinds of behavioral deficits seen in the autistic child. To analyze the autistic child's behavioral deficits, I shall proceed from the general principles of behavior, derived from a variety of species, which describe the kinds of factors that alter the frequency of any arbitrary act (3, 10). The general principles of behavior applied to the specific situations presumably present during the child's developmental period will lead to hypotheses as to specific factors in the autistic child's home life which could produce the severe changes in frequency as well as in the form of his behavior. As an example, consider the effect of intermittent reinforcement, many of the properties of which are comparatively well known from animal experiments. To find how intermittent reinforcement of the autistic child's behavior might produce deficits, we would first determine, in the general case, what specific order of magnitude and kinds of schedules produce weakened behavioral repertoires. The factors in the child's home life could be examined to determine esti-

Reprinted with permission of the Society for Research in Child Development from *Child Development,* 1961, *32*: 437-456.

mates of what kind of circumstances could conceivably cause schedules of reinforcement capable of the required attenuation of the child's behavior. The analysis will emphasize the child's performance as it is changed by, and affected in, social and nonsocial environment. As in most problems of human behavior, the major datum is the frequency of occurrence of the child's behavior. Although the account of the autistic child's development and performance is not derived by manipulative experiments, it may still be useful to the extent that all of the terms of the analysis refer to potentially manipulable conditions in the child's environment and directly measurable aspects of his performance. Such an analysis is even more useful if the performances and their effects on the environment were described in the same general terms used in systematic accounts of behavior of experimental psychology.

Some of our knowledge of the autistic child's repertoire must necessarily come from anecdotal accounts of the child's performance through direct observation. Although such data are not so useful as data from controlled experiments, they can be relatively objective if these performances are directly observable and potentially manipulable. A limited amount of experimental knowledge of the dynamics of the autistic child's repertoire is available through a program of experiments in which the autistic child has developed a new repertoire under the control of an experimental environment (5). These experiments help reveal the range and dynamics of the autistic child's current and potential repertoires. In general, the autistic child's behavior will be analyzed by the functional consequences of the child's behavior rather than the specific form. The major attempt will be to determine what specific effects the autistic child's performance has on that environment and how the specific effects maintain the performance.

Specification of the Autistic Child's Performance

We must first describe the current repertoire of the autistic child before we can describe possible environmental conditions that might produce gross behavioral deficits. A topographic description of the individual items of the autistic child's repertoire would not, in general, distinguish it from the repertoires of a large number of functioning and nonhospitalized children, except perhaps in the degree of loss of verbal behavior. The autistic child's behavior becomes unique only when the relative frequency of occurrence of all the performances in the child's repertoire is considered. In general, the usual diagnostic categories do not adequately characterize the children in the terms of a functional analysis of behavior. Hospitalization of a child usually depends upon whether the parent can keep the child in the home, rather than a functional description of the role of the parental environment in sustaining or weakening the child's performance.

Range of Performances

Although the autistic child may have a narrower range of performances than the normal child, the major difference between them is in the relative frequencies of the various kinds of performances. The autistic child does many things of a simple sort—riding a bicycle, climbing, walking, tugging on someone's sleeve, running, etc. Nevertheless, the autistic child spends large amounts of time sitting or standing quietly. Performances which have only simple and slight effects on the child's environment occur frequently and make up a large percentage of the entire repertoire, for example, chewing on a rubber balloon, rubbing a piece of gum back and forth on the floor, flipping a shoelace, or turning the left hand with the right. Almost all of the characteristic performances of the autistic child may be observed in nonhospitalized children, but the main difference lies in the relative importance of each of these performances in terms of the total repertoire. Conversely, isolated instances of quite "normal" performances may be seen in the autistic child. Again, the relative frequency of the performances defines the autistic child.

Social Control over the Child's Performance

The major performance deficits of the autistic child are in the degree of social control: The kinds of performances which have their major effects through the mediation of other individuals.

The main avenue of social control in a normal repertoire is usually through speech, a kind of performance that is unique because it produces the consequences maintaining it through the mediation of a second person (12). Autistic children almost always have an inadequately developed speech repertoire, varying from mutism to a repertoire of a few words. Even when large numbers of words are emitted, the speech is not normal in the sense that it is not maintained by its effect on a social environment. When normal speech is present, it usually is in the form of a *mand* (12). This is a simple verbal response which is maintained because of its direct reinforcement, e.g., "Candy!" "Let me out." The main variable is usually the level of deprivation of the speaker. It lacks the sensitive interchange between the speaker and listener characteristic of much human verbal behavior, as for example, the *tact* (*see* below). The reinforcement of the mand largely benefits only the speaker. In the case of the autistic child, it frequently affects the listener (parent), who escapes from the aversive stimulus by presenting a reinforcing stimulus relevant to the child's mand. At suppertime, the child stands at the door screaming loudly and kicking the door because the ward attendants in the past have taken the child to supper when this situation became aversive enough. Sometimes, the form of the mand is nonvocal, although still verbal, as when the mand involves tugging at a sleeve, pushing, or jostling. The dynamic conditions which could distort the form of a mand into forms most aversive to a listener will be described below. In contrast to the mand, the tact (12) is almost completely absent. This form of verbal behavior benefits the listener rather than the speaker and is not usually relevant to the current deprivations of the speaker. This is the form of verbal behavior by which the child describes his environment, as, for example, "This is a chair"; "The mailman is coming." This latter kind of verbal control is generally absent or weak, as with other kinds of verbal behavior except an occasional mand.

Atavisms

Tantrums, self-destructive behavior, and performances generally aversive to an adult audience are relatively frequent in the autistic child's repertoire. Most autistic mands depend on an aversive effect of the listener for their reinforcement. To the extent that social behavior is present at all, its major mode is through the production of stimuli or situations which are aversive enough so that the relevant audience will escape or avoid the aversive stimulus (often with a reinforcer). For example, on the occasion of candy in the immediate vicinity, the child screams, flails about on the floor, perhaps striking his head, until he is given some candy. There is evidence that much of the atavistic performance of the autistic child is operant, that is, controlled by its consequence in the social environment. The operant nature of the autistic child's atavisms is borne out by experiments where a child was locked in an experimental space daily for over a year. There was no social intervention, and the experimental session was usually prolonged if a tantrum was underway. Under these conditions, the frequency of tantrums and atavisms declined continuously in the experimental room until they all but disappeared. Severe tantrums and attempts at self-destruction still occurred when sudden changes in the conditions of the experiment produced a sudden change in the direction of nonreinforcement of the child's performances. Severe changes in the reinforcement contingencies of the experiment produced a much larger reaction in the autistic than in the normal child. Consequently, we learned to change experimental conditions very slowly, so that the frequency of reinforcement remained high at each stage of the experiment. Much of the atavistic behavior of the autistic child is maintained because of its effect on the listener.

Reinforcing Stimuli

The reinforcers maintaining the autistic child's performance are difficult to determine without explicit experimentation. Small changes in the physical environment as, for example, direct stimulation of the mouth, splashing water, smearing a sticky substance on the floor, breaking a toy, or repeated tactile sensations, appear to sustain the largest part of the autistic child's repertoire. Nevertheless, these may be weak reinforcing stimuli which appear to be strong, because the response produces its reinforcement continuously and because alternative modes of responding are also maintained by weak reinforcers. The durability and effectiveness of a reinforcer can usually be determined best by reinforcing the behavior intermittently or by providing a strong alternative which could interfere with the behavior in question. In the controlled experiments with autistic children, most of the consequences we supplied to sustain the children's performance, such as color wheels, moving pictures, music, and so forth, were very weak reinforcers compared with food or candy. Food generally appeared to be an effective reinforcer, and most of the performances associated with going to the dining room and eating are frequently intact. In contrast, the normal children could sustain very large amounts of behavior through the nonfood reinforcements. It is difficult to guess the potential effectiveness of new reinforcers, because the estimate depends upon some performance being maintained by that reinforcer.

In the everyday activities of the autistic children, little behavior was sustained by conditioned or delayed reinforcers. But, in a controlled experimental situation, such activities could be sustained by explicit training. For example, (a) The sound of the candy dispenser preceding the delivery of candy served as a conditioned reinforcer. The fine-grain effects of the schedules of reinforcement show this. The difference in performance produced by two different schedules of reinforcement could have occurred only if the effective reinforcer were the sound of the magazine rather than the delivery of a coin. The actual receipt of the coin or food is much too delayed to produce the differences in performances under the two schedules without the conditioned reinforcer coming instantly after a response. (b) With further training, the delivery of a coin (conditioned reinforcer) sustained the child's performances. The coin, in turn, could be used to operate the food or nonfood devices in the experimental room. (c) Still later, coins sustained the child's performance even though they had to be held for a period of time before they could be cashed in. The child worked until he accumulated five coins, then he deposited them in the reinforcing devices. (d) Even longer delays of reinforcement were arranged by sustaining behavior in the experimental room with a conditioned reinforcer as, for example, a towel or a life jacket which could be used later in the swimming pool or in water play after the experimental session terminated. The experimental development of these performances shows that, even though the usual autistic repertoire is generally deficient in performances sustained by conditioned reinforcement and with delay in reinforcement, the children are potentially capable of developing this kind of control.

Little of the autistic child's behavior is likely to be maintained by generalized reinforcement, that is, reinforcement which is effective in the absence of any specific deprivation. A smile or parental approval are examples. The coins delivered as reinforcements in the experimental room are potentially generalized reinforcers, since they make possible several performances under the control of many different deprivations. However, we do not know whether the coin has actually acquired the properties of a generalized reinforcer.

Stimulus Control of Behavior

It is very difficult to determine the stimulus and perceptual repertoire of autistic children. When a child responds to a complex situation, it is not usually clear what aspect of the situation is controlling the child's behavior. In most cases, it is difficult to determine to what extent these children can respond to speech discriminatively, since the situations are usually complex and many stimuli may provide the basis for the simple performances. Similarly with visual repertoires. Controlled experiments showed unequivocally that behavior can come under the control of simple stimuli when differential effects of the performances are correlated with the different stimuli. When a coin was deposited in a lighted coin slot, it operated the reinforcing device. Coins deposited in unlighted slots were wasted. The children soon stopped putting coins in the unlighted slots. The previously developed stimulus control broke down completely when these stimuli were placed in a more complicated context, however. A new vending machine was installed with eight columns, eight coin lights, and eight coin slots, so the child could choose a preferred kind of candy. The slight increase in complexity disrupted the control by the coin light, and it took several months and many experimental procedures before the stimulus control was reestablished. A better designed procedure, in view of the minimal perceptual repertoire of these children, would have been a gradual program by which variations in the specific dimensions of the coin slot and coin light were changed while the reinforcement contingency was held constant in respect to the essential property.

In summary, the repertoire of the autistic child is an impoverished one. Little is known about the perceptual repertoire, but the available evidence suggests that it is minimal. The absolute amount of activity is low, but this deficit is even more profound if the specific items of activity are evaluated in terms of whether they are maintained by significant effects on a social or even nonsocial environment. Most of the child's performances are of a simple sort, such as rubbing a spot of gum back and forth, softening and twisting a crayon, pacing, or flipping a shoelace. Those performances in the child's repertoire having social effects frequently do so because of their effects on the listener as aversive stimuli. Atavisms and tantrums are frequent.

The Emergence of Performance Deficits During the Early Development of the Autistic Child

Having characterized the autistic child's repertoire, the next step is to determine the kinds of circumstances in the early life of these children which could bring about the behavioral deficits. The general plan is to state how the major behavioral processes and classes of variables can drastically reduce the frequency of occurrence of the various behaviors in the repertoire of any organism. Then, the parental environment will be examined to determine circumstances under which the actual contingencies applied by the parental environment to the child's behavior could weaken the child's performance similarly. The datum is the frequency of occurrence of all of the acts in the child's repertoire, and the independent variables are the consequences of these acts on the child's environment, particularly the parental environment. All of the terms in such a functional analysis are actually or potentially directly observable and manipulable. In general, the performances in the child's repertoire will be simultaneously a function of many factors, each contributing to changes in the frequency of the relevant performances. It is important, therefore, to consider relative changes in frequency rather than simple presence or absence of various performances. The datum is the frequency of occurrence of the behavior. In the same vein, singly identifiable factors may be interrelated and functioning simultaneously.

The major paradigm for describing the behavior of an organism is to specify the consequences of the act (reinforcement) which are responsible for its frequency. In this sense, the major cause of an instance of behavior is the immediate effect on the environment (reinforcement). The continued emission of the verbal response "Toast" depends on its effect on the parent in producing toast. Every known behavioral process influencing the frequency of a positively reinforced performance is relevant to the problem of defining conditions under which we may produce a behavioral deficit. Given the variables which maintain it, a performance may be weakened by their absence or by changing the order of magnitude. It is perhaps surprising to discover that large behavioral deficits are plausible without any major appeal to punishment or suppression of behavior by aversive stimuli.

Intermittent Reinforcement and Extinction

Intermittent reinforcement and extinction are the major techniques for removing or weakening behavior in a repertoire. The most fundamental way to eliminate a kind of behavior from an organism's repertoire is to discontinue the effect the behavior has on the environment (extinction). A performance may also be weakened if its maintaining effect on the environment occurs intermittently (intermittent reinforcement).* Behaviors occurring because of their effects on the parent are especially likely to be weakened by intermittent reinforcement and extinction, because the parental reinforcements are a function of other variables and behavioral processes usually not directly under the control of the child. The reinforcement of the verbal response, "Give me the book," may go unreinforced because of many factors which determine the behavior of the listener. He may be preoccupied, listening to someone else, disinclined to reinforce, momentarily inattentive, etc. In contrast, the physical environment reinforces continuously and reliably. Reaching for a book is usually followed by the tactile stimulation from the book. Verbal behavior, particularly, depends entirely for its development and maintenance on reinforcements supplied by an audience (usually a parent). Because of the possibility of prolonged extinction and infrequent, intermittent reinforcement, speech and social behavior are the most vulnerable aspects of the child's repertoire. The young child is particularly vulnerable to the extinction and intermittent reinforcement occurring in social reinforcement because only the parental environment mediates nearly all of the major reinforcers relevant to his repertoire. Large parts of the child's repertoire are reinforced by first affecting a parent who in turn produces the reinforcer for the child. The 2-year-old child who asks for a cookie from a parent and gets no response usually has no alternative audience who will reinforce this vocal behavior. The result will either be the extinction of the child's verbal behavior or the reinforcement of nonvocal verbal forms when the child produces a cookie by a tantrum from which the parent escapes by giving the cookie.

Factors in the Parental Repertoire Affecting the Frequency of Reinforcement of the Child's Performances

To find the conditions under which the child's repertoire will be weakened, therefore, we must look for conditions influencing the parents' behavior, which will alter the parental performances, in turn providing reinforcement of the child's performances. These might be:

1. The general disruption of the parental repertoire. Any severe disruption of the parental repertoire will severely affect the frequency with which the parent reinforces the behavior of the child. Consider, for example, the depressed parent whose general level of behavior is very low. One consequence of this low level of behaving will be a

* The reader may suggest at this point an apparent contradiction with the fact that extinction after intermittent reinforcement is more prolonged than after continuous reinforcement. This aspect of intermittently reinforced behavior's durability is not a general proposition, however, and does not hold for behavior which is still being maintained. Behavior reinforced intermittently will, in general, be emitted less frequently and be more easily weakened by emotional factors, changes in deprivation, punishment, and physiological disturbances than continuously reinforced behavior.

lessened frequency of reacting to the child. Therefore, many items in the child's repertoire will be less frequently reinforced in the depressed than the normal parent. The verbal responses, "May I have some bread" or " I want to go outside," might go unreinforced or be emitted many times without reinforcement. Various kinds of somatic disturbances, such as alcoholic "hangover," drug addiction, severe headache, somatic diseases, etc., could also produce large changes in the over-all reactivity of the parent to a child. To the extent that the child's performances occur because of their effect on the parent, the severely weakened parental repertoire may correspondingly weaken the child's behavior. If the parental extinction of the child's behavior is systematic and periodic, much of a child's behavior could be eliminated.

2. Prepotency of other performances. Whether or not a parent reinforces a child's performance also depends upon the alternative repertoire available to the parent. For example, the parent who is absorbed in various kinds of activities such as housecleaning, a home business, social activities and clubs, active telephoning, and so forth, may at various times allow many usually reinforced performances to go unreinforced. In general, the likelihood of omitting reinforcement would depend upon the strength of the prepotent repertoire. As an example of a prepotent repertoire, the housewife absorbed in a telephone conversation will not be inclined to answer a child or comply with a request. Housecleaning might be another repertoire controlling some parents' behavior so strongly that it is prepotent over behavior in respect to the child. In both cases, the essential result is the nonreinforcement of the child's behavior in competition with the prepotent parental repertoire. Mothers of autistic children often appear to have strong repertoires prepotent over the child. This may be at least a partial reason why mothers of autistic children are so often well-educated, verbal, and at least superficially adequate people.

3. A third factor producing intermittent reinforcement of the child's behavior is related to the first two factors listed above. If the parent finds other reinforcers outside of the home more rewarding than dealing with the child, the child becomes an occasion on which the significant elements of the parental repertoire cannot be reinforced. A parent changing diapers, or otherwise taking care of a child, cannot telephone a friend, be out socializing, be on a job, or doing whatever the autistic mother finds rewarding. The child acquires the properties of a conditioned aversive stimulus because it is an occasion which is incompatible with the parents' normal repertoire. This is of course the major method of aversive control in human behavior—the discontinuation of positive reinforcement. Another basis for establishing the child as a conditioned aversive stimulus to the parent is the emergence of atavisms and a large degree of aversive control of the parent by the child. To the extent that the parent is reinforced by escaping from the child because

of his conditioned aversive properties, the frequency of the parental reinforcement of the child's behavior is further reduced.

The development of the atavistic behavior in the child by the parent is necessarily a very gradual program in which the beginning steps involve small magnitudes of behavior such as whining, whimpering, and crying. As the parent adapts to these or becomes indifferent to them because of the prepotence of other kinds of activity, then progressively larger orders of magnitude become reinforced. The large-magnitude tantrum may be approximated or "shaped" by gradual differential reinforcement. The parents of one autistic child, for example, at one period took turns all night standing in the child's room because one step out of the room would immediately produce a severe tantrum in the child. When the child functions as a conditioned aversive stimulus for the parent, the parent is less likely to reinforce the child's behavior positively. This lack of positive reinforcement, in turn, emphasizes the atavistic responses on the child's part as the major mode of affecting the parent.

The usual limiting factor in preventing excessive development of tantrums is the emergence of self-control on the part of the parent in escaping from the aversive control by the child rather than reinforcing it. Here, again, the repertoire of the patient is relevant. The development of self-control requires a highly developed repertoire which depends for its development on the ultimate aversive consequences of the child's control of the parent. The child's control becomes more aversive to the parent if it interrupts strong repertoires. Specifically, a parent engrossed in a conversation will find a child's interruption more aversive than a parent who is simply resting. If, in fact, there is no strong behavior in the parent, then the child's control is not likely to be aversive, and there is no basis for developing self-control.

All three of the above factors—over-all disturbances in the parental repertoire, prepotent activities, and escape from the child because of his aversiveness—reduce the amount of parental reinforcement of the child's performances. The over-all effect of the nonreinforcement on the repertoire of the child will depend upon the length of time and number of items of the child's repertoire that go unreinforced, as well as the existence of other possible social environments that can alternatively maintain the child's behavior (*see* below).

Differential Reinforcement of Atavistic Forms of Behavior by the Parent

The schedule by which the parent reacts to the child is also relevant to the development of atavistic behavior. Initially, a tantrum may be an unconditioned consequence of parental control as, for example, sudden nonreinforcement or punishment. Eventually, however, the child's tantrums may come to be maintained by their effect on the parental environment, because they present an aversive situation that can be terminated if the parent supplies some reinforcer to the child. The reinforcer presented by the parent to escape from the aversive consequences of the tantrum also increases the subsequent frequency of atavistic responses.

The effect on the parent of the given form and intensity of tantrums will vary from time to time, depending on the conditions maintaining the parents' behavior. This variation in sensitivity of the parent to aversive control by the child results in a variable-ratio schedule of reinforcement of the child's tantrum by the parent—a schedule of reinforcement potentially capable of maximizing the disposition to engage in tantrums. This is the schedule of reinforcement that produces the high frequencies of performances as in gambling (10). The sensitivity of the parent to aversive control by the child will depend on the general condition of the parental repertoire as discussed above. The same factors in the parental repertoire that tend to produce nonreinforcement of the child's behavior—general disruption of the parent or other behaviors prepotent over the child—correspondingly produce reinforcement of large-order-of-magnitude tantrums. The parent whose total repertoire is severely enough disrupted to interfere with the normal reinforcement of the child's behavior will also react only to tantrums that are of large order of magnitude of aversiveness. A range of sensitivity of the parent to aversive control by the child produces ideal conditions for progressively increasing the intensity or frequency of tantrums. A high sensitivity to aversive control guarantees that some tantrums will be reinforced at least periodically. A low sensitivity differentially reinforces tantrums of large orders of magnitude. At one extreme, the parent may be hypersensitive to the child and, at other times, so depressed that only physical violence will produce a reaction. The schedule by which the parent's behavior terminates the tantrum is a second factor which will increase the range of reactivity of the parent. As more behavior is required of the parent to terminate the tantrum, the parent's inclination to do so will fall. When the parent is less inclined to reinforce a given intensity of tantrum, any variation in tantrum intensity is tantamount to differential reinforcement of extreme forms, if the parent now reacts to the larger-order-of-magnitude tantrum.

How much the parent differentially reinforces tantrums in the child depends, in part, upon the child's other positively reinforced repertoires. When, for example, a child's performance suddenly goes unreinforced, as when a parent may refuse a request, the likelihood and severity of a tantrum will in part depend on the parent's ability to "distract" the child. This, in turn, depends upon whether alternative modes of behavior are in fact available to the child. When conditions are present for the progressive reinforcement of more and more severe tantrums, the process is potentially non-self-limiting. Autocatalysis is likely to occur, particularly if the parent has little disposition to reinforce the general items in the child's repertoire for reasons other than terminating the aversive demands of the child.

Nonsocial Reinforcers

Some of the child's behavior is maintained by his direct effect on the physical environment without the intervention of other individuals. In general, very small effects on the environment will sustain performances with which the parent usually has little reason to interfere. For example, the child plays with his own shoelace, moves his fingers in his own visual field, emits minimal nonverbal, vocal responses, and so forth. Larger effects on the physical environment as, for example, moving objects about the house, speaking to the parent, playing with toys, touching and handling usual household objects, are more likely to enter upon the parental repertoire and so may produce a response whose effect is to discontinue the behavior or interfere with its reinforcement. The punishment aspect of the parental interference with the child's activities will be dealt with separately below. The relative possibility of parental interference and nonreinforcement of the hierarchy of performances may account for the large part of the autistic child's repertoire, which consists of behaviors having small, limited effects on the physical environment. Occasionally, even behaviors that are maintained by the most simple effects on the environment are extinguished or punished when they occur in the presence of a parent. For example, the father of one autistic child reports that the child reached for a chandelier while he was holding him. The father instantly dropped the child, with a reaction of considerable disapproval because "You should pay attention to me when you're with me." Aside from the secondary effect on the child, the immediate result of the incident is the nonreinforcement of the child reaching for a common physical object.

The existence of "nonverbal" vocal behavior in some autistic children may be related to forms of vocal behavior with which the parent will or will not interfere. Vocal behavior maintained by its effect on a parent (verbal) is susceptible to weakening by parental extinction. A parent interferes less easily with vocal behavior maintained by its direct effect (nonverbal) comparable with making noise by rubbing a stick over a rough surface. Further, such nonverbal vocal responses can emerge readily at any stage of the child's life, unlike verbal behavior, because it does not depend on a generalized reinforcement.

Failure to Develop Conditioned and Generalized Reinforcers

The normal repertoire of the child consists almost entirely of sequences of behavior that are maintained, in a chain or sequence, by conditioned and generalized reinforcers (10). An example of a chain of responses would be the behavior of the child moving a chair across the room and using it to climb to a table top to reach a key which in turn opens a cupboard containing candy. This complicated sequence of behavior is linked together by critical stimuli which have the dual function of sustaining the behavior they follow (conditioned reinforcement) and setting the occasion for the subsequent response. The chair in the above example is an occasion on which climbing onto it will bring the child into a position where reaching for food on the table top will be reinforced by obtaining food. Once this behavior is established, the chair in position in front of the table may now be a reinforcer, and any of the child's behavior which results in moving the chair into position will be reinforced because of the subsequent role of the chair in the later chain of behaviors. A minimal amount of behavior is necessary before a chain of responses can develop. The development of the control by the various stimuli in the chain, both as discriminative stimuli setting the occasion for the reinforcement of behavior and as reinforcers, depends upon a high level of activity, so that the responses will occur and come under the control of the stimuli. This is even more true for the development of the generalized reinforcer. When the child has moved enough objects about the house and achieved a variety of effects on his environment relative to a range of deprivations and reinforcers, simply manipulating the physical environment may become a reinforcer without reference to a specific level of deprivation. This, of course, is the uniquely human reinforcer that makes possible much of verbal behavior, education in general, and self-control. Again, large amounts of behavior—many chains of behavior with many different kinds of conditioned reinforcers—are a necessary condition for the emergence of a generalized reinforcer. To the extent that the child's repertoire becomes weakened by intermittent reinforcement and extinction, as mentioned above, and punishment and aversive control (*see* below), the possibility of the development of generalized reinforcers, and hence more complex behavior, becomes less and less likely. Parental "attention" is probably one of the most important generalized reinforcers normally maintaining the child's behavior. Parental attention is an occasion upon which the child's performances may have an important effect on the parent. Inattention is an occasion on which the child's responses are likely to have little effect. Hence, the parents' performances in smiling, saying, "Right," "Good boy," or "Thank you." all come to function as conditioned reinforcers. Their emergence as generalized reinforcers again depends upon the existence of a large behavioral repertoire. A large number of chains of responses will produce important positive effects when the parent smiles or says, "Good boy." Lower frequencies of reinforcement follow for these same activities when the parent is frowning or says, "Bad boy."

Any large reduction in the child's over-all performance will interfere with the initial development of conditioned reinforcers or their continued effectiveness. The control by the environment over the child's behavior depends first upon the emission of the behavior. This follows from the manner in which the environment comes to control the child's performance: the successful execution of an act on one occasion, coupled with the unsuccessful act in its absence. Until a child climbs on chairs, as in the previous example, a chair has little chance of becoming a discriminative stimulus. Without the development of stimulus control, conditioned reinforcers cannot develop. The reinforcing effect of the chair in the above example depends upon its being the occasion on which further performances may be reinforced. In this way, a low general level of behavior may impede the enlargement of the child's repertoire because it does not allow stimulus control and in turn prevents reinforcement of new behavior. A limited development of simple conditioned reinforcers in turn prevents the development of a generalized reinforcer. Parental responses, such as smiling, "Good," or "Right," can have little effect on the child if there is not a history by which many different forms of the child's performance have produced various reinforcers on these occasions. Without parental generalized reinforcement, educational processes and positive parental control are all but impossible. This control is normally carried out by the use of praise and parental attention, coupled with mild forms of threats of discontinuing the reinforcers. Even after a generalized reinforcer has acquired its function, its continued effectiveness depends on the various stimuli continuing to stand in a significant relation to the child's performance. The actual form of the parents' generalized reinforcer is not nearly as important as the parents' subsequent reinforcement practices with the child. The reinforcing effects of the smile derive from the reinforcing practices associated with it. A smile usually functions as a generalized reinforcer in most people because a smiling person is more likely to reinforce. The correlation between smiling and reinforcement is by no means inevitable, however. Some individuals may be more disposed to punish than reinforce when smiling in some situations. In a similar vein, if the child has no behavior in his repertoire that will be more likely to be reinforced on the occasion of a parental smile, it matters little what the parent's reinforcing practices are when smiling as against when frowning.

Stimulus Control

The specific occasions on which a child's performances have their characteristic effects on the environment will subsequently determine whether the child acts. In the absence of the characteristic circumstances under which the behavior is normally reinforced, the child will be less disposed to act in proportion to the degree of similarity with the original situation. Changing a stimulus to one which has not been correlated with reinforcement is another way of weakening a repertoire. New stimuli also elicit emotional responses and general autonomic effects that may interfere with established performances. Here, simply repeated exposure to the stimuli may produce adaptation to the stimuli and eliminate their emotional effects. Ordinarily, the infants' performances are under the control of a limited range of stimuli, usually one or two parents in a limited part of a specific home environment. The discriminative repertoire broadens as the child grows older and other individuals come to be occasions on which his performances have significant effects. The parental environment of the very young child narrows the control of the child's performance to a limited range of stimuli, largely because the parent mediates almost all of the important events affecting the child. A major factor which brings the child's behavior more narrowly under the control of the parent is the nonreinforcement of much of the child's behavior in the absence of the parent. The close control of the child's behavior by the parent weakens the child's repertoire in the absence of a parent much more when there has been explicit differential reinforcement than when there has been simply a limited reinforcing environment.

Sudden shifts in the child's environment may or may not produce major performance deficits. At one extreme, a sudden shift of the stimuli in the child's controlling environment will have little influence if the child already has been reinforced on the occasion of a wide range of circumstances and individuals. At another extreme, a repertoire can be eliminated almost completely if the child has had a history in which major kinds of performances have gone unreinforced except on the occasion of a single person in a specific environment. The sudden shifts in the situations and persons controlling the child's behavior may occur under a variety of circumstances, such as a sudden change in a constant companion, death of a parent, or a sudden shift in the physical environment. A sudden shift in the environment of one of the subjects reported in the previously mentioned experiment could conceivably have been the major factor in her autistic development. Many of the activities of the child's mother were prepotent over dealing with the child, and she solved the problem by hiring a teenage baby sitter as a constant companion and nursemaid. After a year, the baby sitter left, suddenly and abruptly, leaving the child with the mother. Within four months, the child began to behave less in general, lost speech, and showed increasing frequency of atavisms. The child's repertoire possibly was under such close control of the baby sitter that the very sudden change to the mother created an environment which in the past had been correlated with nonreinforcement. If the child's behavior were under very narrow control by the baby sitter, because of the nonreinforcement on all other occasions, a sudden shift, as in the loss of the baby sitter, could produce a dramatic deficit in the child's repertoire.

Disruptive Effect of Sudden Stimulus Changes and the Amount, Durability, and Range of Behavior

A novel reinforcing environment will not sustain a child's performance unless the repertoire contains behavior of a sufficient range and durability. The new environment weakens the performance because it nearly always requires slightly different forms of behavior. For example, a new person entering a child's home is not so likely to respond successfully to the incompletely developed verbal behavior of a child as the parent. The possibility of the child's affecting the stranger will depend upon his having verbal responses different from those usually reinforced by the parent and, also, durable verbal behavior that will continue to be emitted under the intermittent reinforcement that is likely to occur. If the child's repertoire is durable and extensive enough so that the verbal response may be repeated several times and supplemented by auxiliary behavior, the child has a greater chance of affecting the new person or of being shaped by him. Similarly with other kinds of social behavior. The wider the range of behavior and the greater the disposition to emit it the more likely that the child's performance will be within the range of responses potentially reinforcible by the new environment.

For a stimulus to acquire control over behavior, the child must first emit behavior in the presence of the stimulus. Consider, for example, the performance of a child at a children's party at which there are lots of toys and games, such as bicycles, swings, and so forth. The likelihood of the child's behavior coming under the control of any of the other children as reinforcers is minimal if the new environment suppresses or makes the child's entire repertoire unavailable because it is a novel stimulus and is an occasion on which the child's behavior has never been reinforced. If the behavior of playing with a swing or riding a tricycle is sufficiently strong that it may be emitted even under the adverse conditions of the very strange party environment, then the simple emission of the previously developed behavior provides a situation under which other children at the party may potentially reinforce or otherwise affect the child's repertoire. Simply the acts of eating cake, candy, or ice cream, or picking up a toy put some of the child's behavior under the control of the new environment. Each new performance which can potentially occur at the party provides a basis for the child's reinforcing some behavior of other children at the party or of his coming under the control of the other children's reinforcers. On the other hand, a sudden exposure to a new environment with a weak and narrow repertoire may produce a severe behavioral deficit. In any case, the child will be much less disposed to go to the party if he had behaved unsuccessfully in the new environment. This lower disposition to attend and engage in the party would in turn make it less likely that the child will emit behavior that would be reinforced in the party environment.

Adaptation

The emotional and elicited autonomic effects of novel environments may also interfere with a child's performances. Adaptation to new environments occurs with gradual exposure. A sudden exposure to a new environment will produce gross emotional and autonomic responses which will in turn interfere with, or even completely suppress, the emission of possible operant behavior potentially reinforcible by the new environment. The rate at which the child is exposed to the new environments will determine the magnitude of disturbance. Exposure to a new environment and adaptation of the emotional responses do not necessarily create the potential basis for responding, however. A repertoire that will make contact with the new environment is also necessary.

Amount of Prior Nonreinforcement

The more closely controlled the child's performances are by specific stimuli, the more likely a sudden shift in the environment will produce a cessation of responding. For example, the child receiving minimal care from a parent probably will be less affected by a sudden shift in environment than a child closely affected and controlled by parental response. It is paradoxical that the parent who responds sensitively to the child's performance may be potentially weakening it more than the parent who exerts little control over the child. It is the alternate reinforcement and nonreinforcement that place the child's behavior narrowly under the control of very specific stimuli so that it is much more vulnerable to sudden changes. The range of stimuli in whose presence the child's behavior goes unreinforced will determine the narrowness of the stimulus control.

Cumulative Effects of a Behavioral Deficit

The continuous development of more and more complex forms of a child's behavior is normally achieved because the parents and community approximate the required performances. At each stage of the child's development, the community reinforces the child's current repertoire even though it is more disposed to react to small increments in the child's performance in the direction of the required complex performances. Should any of the above processes produce a deficit in performance or an arrest in the development of the child's performance, further development of a repertoire would depend upon the community's relaxing its requirements and reinforcing performances in an older child that it normally accepts only from a younger one. Ordinarily, the reinforcing practices of the community are based on the chronological age and physical development of the child.

Only between the ages of 1½ to 4 years does the parent have sufficient control of the child to weaken his performance to the degree seen in infantile autism. This is a critical period in the child's development during which his behavior is especially susceptible to extinction, because the traditional social pattern in the usual family restricts the child's experience to one or two parents. Before the age of 1½, the child has few performances with which the parent will interfere or that have important effects on the parent. Much of the infant's behavior is maintained by simple and direct effects on its environment. As the child approaches 2 years, the rapid development of a behavioral repertoire, particularly social and verbal behavior, makes possible extinction and other forms of weakening. The effectiveness of the parental environment in weakening the child's repertoire depends upon the availability of concurrent audiences for the child's behavior. In general, the 2-year-old child is limited to the home and comes into increasing contact with other environments as he grows older, perhaps reaching a maximum at school age. The presence of an older sibling might appear to preempt the possibility of a sufficient degree of isolation to account for an aversive behavioral deficit. A sibling could provide an alternative to the parent as a reinforcing environment. The behavioral or functional influence of a sibling would depend on the amount and nature of interaction between the children. For example, an older child might possibly completely avoid the younger one or tend to have the same patterns of reaction as the parent. In many cases, the older sibling has playmates outside the home to the complete exclusion of the younger child. The older sibling, in many circumstances, punishes as well as extinguishes the younger child for any attempted participation in his play. There are very few facts as to the exact nature of the interactions in most cases.

The parent as the sole maintainer of the child's behavior is perhaps even more likely when the child is raised in a rural or isolated community, and perhaps with one of the parents largely absent. The above analysis suggests that a survey of severely autistic children would, in general, show them to be first-born children; or, if other siblings were available, they would have provided little interaction with the child. It also suggests that the child would be raised in a house physically or socially isolated from other families or children such that there were no alternative social environments that could provide reinforcement for the child's behavior. With the child was exposed to both parents, it would be expected that both parents were consistent in their nonreinforcement of the child's performances.

Aversive Control and Punishment

It has been possible to describe conditions which might produce major behavioral deficits without dealing with punishment or aversive control. A similar account might present a functional analysis of how performance deficits might occur as a result of aversive control. Many writers have already described some of these factors by extending general principles of aversive control to human behavior (7, 8, 11). For the purposes of the analysis presented in this paper, I should like to restrict the discussion of aversive control to its relation to positive reinforcement. Much of human aversive control is carried out by discontinuing or withdrawing reinforcement (3, 10). For example, a frown or criticism may function as an aversive stimulus because these are occasions on which reinforcements are less likely to occur. Even when corporal punishment is given, it is not clear as to whether the resulting effect on the child's behavior is due to a slap or to the lower inclination of a punishing parent to reinforce. Most parents who spank a child will be indisposed to act favorably toward the child for some period of time subsequently. As a result, one major by-product of frequent punishment may be a larger order of interference with the child's normal repertoire along the lines of the positive reinforcement deficits described above.

The obvious effectiveness of punishment in some kinds of human control appears to contradict experimental findings with animals which show punishment to have only a temporary effect on behavior (1, 2, 9). The role of positive reinforcement factors helps resolve the dilemma. The effectiveness of punishment depends on how strongly the punished behavior is maintained by positive reinforcement. The apparent effectiveness of punishment in the control of children may occur when weak repertoires are punished or when the punishment indirectly produces extinction. Most animal experiments using electric shock as an aversive stimulus have used strongly maintained positively reinforced operant behavior as the base-line performance to be punished. The aversive control might be more effective when the performances to be punished are less strongly maintained.

Conclusion

As might be expected from the relatively low frequency of infantile autism, the combination of circumstances hypothesized above would occur only rarely. The above hypothesis provides a framework for investigating the circumstances surrounding the development of the autistic child. All of the variables that might weaken the behavior of a child are directly or potentially observable. The data required are the actual parental and child performances and their specific effects on each other, rather than global statements such as dependency, hostility, or socialization. Not all of the factors responsible for a child's performance may be present currently. Using retrospective accounts, however, makes it difficult to determine the actual correspondence between the verbal statements of the parent and their actual practices in raising the child. The alternatives are, first, an objective assessment of the child's repertoire in a wide enough range of environments so as to allow an assessment of the nature of the environmental control of the child's current behavior; and, second, actual home observations of the specific social consequences of the child's performances early in the development of the disease.

The same kind of functional analysis can be made for the performance of the adult psychotic although the specific deficits observed in autistic children and their manner of occurrence may not be relevant. In particular, the analysis of the adult's behavior would be more concerned with the factors which weaken behavior already in the repertoire rather than the development of new repertoires as with the analysis of the autistic child's behavior. Maintaining already-established behavior is more at issue in the adult than the initial development of a performance as in the case of the child (3).

References

1. Azrin, N. H.: Punishment and recovery during fixed-ratio performance. *J. exp. anal. Behav.*, 1959, *2*: 301-305.
2. Estes, W. K.: An experimental study of punishment. *Psychol. Monogr.*, 1944, *57*: No. 3 (Whole No. 623).
3. Ferster, C. B.: Reinforcement and punishment in the control of human behavior by social agencies. *Psychiat. Res. Repts. 10,* 1958, *12*: 101-118.
4. Ferster, C. B., and DeMyer, M. K.: A method for the experimental analysis of the behavior of autistic children. *Amer. J. Orthopsychiat.*, in press.
5. Ferster, C. B., and DeMyer, M. K.: The development of performances in autistic children in an automatically controlled environment. *J. chronic Dis.*, 1961, *13*: 312-345.
6. Kanner, L.: Early infantile autism. *J. Pediat.*, 1944, *25*: 211-217.
7. Miller, N. E., and Dollard, S.: *Personality and psychotherapy*. New York: McGraw-Hill, 1950.
8. Rotter, Julian: *Social learning and clinical psychology*. New York: Prentice-Hall, 1954.
9. Skinner, B. F.: *The behavior of organisms*. New York: Appleton-Century-Crofts, 1938.
10. Skinner, B. F.: *Science and human behavior*. New York: Macmillan, 1953.
11. Skinner, B. F.: Some contributions of an experimental analysis of behavior to psychology as a whole. *Amer. Psychologist*, 1953, *8*: 69-78.
12. Skinner, B. F.: *Verbal behavior*. New York: Appleton-Century-Crofts, 1957.

23

THE PSYCHIATRIC NURSE AS A BEHAVIORAL ENGINEER

by Teodoro Ayllon, Ph.D., and Jack L. Michael, Ph.D.

The behavior which leads to a person's admission to a mental hospital often involves danger to himself or others, withdrawal from normal social functions, or a dramatic change from his usual mode of behaving. The professional staff of the psychiatric hospital directs its major efforts toward the discovery of the flaw in the patient's mental apparatus which presumably underlies his disturbing and dangerous behavior. Following the medical paradigm, it is presumed that once the basic disfunction has been properly identified the appropriate treatment will be undertaken and the various manifestations of the disfunction will disappear.

While diagnosis is being made and during subsequent treatment, the patient is under the daily care of the psychiatric nurses* in the ward. There, he often exhibits annoying and disrupting behavior which is usually regarded as a further manifestation of his basic difficulty. This behavior is sometimes identical with that which led to his admission; but at other times it seems to originate and develop within the hospital setting. Although it is still regarded as a reflection of his basic problem, this disruptive behavior may become so persistent that it engages the full energies of the nurses, and postpones, sometimes permanently, any effort on their part to deal with the so-called basic problem.

Disrupting behaviors usually consist in the patient's failure to engage in activities which are considered normal and necessary; or his persistent engagement in activities that are harmful to himself or other patients, or disrupting in other ways. For example, failures to eat, dress, bathe, interact socially with other patients, and walk without being led are invariably disruptive. Hoarding various objects, hitting,

* As used in this paper, "psychiatric nurse" is a generic term including all those who actually work on the ward (aides, psychiatric nurses, and registered nurses).

Reprinted with permission from the *Journal of the Experimental Analysis of Behavior,* 1959, vol. 2, pp. 323-334.

pinching, spitting on other patients, constant attention-seeking actions with respect to the nurses, upsetting chairs in the dayroom, scraping paint from the walls, breaking windows, stuffing paper in the mouth and ears, walking on haunches or while in a squatting position are disruptive when they occur frequently and persistently.

At present, no systematic approach to such problems is available to the nurses. A psychodynamic interpretation is often given by psychiatrists and psychologists; and, for that matter, the nurses sometimes construct "depth" interpretations themselves. These interpretations seldom suggest any specific remedial actions to the nurses, who then have no other recourse than to act on the basis of common sense, or to take advantage of the physical therapy in vogue. From the point of view of modern behavior theory, such strong behaviors, or behavioral deficits, may be considered the result of events occurring in the patient's immediate or historical environment rather than the manifestations of his mental disorder. The present research represents an attempt to discover and manipulate some of these environmental variables for the purpose of modifying the problem behavior.

Research Setting

The research was carried out at the Saskatchewan Hospital, Weyburn, Saskatchewan, Canada. It is a psychiatric hospital with approximately 1,500 patients. Its most relevant features in terms of the present experiment are:

1. The nurses are trained as psychiatric nurses in a 3-year program.
2. They are responsible for the patients in their wards and enjoy a high degree of autonomy with respect to the treatment of a patient. The psychiatrists in the hospital function as advisers to the nursing staff. This means that psychiatrists do not give orders, but simply offer advice upon request from the psychiatric nurses.
3. The nurses administer incoming and outgoing mail for the patients, visitor traffic, ground passes, paroles, and even discharge, although the last is often carried out after consultation with a psychiatrist. The nurses also conduct group therapy under the supervision of the psychiatric staff.

The official position of the senior author, hereafter referred to as *E*, was that of a clinical psychologist, who designed and supervised operant-conditioning "therapy" as applied by the nurses. Once his advice had been accepted, the nurses were responsible for carrying out the procedures specified by *E*. It was the privilege of the nurses to discontinue any treatment when they believed it was no longer necessary, when they were unable to implement it because of lack of staff, or when other ward difficulties made the treatment impossible. Whenever termination became necessary, *E* was given appropriate notice.

Subjects

The subjects used in this investigation were all patients in the hospital. Of the total 19 patients, 14 had been classified as schizophrenic and 5 as mentally defective. Except for one female patient who was resident for only 7 months, all patients had been hospitalized for several years. Each subject presented a persistent behavior problem for which he had been referred to *E* by the nursing staff. None of the *S*s was presently receiving psychotherapy, electroconvulsive therapy, or any kind of individual treatment.

The behaviors which were studied do not represent the most serious problems encountered in a typical psychiatric hospital. They were selected mainly because their persistence allowed them to survive several attempts at altering them.

Procedure

Prior to a systematic observational study of the patient's behavior the nurses were asked about the kind and frequency of naturally occurring reinforcement obtained by the patient, the duration and frequency of the problem behavior, and the possibility of controlling the reinforcement. Next, a period of systematic observation of each patient was undertaken prior to treatment. This was done to obtain objective information on the frequency of the behavior that was a problem to the nurses, and to determine what other behaviors were emitted by the patient.

Depending on the type of behavior, two methods were used for recording it. If the behavior involved interaction with a nurse, it was recorded every time it occurred. Entering the nurses' office, and eating regular meals are examples of such behavior.

Behavior which did not naturally involve contact with the nurse was recorded by a time-sampling technique. The nurse who was in charge of the program was supplied with a mimeographed record form. She sought out the patient at regular intervals; and without interaction with him, she recorded the behavior taking place at that time. She did not actually describe the behavior occurring, but rather classified it in terms of a pre-established trichotomy: (a) the undesirable behavior; (b) incompatible behavior which could ultimately displace the undesirable behavior; and (c) incompatible behavior which was not considered shapeable, such as sleeping, eating, and dressing. (Although these latter acts are certainly susceptible to the influence of reinforcement, they were regarded as neutral behaviors in the present research.) The period of observation varied from 1 to 3 minutes. After making an observation, the nurse resumed her regular ward activities until the next interval was reached, whereupon she again sought out the patient. Except for one patient, who was observed every 15 minutes, such observations were made every 30 minutes.

The relevant aspect of the data obtained by the time-check recording is the proportion of the total number of observations (excluding observations of neutral behavior) during which the patient was engaging in the behavior being altered. This will be called the relative frequency of the behavior. As an example, on the first day of the program of extinction for psychotic talk in the case of Helen (see below), 17 non-neutral behaviors were recorded. Of these, nine were classed as psychotic talk and eight as sensible talk; the relative frequency of psychotic talk was 0.53.

Although it would have been desirable, a long pretreatment period of observation was precluded by the newness of this approach and the necessity of obtaining the voluntary cooperation of the nurses.

After the pretreatment study had been completed, *E* instructed the ward nurses in the specific program that was to be carried out. In all cases the instruction was given at ward meetings and usually involved the cooperation of only two shifts, the 7 a.m. to 3 p.m., and 3 p.m. to 11 p.m., since the patients were usually asleep during the 11 p.m. to 7 a.m. shift.

The pretreatment studies indicated that what maintained undesirable behavior in most of the patients was the attention or social approval of the nurses toward that behavior. Therefore, the emphasis in instructing the nursing staff was on the operation of giving or withholding social reinforcement contingent upon a desired class of behavior. What follows illustrates the tenor of *E*'s somewhat informal instructions to the nurses. "Reinforcement is something you do for or with a patient, for example, offering candy or a cigarette. Any way you convey attention to the patient is reinforcing. Patients may be reinforced if you answer their questions, talk to them, or let them know by your reaction that you are aware of their presence. The common-sense expression 'pay no attention' is perhaps closest to what must be done to discourage the patient's behavior. When we say 'do not reinforce a behavior,' we are actually saying 'ignore the behavior and act deaf and blind whenever it occurs.' "

When reinforcement was given on a fixed-interval basis, the nurse was instructed to observe the patient for about 1 to 3 minutes at regular intervals, just as in the pretreatment observation period. If desirable behavior was occurring at the time of observation, she would reinforce it; if not, she would go on about her duties and check again after the next interval had passed. Strictly speaking, this is fixed interval with a limited-hold contingency (2). During a program of extinction the nurse checked as above; however, instead of reinforcing the patient when he exhibited the behavior being altered, she simply recorded it and continued her other work. Except for specific directions for two patients, the nurses were not given instructions on the operation of aversive control.

The programs requiring time-sample observations started after breakfast (around 9 a.m.) and ended at bedtime (around 9 p.m.), and were usually carried out by only one of the 6 to 12 nurses on each shift. Because of the daily shift changes, the monthly ward rotations, and a systematic effort to give everyone experience at this new duty, no patient's program was followed by any one nurse for any considerable length of time. Nineteen, as a minimum, different nurses were involved in carrying out each patient's program. Over 100 different nurses participated in the entire research project.

Most social ward activities took place in the dayroom, which was a large living room containing a television set, card tables, magazines, and games. It was here that reinforcement was given for social behaviors toward patients, and for nonsocial behaviors which were strengthened to compete with undesirable behaviors. The fact that the research was carried out in five wards distributed far from each other in a four-floor building made it impossible for *E* to observe all the nurses involved in the research at any one time. Because of the constant change in nursing personnel, most of *E*'s time was spent in instructing new people in the routines of the programs. In addition, since *E* did not train the nurses extensively, he observed them, often without their knowledge, and supervised them in record keeping, administering reinforcement, extinction, etc. That the nurses performed effectively when *E* was absent can be at least partially determined by the ultimate results.

Results

The results will be summarized in terms of the type of behavior problem and the operations used in altering the behavior. In general, the time required to change a specific behavior ranged from 6 to 11 weeks. The operations were in force for 24 hours a day, 7 days a week.

Strong Behavior Treated by Extinction, or Extinction Combined with Reinforcement for Incompatible Behavior

In the five cases treated with this program, the reinforcer was the attention of the nurses; and the withholding of this reinforcer resulted in the expected decline in frequency. The changes occurring in three of the behavior problems, scrubbing the floor, spending too much time in the bathroom, and one of the two cases of entering the nurses' offices, were not complicated by uncontrollable variables. Lucille's case is presented in detail as representative of these three. The interpretation of the changes occurring in the other two behavior problems, entering the nurses' offices, and psychotic verbal behavior, is not so clear-cut. Helen's case illustrates this point. For details concerning the cases not discussed in this paper, see Ayllon (1).

Lucille. Lucille's frequent visits to the nurses' office interrupted and interfered with their work. She had been doing this for 2 years. During this time, she had been told that she was not expected to spend her time in the nurses' office. Frequently, she was taken by the hand or pushed back bodily into the ward. Because the patient was classified as mentally defective, the nurses had resigned themselves to tolerating her behavior. As one of the nurses put it, "It's difficult to tell her anything because she can't understand—she's too dumb."

The following instructions were given to the nurses: "During this program the patient must not be given reinforcement (attention) for entering the nurses' office. Tally every time she enters the office."

The pretreatment study indicated that she entered the office on an average of 16 times a day. As Fig. 1b shows, the average frequency was down to two entries per day by the seventh week of extinction, and the program was terminated. Fig. 1a shows the same data plotted cumulatively.

Helen. This patient's psychotic talk had persisted for at least 3 years. It had become so annoying during the last 4 months prior to treatment that other patients had on several occasions beaten her in an effort to keep her quiet. She was described by one of the psychiatrists as a "delusional" patient who "feels she must push her troubles onto somebody else, and by doing this she feels she is free." Her conversation centered around her illegitimate child and the men she claimed were constantly pursuing her. It was the nurses' impression that the patient had "nothing else to talk about."

A 5-day pretreatment observation of the patient was made at 30-minute intervals to compare the relative frequencies of psychotic and sensible content in her talk. Some of the nurses reported that, previously, when the patient started her psychotic talk, they listened to her in an effort to get at the "roots of her problem." A few nurses stated that they did not listen to what she was saying but simply nodded and remarked, "Yes, I understand," or some such comment, the purpose of which was to steer the patient's conversation onto some other topic. These reports suggested that the psychotic talk was being maintained by the nurses' reaction to it. While it is recognized that a distinction between psychotic and normal talk is somewhat arbitrary, this case was included in the research because of its value as a problem involving primarily verbal behavior.

The following instructions were given to the nurses: "During this program the patient must not be given reinforcement (attention) for her psychotic talk (about her illegitimate child and the men chasing her). Check the patient every 30 minutes, and (a) tally for psychotic talk; and (b) reinforce (and tally) sensible talk. If another patient fights with her, avoid making an issue of it. Simply stop the other patient from hurting her, but do so with a matter-of-fact attitude."

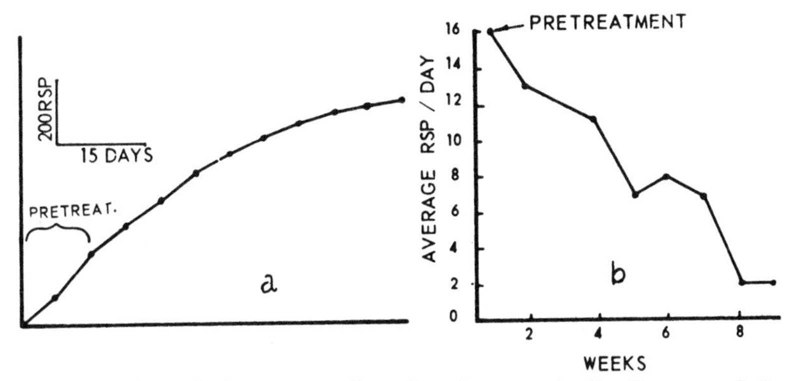

FIG. 1. Extinction of the response "entering the nurses' office;" a. cumulative record, b. conventional record.

The 5-day observation period resulted in a relative frequency of psychotic talk of 0.91. During treatment (Fig. 2), the relative frequency dropped to less than 0.25; but, later on, it rose to a value exceeded only by the pretreatment level. The sudden increase in the patient's psychotic talk in the ninth week probably occurred because the patient had been talking to a social worker, who, unknown to the nurses, had been reinforcing her psychotic talk. The reinforcement obtained from the social worker appeared to generalize to her interaction with other patients and nurses. The patient herself told one of the nurses, "Well you're not listening to me. I'll have to go and see Miss ——— (the social worker) again, 'cause she told me that if she would listen to my past she could help me."

In addition to the reinforcement attributable to the social worker, two other instances of bootleg reinforcement came to light. One instance occurred when a hospital employee came to visit the ward, and, another, when volunteer ladies came to entertain the patients. These occasions were impossible to control, and indicate some of the difficulties of long-term control over verbal behavior.

It is of interest to note that since the reinforcement program began, the patient has not been attacked by the other patients and is only rarely abused verbally. These improvements were commented upon by the nurses, who were nevertheless somewhat disappointed. On the basis of the improvement shown in verbal behavior, the nurses had expected a dramatic over-all change which did not occur.

Strong Behavior Treated by Strengthening Incompatible Behavior

This case represented an attempt to control violent behavior by strengthening an incompatible class of responses, and to recondition normal social approaches while the violence was under control. The

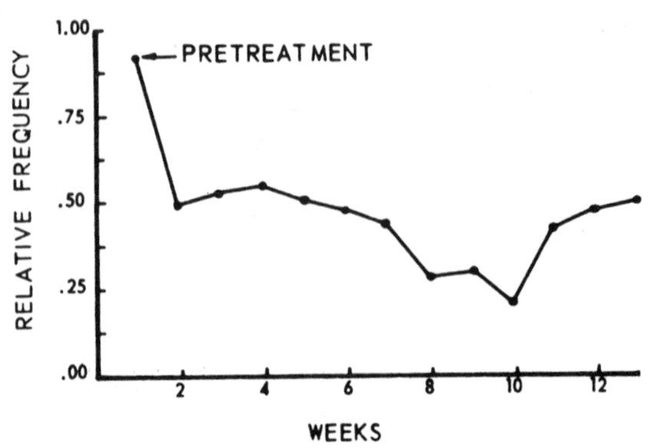

FIG. 2. Extinction of psychotic talk.

first phase was quite successful; but errors in strategy plagued the last half of the program, and it was terminated by the nurses because the patient became more violent.

The immediate reason for referral was that the patient, Dotty, had become increasingly violent over the last 5 years, and recently attacked several patients and hospital personnel without any apparent reason. Since admission and up to the present, she had received many electroconvulsive-therapy treatments aimed at reducing this violence, with little or no success. In 1947, a physician recommended her as a good case for psychosurgery. In December of the same year, she attempted to strangle her mother who was visiting her at the time. In July 1948, the patient had a leucotomy. The situation had recently become so serious that at the least suspicious move on her part the nurses would put her in the seclusion room. She spent from 3 to 12 hours daily in that room.

A 5-day pretreatment study, at 15-minute intervals, indicated that one of the nonviolent behaviors exhibited fairly often was "being on the floor" in the dayroom. The response included lying, squatting, kneeling, and sitting on the floor. Strengthening this class of responses would control the violence and, at the same time, permit the emotional behavior of other patients and nurses toward her to extinguish. To strengthen the patient's own social behavior, her approaches to the nurses were to be reinforced. The response "approach to nurse" was defined as spontaneous requests, questions or comments made by the patient to the nurse. Ultimately, the plan was to discontinue reinforcing being on the floor once the patient-nurse social interaction appeared somewhat normal. Presumably, this would have further increased the probability of approach to the nurses.

For the duration of the program, continuous social reinforcement was to be available for her approach to the nurses. Social reinforcement was to be available for the first 4 weeks only, on a fixed interval of 15 minutes, contingent on the response being on the floor. For the last 4 weeks, social reinforcement was to be withheld for being on the floor.

The following instructions were given to the nurses for the first 4 weeks of the program: "Reinforce (and tally) her approaches to you every time they occur. Check the patient every 15 minutes, and reinforce (and tally) the behavior being on the floor."

From the fifth week on the instructions were modified as follows: "Continue reinforcing (and tallying) her approaches to you every time they occur. Check the patient every 15 minutes, and tally but do not reinforce the behavior being on the floor."

During the period of reinforcement, as shown in Fig. 3, the relative frequency of the response being on the floor increased from the pretreatment level of less than 0.10 to a value of 0.21. During the succeeding 4 weeks of extinction, the frequency of being on the floor returned to the pretreatment level.

It was clear that being on the floor was incompatible with the fighting behavior and that the latter could be controlled by reinforcing the former. During the period of reinforcement for being on the floor, she attacked a patient once; but during the period of extinction, she made eight attacks on others. Her approaches to nurses increased over-all during the 4 weeks of reinforcement, but they decreased during the last 4 weeks, even though they were still being reinforced. This decrease paralleled the decrease in being on the floor. While being on the floor was undergoing extinction, attacks on the patients and nurses increased in frequency, and the nurses decided to return to the practice of restraining the patient. The program was terminated at this point.

The patient's failure to make the transition from being on the floor to approaching the nurses suggests that the latter response was poorly chosen. It was relatively incompatible with being on the floor. This meant that a previously reinforced response would have to be extinguished before the transition was possible, and this, too, was poor strategy with a violent patient.

Weak Behavior Strengthened by Escape and Avoidance Conditioning

Two female patients generally refused to eat unless aided by the nurses. One, Janet, had to be forcefully taken to the dining room, where she would permit the nurses to spoonfeed her. The other patient, Mary, was spoonfed in a room adjacent to the dining room. Both patients had little social contact with others and were reported to be relatively indifferent to attention by the nurses. Both were also reported to care only for the neat and clean appearance of their clothing. Mary had been at the hospital for 7 months, and Janet had been there for

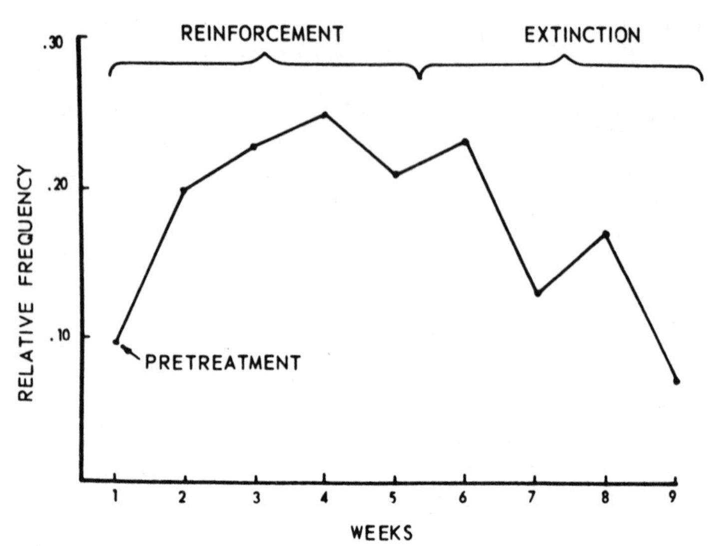

FIG. 3. Reinforcement and subsequent extinction of the response "being on the floor."

28 years. These two patients were in different wards and apparently did not know each other.

The program involved a combination of escape and avoidance conditioning, with food spilling as the aversive stimulus. All spoonfeeding was to be accompanied by some food spilling which the patient could escape by feeding herself after the first spilling, or avoid by feeding herself the entire meal. Social reinforcement was to be given contingent on feeding herself.

It was hoped that once self-feeding began to occur with some regularity, it would come under the control of environmental variables which maintain this behavior in most people, such as convenience, social stimulation at meal time, etc. In both cases, the program ultimately resulted in complete self-feeding, which now has been maintained for over 10 months. Janet's behavior change was complicated by a history of religious fasting, and her change took a little longer. Mary's case will be given here in detail.

The following instructions were given to the nurses: "Continue spoonfeeding the patient; but from now on, do it in such a careless way that the patient will have a few drops of food fall on her dress. Be sure not to overdo the food dropping, since what we want to convey to the patient is that it is difficult to spoonfeed a grown-up person, and not that we are mean to her. What we expect is that the patient will find it difficult to depend on your skill to feed her. You will still be feeding her, but you will simply be less efficient in doing a good job of it. As the patient likes having her clothes clean, she will have to choose between feeding herself and keeping her clothes clean, or being fed by others and risking getting her clothes soiled. Whenever she eats on her own, be sure to stay with her for a while (3 minutes is enough), talking to her, or simply being seated with her. We do this to reinforce her eating on her own. In the experience of the patient, people become nicer when she eats on her own."

During the 8-day pretreatment study, the patient ate 5 meals on her own, was spoonfed 12, and refused to eat 7. Her weight at this time was 99 pounds. Her typical reaction to the schedule was as follows: the nurse would start spoonfeeding her; but after one or two "good" spoonfuls, the nurse would carelessly drop some food on her dress. This was continued until either the patient requested the spoon, or the nurse continued spoonfeding her the entire meal. The behaviors the patient adopted included (a) reaching for the spoon after a few drops had fallen on her dress; (b) eating completely on her own; (c) closing her mouth so that spoonfeeding was terminated; or (d) being spoonfed the entire meal. Upon starting the schedule, the most frequent of all these alternatives was the first; but after a while, the patient ate on her own immediately. The relevant data are shown in Fig. 4. On the 12th day, the patient ate all three meals on her own for the first time. Four meals were refused out of the last 24: one meal was missed because she stated she didn't like "liver" and the other three because she said she was not hungry. Her weight when she left the hospital was 120 pounds, a gain of 21 pounds over her pretreatment weight.

Mary's relapse in the fifth week, after she had been eating well for 2 weeks, was quite unexpected. No reasonable explanation is suggested by a study of her daily records; but, after she had been spoonfed several meals in a row, the rumor developed that someone had informed the patient that the food spilling was not accidental. In any event, the failure to feed herself lasted only about 5 days.

Since the patient's hospital admission had been based on her refusal to eat, accompanied by statements that the food was poisoned, the success of the program led to her discharge. It is to be noted that although nothing was done to deal directly with her claims that the food was poisoned, these statements dropped out of her repertoire as she began to eat on her own.

Strong Behavior Weakened Through a Combination of Extinction for Social Attention and Stimulus Satiation

For 5 years, several mentally defective patients in the same ward, Harry, Joe, Tom, and Mac, had collected papers, rubbish, and magazines and carried these around with them inside their clothing next to their body. The most serious offender was Harry, whose hoarding resulted in skin rashes. He carried so much trash and so persistently

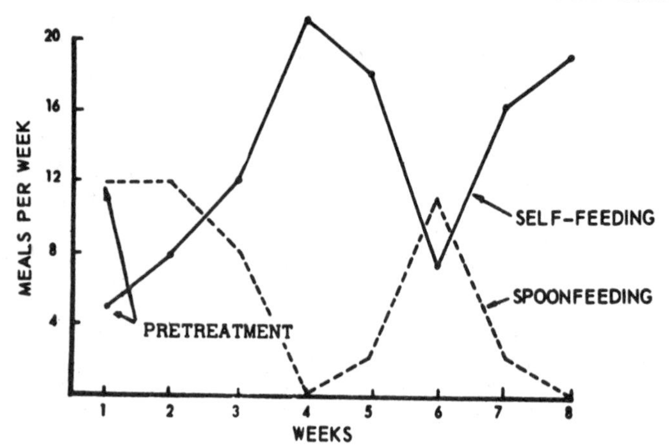

FIG. 4. Escape and avoidance conditioning of self-feeding.

that for the last 5 years the nurses routinely "dejunked" him several times during the day and before he went to bed.

An analysis of the situation indicated that the patient's hoarding behavior was probably maintained by the attention he derived because of it and by the actual scarcity of printed matter. There were few papers or magazines in the ward. Some were brought in occasionally; but since they were often torn up and quickly disappeared, the nurses did not bring them in very often.

It was expected that flooding the ward with magazines would decrease the hoarding behavior after the paradigm of satiation. Similarly, the availability of many magazines was expected to result in their being the major object of hoarding. The latter would facilitate an easier measurement of this behavior.

In addition, social reinforcement was to be withheld for hoarding magazines and rubbish. The results for all patients were essentially similar: a gradual decrease in hoarding. After 9 weeks of satiation and extinction, the program was terminated, since hoarding was no longer a problem. This improvement has been maintained for the last 6 months.

The following instructions were given to the nurses: "During this program the patients Harry, Mac, Joe, and Tom must not be given reinforcement (attention) for hoarding. There will be a full supply of magazines in the dayroom. Every night, after all patients have gone to bed, replenish the magazine supply in the dayroom. Every night while the patients are in bed, check their clothes to record the amount of hoarding. Do not, however, take their hoarding from them."

The original plan was to count the number of magazines in the patients' clothing after they had gone to bed. This is, in fact, the dependent variable shown in Fig. 5 for Joe, Tom, and Mac. The re-

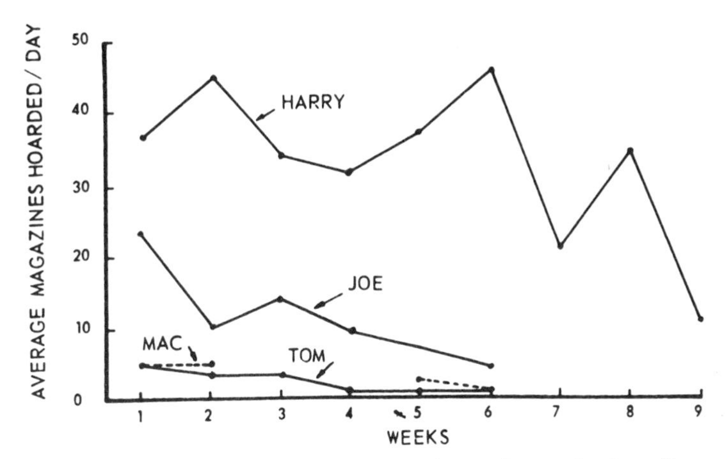

FIG. 5. Satiation and extinction of two forms of magazine hoarding.

cording for Harry had to be changed, however; after 4 days of the program, he no longer carried the rubbish or magazines in his clothing. Instead, he kept a stack of magazines on his lap while he was sitting in the dayroom. The number of magazines in his stack was counted when he left the dayroom for supper, and this is the dependent variable shown for Harry in Fig. 5. (Mac was out of the ward for 3 weeks because of illness.)

Prior to the program, one of the nurses questioned the possibility and even advisability of changing Harry's behavior. Her argument was that "behavior has its roots in the personality of the individual. The fact that he hoards so much indicates that Harry has a strong need for security. I don't see how we are going to change this need, and I also wonder if it is a good thing to do that." This was a point of view commonly encountered, especially regarding relatively nonverbal patients.

It would seem in this case that Harry transferred his security needs from hoarding rubbish and magazines to sitting in the dayroom and looking at magazines, especially during TV commercials. The transfer occurred with no apparent signs of discomfort on his part.

Other Cases

Combinations of extinction, reinforcement, and avoidance programs were set up for three patients; in two of these the problem behavior was eliminated in only a few weeks. The program of the third patient was followed for 20 days and then terminated since he had shown no changes by that time. An interpretation of the outcome of each of these programs is rendered questionable by the number of controlling variables involved and the nature of the changes.

The pretreatment study of four additional patients showed that the problem behavior of three of them did not occur often enough to justify carrying through a program; and in the fourth case, no easily controllable variables were available and, again, no program was undertaken.

Discussion

It is hoped that the results will provide encouragement to those who are in a position to conduct similar research. Therefore, it will be useful to mention a few other aspects of this work.

A major problem concerns the use of nurses as experimental assistants as well as substitutes for the recording and programming apparatus of the laboratory. There is no question as to the greater reliability of the ordinary laboratory component. In large part, however, the nurses' failures in carrying out *E*'s instructions were unsystematic with respect to the results obtained, and although undesirable, they do not by any means render this kind of work uninterpretable. Systematic errors in observation can be reduced to some extent by dealing with response classes that are relatively easily identified. But, of course, this problem will become more serious as efforts are made to alter more subtle aspects of behavior. Perhaps the only solution is to be dissatisfied with one's techniques and principles until the behavioral changes are so obvious as to render statistical analysis superfluous.

Another question concerns the acceptability of this approach to the hospital staff. The nurses and psychiatrists who were familiar with the "reinforcement programs," as they were called, were given questionnaires and interviews to determine their attitudes toward this work. The results indicate a mildly favorable reception in general, with some enthusiastic support from both nurses and psychiatrists.

Regarding time actually spent in carrying out the programs, it might seem unreasonable to expect the already overworked nurse to devote 2 or 3 minutes every half-hour to observation and recording. However, this is only about 40 minutes of an 8-hour shift; and, besides, much of her work stems from patients' behavior problems, the elimination of which would make the 40 minutes an excellent investment of time.

Two sources of possible misunderstanding between *E* and nurses should be pointed out. First, when nurses were asked about the sort of problems they had in the ward, if no dramatic behaviors, such as attempts at suicide, or violent acts, had been recently reported, they often denied having any problems. Problems also went unrecognized because they were considered unsolvable. For example, since most nurses attributed the behavior of a patient to his diagnosis or age, little or no effort was made to discover and manipulate possibly relevant environmental variables.

Second, even after a behavior had been modified, it was not uncommon to hear nurses remark, "We've changed her behavior. So what? She's still psychotic." It seemed that once a persistent problem behavior was eliminated, its previous importance was forgotten and other undesirable aspects of the patient's repertoire were assumed to be the most important ones. In general, their specific expectations were unclear or unverbalized, and they tended to be somewhat dissatisfied with any change less than total "cure."

Finally, an objection often raised against this approach is that the behavior changes may be only temporary. However, permanent elimination of ward behavior problems requires a permanent elimination of the environmental variables that shape them up and maintain them. The clinical belief that a favorable behavioral change, if properly accomplished, will be permanent probably rests on a faulty evaluation of the role of environmental variables in controlling behavior. Certainly, it is not based on any actual accomplishments in the field of mental health.

References

1. Ayllon T. The application of reinforcement theory toward behavior problems. Unpublished doctoral dissertation, University of Houston, 1959.
2. Ferster, C. B., and Skinner, B. F.: *Schedules of reinforcement.* New York: Appleton-Century-Crofts, 1957.

24

EXPERIMENTAL ANALYSIS OF HYSTERICAL BLINDNESS

by John Paul Brady, M.D., and Detlev L. Lind, A.B.

Introduction

The viewpoint adopted for experimental purposes in this study was that the behavior of an organism is generated and maintained chiefly by its consequences on the environment. Over a wide range of conditions, a hungry rat, placed in a so-called "Skinner box," will persist in pressing a bar if, as a consequence of this response, a pellet of food is delivered to it at least some of the time. This exemplifies the principle of reinforcement which is at the core of current behavior theory. Conditioning of this type is termed operant (instrumental) to distinguish it from respondent (classical Pavlovian) conditioning. The probability of a given response in relation to the conditions of reinforcement of that response has been the subject of much study of Skinner (4), Ferster and Skinner (2) and others. Recently, controlled experiments conducted with human subjects using cubicles analogous to the "Skinner box" have demonstrated the existence of these same relationships in human behavior and the feasibility of analyzing human behavior within this methodological framework (3). However, the relationships between an organism's behavior, its environmental consequences, and the disposition or probability of the organism to repeat a particular response often is obscure in so complex a psychobiological unit as man. For example, when a man behaves in a given way, the most important consequence of his activity, from the standpoint of reinforcement, may be its effect on some part of his intricate social or intrapersonal environment. Further, the given behavior or its effect may be readily understood only in terms of its "symbolic meaning." Nevertheless, much of man's behavior, both normal and aberrant, can be analyzed in terms of these general principles and influenced by their systematic application (5).

Reprinted from the *Archives of General Psychiatry,* April 1961, Vol. 4, pp. 331-339.

The present report concerns the application of operant conditioning methodology in the study of a patient with hysterical blindness. In the course of this study, the patient, who had been totally blind for 2 years, regained his sight. It is not the primary purpose of the present report to argue the utility of these techniques for the removal of hysterical symptoms or for psychiatric therapy generally. Rather, the intent is to demonstrate the unique advantages this methodological approach offers for the systematic analysis of symptomatic behavior within a controlled, experimental context. In the present instance, some of the variables of which the patient's seeing or not seeing were a function were studied by operant conditioning techniques. An attempt was made to influence his disposition to see by manipulating some of these variables in accordance with experimentally demonstrable principles. In the course of the study, note was taken of the patient's verbal and social behavior in addition to the operant response (pressing a button) being measured. Some of these clinical observations, elicited in part by the conditioning procedure, were quite understandable in terms of the conventional psychodynamic concept of hysteria.

Report of Case

The patient, now 40 years of age, was born on a farm in rural Indiana, the youngest of 4 children in a poor family. The father was described as an irresponsible man, who quit the family group entirely when the patient was 11, and has not been heard from since. He depicts his mother as the strong and determining force in the family group especially with respect to him during his early years. It is of interest that the patient had 2 maternal aunts who were totally blind during their last years. He refers to them as "nice old ladies."

The patient was shy and retiring during his childhood and left school (the eighth grade) at the age of 16 because he "liked work better." He held a variety of jobs, chiefly unskilled, but never stayed at any more than a few months.

He was married in 1942, after a very brief courtship, to a woman who worked as a welder in the factory at which he also was employed. The patient describes her as "often nervous and upset," but it is clear that she makes the important decisions in the house and that he is greatly dependent on her. From his description of his married life, one gets the picture of almost constant harassment from his wife and mother-in-law. Nonetheless, he speaks of his wife only in the most endearing terms. They have 2 children, a boy 13 and a girl 17.

Shortly after his marriage, the patient, then 23, was drafted into the Army where he served for 3 years. He did not see active combat, but worked as a teletype operator and truck driver in the United States and England. One incident is of interest. While driving an Army truck in England, he had an accident with a civilian driving a sports car in which the civilian was seriously injured. He states that he can now recall nothing of the accident scene or the period of investigation by civilian and military authorities which immediately followed, although he himself was not injured in any way. This is one of several examples of the patient's ability to repress large areas of experience, visual and other, with remarkable facility. While still in the Army, the patient developed dendritic keratitis of the right eye, following a tonsillectomy. Corneal scarring resulted, and the visual acuity of the right eye was reduced to 20/80. Shortly after this, he was given a medical discharge from the Army and was awarded a small pension because of the loss of vision.

After release from service, the patient had a succession of semiskilled jobs, remaining at none for more than a year. He seemed to tolerate responsibility poorly and was very sensitive to criticism. During this period, there were 3 minor recurrences of his eye infection which were treated conservatively in the hospital. On each occasion, he requested an increase in his pension, but this was denied since the visual acuity of the affected eye had not decreased. Between his discharge from the Army in 1945 and the occurrence of his total blindness 12 years later, his general adjustment was poor. He depended greatly on public assistance and financial aid from relatives because of frequent periods of unemployment and poor planning in general.

Three days before Christmas in 1957, the patient, while shopping in a supermarket with his wife and mother-in-law, suddenly became totally blind in both eyes. He is able to recall few details of the episode, and no immediate precipitating event is apparent. It did occur at a time when his wife and mother-in-law were being more demanding than usual, requiring him to work nights and weekends at various chores under their foremanship. One immediate consequence of his blindness was, then, partial escape from this situation. The family group first interpreted the blindness in theurgic rather than medical terms and sought counsel from its Fundamentalist minister. Several days later, however, the patient was admitted to a veterans' hospital, where he remained for 2 weeks. Neurological and ophthalmological examinations were negative except for the small corneal scar in the right eye described previously. A diagnosis of total hysterical blindness was made. At the time, the patient did not seem greatly alarmed by his loss of sight, but instead had an attitude of patient forbearance. The obvious discrepancy between his report of total blindness and his ability to get about on the ward was apparent. He was not concerned with this, but felt hurt and unjustly accused when other patients pointed out this discrepancy to him. The nature of his illness was explained to him, and interviews under sodium pentothal were conducted in an effort to increase his vision. Blindness persisted, however. Immediately after release from the hospital, the patient applied for training for the blind through an appropriate public agency. Several months later, he was admitted to a veterans' diagnostic center, where several additional neurological and ophthalmological examinations were conducted with similar negative results, and the diagnosis of hysterical blindness was confirmed. Although the blindness was not considered service-connected, a special pension was awarded because of his total disability. During the 18 months which intervened between his discharge from the diagnostic center and the beginning of the present treatment program, the patient was treated at an outpatient psychiatric clinic 2 hours weekly, without results. Various drugs were used as adjuvant treatments, as well as sodium pentothal interviews, but to no avail.

Because of the long history of generally poor adjustment, the fixity and duration of the symptoms, and the patient's resistance to psychotherapeutic intervention, a program of rehabilitation for the totally blind was recommended. His subsistence was derived from his government pension, financial aid from the local community to his underage children, some financial assistance from relatives, and other community resources on which he came to depend more and more. During these 18 months, he seldom left his house, but spent most of his time listening to radio or recorded reading supplied to him by an agency for the blind. Although he made some effort to learn Braille and to rehabilitate himself in other ways, he gradually came to depend on his wife more and more to meet his ordinary needs.

In summary, this is a man who developed total hysterical blindness which proved refractory to psychiatric intervention of various sorts for 2 years. Although the immediate precipitating cause of his blindness is not clear, one might conjecture, in dynamic terms, that somatically converted angry feelings toward a controlling wife upon whom he was greatly dependent were an important factor. Several items from the history could well support hysterical blindness as a symptom choice in this man: his exposure as a child to his 2 totally blind aunts; a recurrent eye infection which did leave him with some loss of vision and for which he was compensated financially; his immaturity, and his tendency to use amnesic repression as a means of adjustment. The long duration of the symptom despite psychiatric treatment may be accounted for, in part, by his passivity, the dependency needs which the symptom helped him satisfy, and the sizeable pension he was receiving for the disability.

Behavioral Principles

A patient with total hysterical blindness is generally able to get around better than a patient with total blindness from an organic lesion. He states he can see nothing, yet is able to avoid large obstacles in walking, handle eating utensils, reach accurately for small objects, etc. This indicates that the hysterical patient does "see" in some sense. *Dynamically,* one would say that the patient reports being blind because he is consciously unaware of seeing. *Behaviorly,* one would say that the patient is not making full use of visual cues as evidenced by the fact that his behavior is not adequately under control. In order to study experimentally the effects of visual cues on the control of behavior, it is necessary first to generate some relatively stable behavior upon which the effect of visual stimuli can be measured. For this purpose, an operant-conditioning situation was selected in which the behavioral requirement for reinforcement (reward) would be the spacing of responses (button-pressing) in a prescribed way. Specifically, the patient would be required to space his responses between 18 to 21 seconds. In other words, a response which followed the preceding response by less than 18 seconds or more than 21 seconds would not be reinforced, but would simply reset the apparatus for the start of another period. A response which followed the preceding response within the specified time interval (18 to 21 seconds) would be reinforced. Technically, such a schedule of reinforcement is termed a differential reinforcement of low rate (DRL) of 18 seconds, with a limited hold of 3 seconds.

It is convenient to study the performance of an individual on such a schedule by recording the actual intervals between responses (the inter-response times) over class intervals of 3 seconds each. The number of responses in each 3-second interval is recorded automatically and the number falling in the 18-to-21 second interval constitutes the patient's "score" for that session. After a stable distribution of inter-response times had been generated in this way, visual stimuli could be introduced to serve as cues for the correct spacing of responses. In other words, the patient can acquire more reinforcements (improve his score) by making use of visual cues. Hence, the effects of such cues on his operant performance and behavior in general can be systematically studied. One might wonder how so fixed a symptom as this man's blindness could be manipulated by simply differentially reinforcing responses that are contingent upon his making use of visual cues. However, use can be made of several behavioral principles demonstrable by the controlled study of operant behavior in lower animals.

Choice of Reinforcers. The potency of a reinforcer in maintaining behavior is a function of its importance to the organism. Rather than a single specific reinforcer, such as candy, multiple, generalized reinforcers were used. Use was made of the patient's great need for approval and sensitivity to criticism in bringing his behavior under experimental control. When he did well during testing, i.e., made a high score, he was given praise and approval. Conversely, when he did poorly, i.e., made a low score, disapproval and criticism were expressed toward him. These social reinforcers were supplemented by more tangible rewards and punishments, such as special privileges and trips to the hospital canteen, or withdrawal of these when he did poorly.

Immediacy of Reinforcement. The effectiveness of a reinforcer is a function also of the temporal proximity of the behavior and the reinforcing event. This is seen especially in the child who repeatedly eats green apples for the immediate pleasure it gives, although he knows they will give him a stomach-ache several hours later. Such behavior is characteristic also of the immature adult. Much of the present patient's financial and social difficulties are related to this. Hence, maximum use can be made of approval, praise, and other reinforcers by delivering them immediately after each testing session. The environmental consequences of his blindness which tend to favor its continuation are more remote in time.

Successive Approximation. This is the technique of developing complex responses in an organism by starting with some behavior in his present repertoire, and, by a series of small steps and the use of appropriate reinforcement, gradually approaching the desired behavior. Very complex responses involving difficult discriminations can be developed in lower animals by this technique. In the present study, the patient would be expected to show small but steady improvement in his score on successive sessions. His behavior first would come under the control of gross visual stimuli, and, later, after a series of small steps, under the control of finely discriminative stimuli.

Stimulus Generalization. After a stimulus has been conditioned to evoke a given response, similar stimuli tend to evoke the same response. In the present instance, it was anticipated that the control exerted over the patient's behavior by the visual stimuli in the experimental room would gradually generalize to visual stimuli produced in other situations (on the ward, home on visits, etc.). These visually cued responses then would be reinforced outside the testing room by the consequences of seeing which generally support this behavior in the community (e.g., enjoying television, ambulating easily, sight of a friend, etc.).

Testing Procedure

The present program tested started 2 weeks after the patient entered the hospital for the fourth time since the onset of his blindness. At this time, he was complaining not of his blindness, but of a variety of minor gastrointestinal symptoms, without structure change. He was told that his digestive symptoms and blindness were related and that both would be treated by "reconditioning therapy." With no further explanation, the patient was started on a program of operant conditioning entailing two ½ hour sessions daily, 5 days a week.

At the start of each session, the patient was led into a small rectangular room and seated alone at a desk. His hand was placed on a small button mounted in a box (Fig. 1). He was instructed to try to space his responses between 18 and 21 seconds as described earlier. For the remainder of the session, he was then left alone in the room. A correctly spaced response (18-21 seconds since the previous) caused a buzzer to sound, while an incorrectly spaced response (less than 18 or more than 21 seconds) caused no buzzer to sound but merely reset the apparatus for the start of another interval. After several practice sessions, visual stimuli of varying intensity and topography were introduced in the room in a manner described below. The entire experimental procedure was programmed automatically by appropriately designed switching circuits. This equipment, along with devices for recording the inter-response times (IRT's) automatically was housed in an adjoining room.

Results

It will be convenient to discuss the results of the study in 5 phases corresponding to 5 experimental conditions.

I. (*Sessions 1 Through 6*). During Phase I, the illumination of the testing room was held constant, and there were no visual cues for the 18-to-21 second intervals.

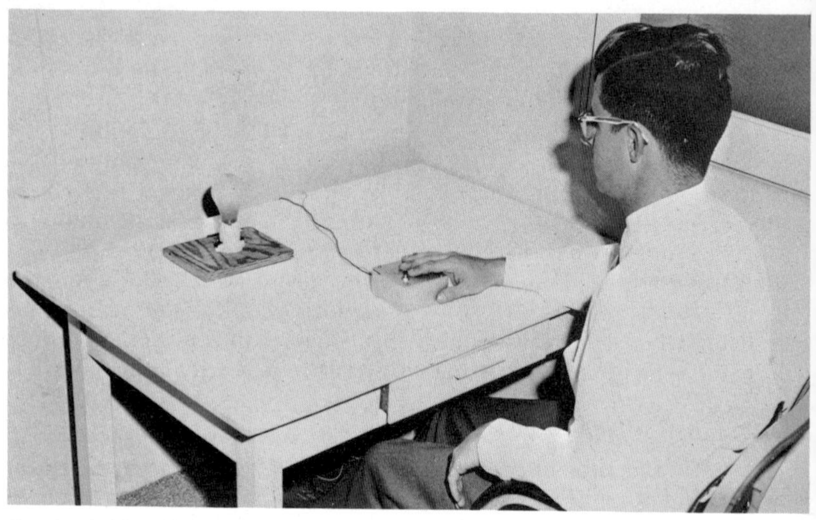

FIG. 1. Subject in experimental room. The light bulb was present as shown during Phases III and IV only.

After several days, the patient's performance became stable. Most responses fell within the correct interval, i.e., spaced 18-21 seconds apart, which rang the buzzer (reinforcement) and added to the patient's score for that day. Fig. 2 shows the distribution of inter-response times (IRT's) for the sixth session. Note that in addition to the peak in the 18-to-21 second interval, a second peak appears in the first or 0-to-3 second interval. These first interval responses do not represent gross inaccuracies in the patient's effort to space his responses 18-21 seconds apart, but rather, "multiple" responses. On these occasions, the patient has pressed the button 2 or more times in rapid succession instead of making one discrete response. In some animal experiments, "multiple" responses on a schedule of this type (DRL) are considered to be related to the "emotionality" of the animal during testing. In the present study, they appeared to correlate with the patient's manifest anxiety. Indeed, the percentage of responses falling in this first interval may serve as an independent behavioral measure of the patient's affective state.

Clinically, the patient was moderately anxious during this phase of the study. The gastrointestinal symptoms which occasioned his admission to the hospital gradually disappeared, but there was no change in his blindness.

II. (*Sessions 7 Through 16*). During this phase, a light bulb was present in the room located where it could not be seen directly by the seated patient. The voltage delivered to the bulb was reduced by means of a variable voltage transformer so that, when lit, the illumination in

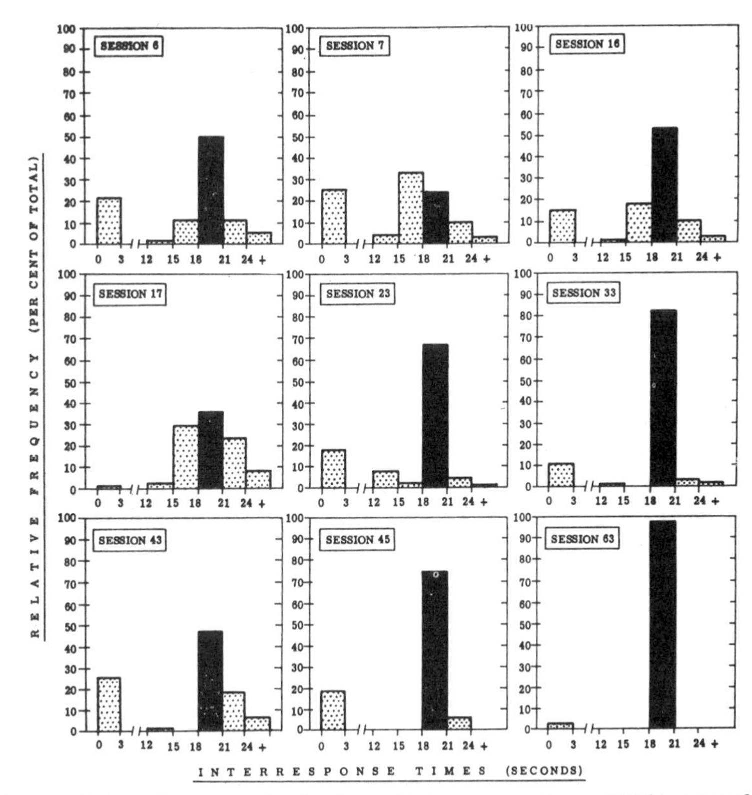

FIG. 2. Relative frequency distributions of interresponse times (IRT's) grouped into class intervals of 3 seconds each. Responses falling in the 18-to-21 second interval (black) are reinforced. IRT's between 3 and 12 seconds (occurring only rarely) have been omitted.

the room was increased by a barely perceptible amount. The light was programmed to go on after 18 seconds had elapsed since the last response and to go off again 3 seconds later. In other words, the appearance of the light corresponded exactly with the period during which a response would be reinforced (causing the buzzer to sound and adding to the patient's score for that session). The patient could greatly improve his score by making use of the visual cue thus provided.

Introducing this barely perceptible light had a profound influence on the patient's operant responding. Note the marked deterioration in the percentage of correct responses when the light was first introduced (Session 7 of Fig. 2). The introduction of this visual cue, then, was accompanied by deterioration rather than improvement in score. The greatest number of responses was made prematurely, in the 15-to-18 second interval. Premature responses reset the apparatus and hence postponed the appearance of the light. In other words, the approach of the crucial 18-to-21 second interval, now accompanied by a light, constituted a *preaversive situation*. By responding prematurely, the patient precluded the appearance of the light and thereby avoided an aversive experience. Note also the large number of responses in the first interval (multiple responses).

The *clinical* effect of introducing visual cues was equally dramatic. The patient came out of the seventh session trembling and perspiring and reported feeling "very frightened." He was unable to account for his marked distress, but reported simply that he suddenly became very afraid during the testing session. He gave no indication of being consciously aware of a light in the room. While still very apprehensive, at the end of the session, the patient made some spontaneous comments regarding his relationship with his wife. He recounted several episodes in which he became extremely angry at her.

With reassurance, the patient returned to the testing situation the next day, and his score gradually improved again in the sessions which followed. By the 12th session, the percentage of correct responses was back to the level obtained before the light was introduced (Phase I). There was also less anxiety. He then seemed to reach a plateau, with about 50% of his responses correctly spaced (as in Session 16, Fig. 2). In an effort to account for the patient's failure to improve his score beyond that obtained when no light was present (Phase I), he was observed directly during Session 16. This was done without his knowledge by means of a peephole drilled in the wall of a closet in the room. He was observed to be resting his head on the table, his eyes covered by his forearm, during the entire session. In other words, he learned to avoid the now aversive and anxiety-provoking light by the simple expedient of covering his eyes. Since he was not told that a visual cue would be provided, and was not "consciously aware" of the light, this was acceptable and appropriate behavior in the situation.

III. (*Sessions 17 Through 23*). It was decided to place the light at its full intensity (about 100 watts) in clear view in front of the patient and to tell him of its presence (Fig. 1). He was told that the light would help him determine when to press the button and eventually enable him to make a perfect score and to see normally again. He expressed doubt about regaining his sight, but agreed to the new testing arrangements. Again, the light went on only during the 3-second interval during which a response would be reinforced.

Fig. 2 shows the distribution of IRT's for the first session under these conditions (Session 17). Again, the number of correctly spaced responses fell (36% of total). The patient expressed concern over his poor performance and sought approval; he did not appear more anxious than usual, however. In the new situation making the presence of the visual cues known to the patient seemed to avoid the recurrence of anxiety, even though the performance was disrupted as before. The percentage of multiple (first-interval) responses was small, again in keeping with the level of overt anxiety present.

By making continued approval and acceptance contingent upon a continually improving score, the patient's percentage of correct responses gradually increased. In Session 23, 67% of his responses were correctly spaced (Fig. 2), but he was still unaware of seeing. He accounted for his high percentage of correctly spaced responses by reporting that he could feel the heat thrown off by the light bulb when it came on. This was clearly an unconscious rationalization for his use of visual cues, however, since the temperature changes were too small to be detected. There was some return of anxiety, again reflected in the percentage of 0-3 second IRT's.

IV. (*Sessions 24 Through 45*). It was decided to decrease the intensity of the light by means of the variable voltage transformer in the circuit. The patient was told that this would be done gradually, so that he would switch over from feeling the heat of the bulb (which he admitted would become too small to be detected) to seeing it. As rewards continued to be delivered or withdrawn in accordance with his performance the patient's score continued to improve while the intensity of the light was reduced in small decrements. Eighty-two per cent of his responses were correctly spaced in Session 33 (Fig. 2).

The patient's score continued to improve in the sessions which followed.* His adjustment on the ward and his relationships with others also improved. He became less defensive about his blindness and less guarded in his behavior, entering into ward activities and aiding the nurses in various chores. Although he still reported seeing nothing, he used visual metaphors with increasing frequency, especially in the context of angry feelings toward his wife or mother-in-law. For example, he frequently spoke of not "seeing eye to eye" with his wife or having felt so angry toward her he "couldn't see straight."

The patient's operant behavior changed abruptly in Session 43 (Fig. 2). The percentage of responses during the correct interval dropped to half its previous value (48%), and the number of multiple responses (first-interval) rose sharply. At the end of the session, the patient came out of the room exclaiming that he could see the light. He appeared both anxious and exhilarated, and sought praise and approval for his accomplishment. He accounted for his poor score during this session despite his awareness of visual cues by stating that he felt almost para-

* During four of the sessions (No.'s 34, 40, 49, and 55) the interval that was reinforced, and the corresponding visual cues, was varied randomly among the 15-to-18, 18-to-21, and 21-to-24 second intervals to ascertain that the patient was not relying on the temporal cue of 18 seconds to guide his responses. Since the patient obtained a high score during these sessions also, reliance on a temporal cue was ruled out.

lyzed by the light. His score improved rapidly over the next 2 sessions, however, and he became less anxious (Session 45, Fig. 2).

V. (*Sessions 46 Through 63*). Now that the patient was able to make use of the visual cues provided by the 40-watt bulb on the desk in front of him, it was decided to introduce more difficult discriminative stimuli. At first, a stimulus board of 4 small lights mounted in a row was substituted for the single large bulb. This was programmed so that a change in pattern of the lights (the end two going off and the middle two coming on) signaled that 18 seconds had elapsed since the previous response. After this, a stimulus panel was used which consisted of a small pane of translucent glass on which various geometrical designs could be projected. With each change in experimental conditions, the correct spacing of responses was contingent upon making finer visual discriminations. With each new discriminative problem, the patient's performance was poorer for a few sessions and then gradually improved. Fig. 2 shows the distribution of IRT's for the patient's last session (No. 63), in which a difficult visual discrimination was used. Except for a few multiple responses, all the presses were separated by 18-21 seconds, indicating a reinforcement on each occasion. The formal operant sessions were discontinued at this point.

During this phase of the study, the patient's clinical condition continued to improve. He used the visual modality (and was aware of seeing) more and more on the ward and at home during visits. After operant conditioning was discontinued, more conventional therapy was instituted. This consisted largely of support and efforts to rehabilitate him socially and vocationally.

Comment

In this study a chronic hysterical symptom has been analyzed and manipulated by operant conditioning techniques. The experimental program was such that the number of correctly spaced responses served as an index of the patient's use of visual cues and the number of multiple (first interval) responses a behavioral measure of his anxiety.

When visual cues were first introduced in the testing situation, profound effects were noted in the patient's clinical condition and operant behavior which are of interest from a psychodynamic point of view. Modern psychoanalytic theory would regard the patient's blindness as a manifestation of repression and his relative freedom from overt anxiety as an indication of the "success" of this repression. Put another way, anxiety maintains the repression, and any threat to this repressive defense would be accompanied by an increase of anxiety. In the present study, the patient was only moderately anxious in the testing situation when the spacing of responses was not cued by visual stimuli (Phase I). However, when such cuing was first introduced in Phase II, the responses were reinforced only in the presence of a visual stimulus, the coincidence of light and response simulated the visual *control* of his responses, and intense anxiety was observed. It may be argued that the patient's repression was weakened momentarily and anxiety was generated. As mentioned earlier, the aversive property of the light is evidenced by the shift in mode of the distribution of the IRT's to the earlier 15-to-18 second interval (Session 7 of Fig. 2). The patient's spontaneous remarks at this time suggested the areas of life experience and feelings which occasioned the development of the neurosis. This was confirmed by later clinical observations. These findings would seem to corroborate experimentally the dynamic view of hysterical blindness as a manifestation of repression, which, in turn, is maintained by anxiety.

In Phase III the patient was told that visual cues would be present. Again a disruption in performance was seen but little anxiety. It appears that alerting the patient to the presence of the light facilitated its repression and little anxiety was generated. In the sessions that followed the patient's behavior came more and more under control of visual cues; anxiety gradually mounted again and he defended himself for a time against conscious awareness of the cues by the rationalization that he could feel the bulb's heat. When he finally reported seeing, he was intensely anxious for a short time. After this it was possible to bring the patient's responding under finer and finer visual stimulus control until a high degree of visual acuity was demonstrated. This generalized to outside the testing situation.

The issue of therapy per se has been largely omitted by intention, but a few comments are in order. Eysenck (1) has recently reviewed the treatment of neurotic symptoms by techniques derived from learning theory, and Walton and Black (6, 7) have reported on the treatment of hysterical aphonia and other disorders by conditioning techniques, but within a different theoretical framework than the present essay. The treatment of psychiatric disorders by operant conditioning techniques is being studied at several centers in the United States. In the present study, it might be argued that the whole testing procedure constituted "psychotherapy" in the broad sense of the term, and that the specific conditioning procedures were incidental. This argument would be more persuasive, however, had the patient not proved so refractory to the many, but more usual, psychotherapeutic measures that were taken over a long period. Further, the systematic reappearance of anxiety, the occurrence of preaversive avoidance behavior, and the evolution of behavior clearly under the control of environmental cues support the authors' contention that return of visual function was specifically related to the events programmed in the testing procedure. Once visual function was regained by the process of successive approximation described earlier, the patient was amenable to more conventional rehabilitative techniques. For a time he worked at a community rehabilitation center during the day and stayed at the hospital at night. Seven months ago he was discharged from the hospital and returned to his own community.

He now returns to the hospital laboratory at monthly intervals for follow-up evaluation and general support; he is in on other treatment at this time. For several months his visual ability has been unchanged. On testing he is able to read small case newspaper print, to identify geometrical patterns, and to identify small objects. In a social situation, his performance is more variable. Sometimes he is slow to recognize the faces of persons who knew him when he was blind. Also, in the presence of these same persons, he walks with the awkward gait he exhibited when totally blind. Perhaps a more meaningful index of his present clinical condition, however, is his performance in the everyday business of living. He is gainfully employed in his community (as a switchboard operator), and is managing his family responsibilities and other affairs in a satisfactory manner. It is now 13 months since he first reported seeing.

Summary

An experimental analysis of hysterical blindness by operant conditioning techniques is reported to illustrate the utility of this method for the study of psychiatric conditions. Clinical data, in part evoked by the conditioning procedure, also are reported. These are usually conceptualized within a "psychodynamic" framework. Some areas of *rapprochement* between concepts derived from dynamic theory and operant conditioning are suggested. Brief comments are made on some therapeutic aspects of the study.

References

1. Eysenck, H. J.: Learning theory and behaviour therapy. *J. Ment. Sci., 105*: 61-75, 1959.
2. Ferster, C. B., and Skinner, B. F.: *Schedules of Reinforcement*. New York: Appleton-Century-Crofts, 1957.
3. Lindsley, O. R.: Characteristics of the behavior of chronic psychotics as revealed by free-operant conditioning methods. *Dis. Nerv. Syst., 22*: 66-78, 1960.
4. Skinner, B. F.: *The Behavior of Organisms*. New York: Appleton-Century-Crofts, 1938.
5. Skinner, B. F.: *Science and Human Behavior*. New York: Macmillan, 1953.
6. Walton, D., and Black, D. A.: The application of learning theory to the treatment of stammering, *J. Psychosom. Res., 3*: 170-179, 1958.
7. Walton, D., and Black, D. A.: The application of modern learning theory to the treatment of chronic hysterical aphonia, *J. Psychosom. Res., 3*: 303-311, 1959.

25

REDUCTION IN RATE OF MULTIPLE TICS BY FREE-OPERANT CONDITIONING METHODS

by Beatrice H. Barrett, Ph.D.

The experimental investigation of neuromuscular tics has probably been most limited by difficulties in developing sensitive and reliable behavioral measurement techniques. The closest approximation to an experimental study of tics, by Yates (18), was based on a patient's records of her ability to reproduce her tic symptoms. Yates did not attempt to obtain objective records or measurement of the patient's tics.

The method of free operant conditioning, originally developed by Skinner (15) to study animal behavior and later modified by Lindsley (9) to study the behavior of chronic psychotics, has provided precise techniques of behavioral measurement and control. These techniques have been extended to the investigation of such pathological behaviors as vocal hallucinatory episodes (10, 11, 12), pressure of speech (13), and stuttering (7). By the application of free operant techniques, Ferster (5) succeeded in expanding the very limited behavioral repertories of two autistic children, and Brady and Lind (3) performed an experimental analysis with therapeutic results in a patient with hysterical blindness.

The basic datum of the free operant method is the frequency of a specific and reliably defined response within a controlled experimental environment. The method is most readily applied, therefore, in cases where changes in the rate of a repeated movement are of primary concern. The present report describes an application of free operant methods to the control of multiple neuromuscular tics.

Method

Patient

The patient in this experiment was a 38-year-old veteran, hospitalized in the Neurology Service of a local Veterans Administration hos-

Reprinted from *The Journal of Nervous and Mental Disease,* Vol. 135, No. 3, September, 1962, pp. 187-195.

pital.* His extensive multiple tics started approximately 14 years ago, during his term of duty in the armed services. Although a medical discharge was available to him, the patient chose to continue in the service, eventually serving overseas, until regular discharge. Since then he has been employed as an accountant by a single firm.

An interview prior to the experiment revealed that the patient knew of no traumatic experience preceding the abrupt onset of tics. He told of awakening during the night with a choking sensation accompanied by a momentary inability to breathe or swallow. He recalled this as a frightening experience and was puzzled by the subsequent development of tics. Within a few months, spasmodic movements had developed in much of his body. At the time of this experiment, his major movements included contractions of neck, shoulder, chest, and abdominal muscles, head nodding, bilateral eye blinking, opening of the mouth, and other comparatively mild facial movements.** The patient complained of difficulty in swallowing, hence of slow ingestion. His clear, intelligent speech was marked only occasionally by barely noticeable hesitation.

In recent years the patient was not fully aware of the presence of his tics. On occasion, when he thought himself relatively free of them, his wife reported that there was no reduction in his twitching. The patient did feel, however, that his movements were reduced in frequency while he was playing his saxophone in a local band on weekends. His greatest concern was the extent to which his tics made him conspicuous to strangers and limited his business advancement. In general, little was known of the patient's personal history.

The patient had undergone psychological counseling for a number of months and had received pharmacological treatment which included a variety of tranquilizing and muscle-relaxing drugs. Neither treatment had afforded symptomatic relief. The patient displayed no outstanding symptoms of psychopathology. His tics were considered symptomatic of an extrapyramidal system disturbance and untreatable by conventional methods.

Since he had experienced no success with other methods, the patient was highly motivated to participate in this experiment. Although he was soon discharged to return to work in a neighboring state, he voluntarily rehospitalized himself two months later for continuation of the experiment.

* The author is grateful to Norman Geschwind, M.D., Department of Neurology, Boston VA Hospital, who suggested the experimental behavioral study of this patient and who arranged for space and the loan of various apparatus components.

** Some of the patient's movements were so strong that, when he was seated in a chair on casters, they caused slight rolling.

Arrangement of Apparatus

Patient's enclosure. A quiet, well ventilated room with observation facilities was equipped with a comfortable swivel-tilt armchair, an ashtray, a set of comfortable earphones which the patient wore throughout all experimental sessions, and a Grass EEG console (see Fig. 1).

Operandum. A large U-shaped magnet, securely attached to the outside of the chair back, served as a convenient device for summating multiple tics. Although the swivel arc of the chair was restricted and the chair's casters removed, its tilt was freely operative. An induction coil rested in a "nest" of electrical tape strung between the poles of the magnet.* Slack in the tape was adjusted so that when the patient was seated in the chair his most noticeable spasmodic movements, regardless of locus or amplitude, created a slight movement of the coil in the magnetic field.

Response definition and recording. The current induced in the moving coil was amplified by one channel of an EEG recorder to operate a sensitive relay. The operations of this relay were directly recorded as tics. The duration and amplitude of the recorded tics were determined by setting the amplifier gain so that each strong and obvious tic would operate the response relay and cumulative response recorder. After initial selection, this amplifier gain was held constant throughout the experiment.

Response-contingent Events

In free operant conditioning, the frequency of a response is altered by programing particular consequences contingent upon the emission of that response. Generally this method has been used to generate steady rates of responding or to increase the frequency of a given response. When *reduction* in the frequency of a symptom is desired, the event contingent upon symptom occurrence may be 1) the removal of a positive stimulus or 2) the presentation of an aversive stimulus. In this experiment, both types of tic-contingent events were used.

By the use of a tape recorder, a positive stimulus (music) could be removed or an aversive stimulus (noise) presented when a tic occurred. Pulses from the response relay were transmitted through a timer to a circuit which controlled the tape recorder output to the patient's earphones (see schema in Fig. 1). All recording and controlling equipment was located in a nearby room.**

* Michael J. Malone, M.D., offered the general idea of the "tic chair" and magnetic pickup.

** The cooperation, assistance, and patience of David Adkins and the staff of the EEG laboratory at the Boston VA Hospital made possible the occupancy of sufficient space to approximate good environmental control.

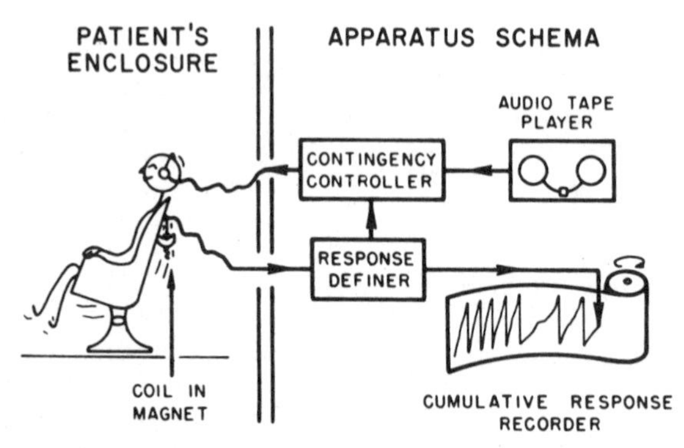

FIG. 1. Schema of apparatus used to pick up, automatically record, and program the contingent consequences of multiple ties.

Music. In order to maximize the patient's interest, the music used in the experiment was selected by the patient himself from the hospital's music library. Boredom and satiation were minimized by using several selections with no repetitions.

The contingency arrangement was programed so that each tic produced a 1.5 second interruption of music. If the patient did not tic for at least 1.5 seconds, he could hear the music until it was automatically interrupted by the next tic. In effect, this schedule differentially reinforced time intervals between tics of 1.5 seconds or more.†

Noise. Azrin (1) found that responses could be eliminated by making the presentation of white noise contingent upon their occurrence; and Flanagan, Goldiamond and Azrin (7) successfully reduced chronic stuttering by presentation of a stutter-produced loud tone. In the present experiment a tape loop of white noise (60 db) was used as a tic-produced aversive stimulus.

The contingency was arranged so that each tic produced 1.5 seconds of noise over the patient's earphones. When the patient was tic-free for at least 1.5 seconds, the noise was automatically interrupted and did not recur until the next tic.

Contingency Testing

As a control measure to test the effect of the contingencies described above, periods of continuous music and continuous noise were used. This amounted to removal of the contingency requirement which, in the case of music, more nearly approximated the conditions of music therapy.

† In technical terms, this schedule is a time contingent crf drl of 1.5 seconds with an unlimited hold (6).

Self-control

The effects of music and noise were compared with the patient's own efforts to control his tics. A signal light (60 watt bulb) was introduced and the patient was instructed to control his tics by his most frequently used methods for as long as the light was on.

Experimental Sessions

The patient was informed that we would be studying the effects of various conditions on his tic rate. He had selected a lasting supply of music tapes with the understanding that he would hear them at least some of the time during the experiment. He was instructed to make himself comfortable and to remain seated in the chair, with earphones on, throughout the sessions. Aside from previously mentioned instructions concerning the signal light, no further explanation was given. The experimental room was closed, and recording was begun. Experimental conditions were changed without interruption by adjusting the controlling equipment. The duration of sessions varied from two to three hours depending on meal schedules and other hospital routines. No attempt was made to set up predetermined time intervals for each experimental condition. With a few exceptions due to time limits, each condition was run long enough to show its maximal effect when compared with the normal tic rate or operant level.

Results

Cumulative records of the first four sessions showing the effects of music and noise on tic rate are shown in Fig. 2.* These sessions were conducted during a 48-hour period prior to the patient's discharge. The remaining sessions were held two months later when the patient voluntarily rehospitalized himself for continuation of the experiment.

To facilitate comparison of tic rates under the various experimental conditions, the continuous records in all figures have been telescoped and grouped. The steeper the slope of the curves, the higher the tic rate. Rate estimates may be made by reference to the grid showing rates for representative slopes.

Operant level determinations. The patient's normal tic rate (operant level) ranged between 64 and 116 tics per minute (tpm), with some decrease in the short run at 4E during the last session in Fig. 2. No diurnal variations in tic rate were noted. Although sessions were run

* The cumulative response recorder feeds paper at a constant speed while each tic impulse moves the recording pen one step in a vertical direction. After 450 tics have been recorded, the pen automatically resets to the base and is ready to step up with the next tic (see Fig. 1). Horizontal lines in the curves are periods when no tic impulses occurred.

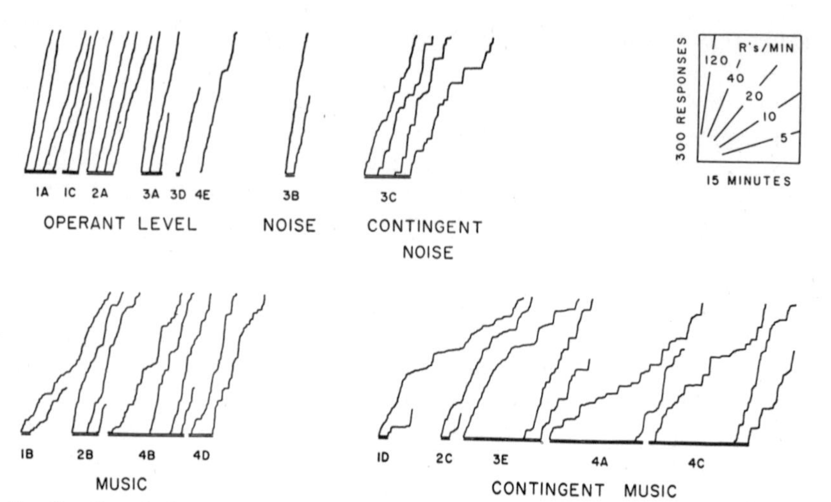

FIG. 2. Cumulative response records of the first four experimental sessions showing changes in tic rate under conditions of tic-contingent noise and tic-contingent interruption of music and control runs of both noise and music without the contingency requirement. The experimental sessions are numbered and the sequence of conditions within each session identified by letters. Double bars connect all immediately successive curves under designated conditions. Breaks in double bars indicate a change of conditions.*

* For example, the first four pen excursions labeled 1A were continuously recorded tics during a 26-minute period at the start of the first session to get an operant level. Without interruption, the 1B curves follow, showing 27 minutes of tics under continuous music. The two curves labeled 1C record a return to the operant level for 10 minutes, followed immediately by the 1D period of 34 minutes with each tic producing interruption of the music. The 2A curves show operant level rates at the start of session 2, followed by 25 minutes of continuous music (2B), then 21 minutes of tic-contingent interruption of music (2C), and so on. The same identification system is used in Fig. 4 for sessions 7 and 8.

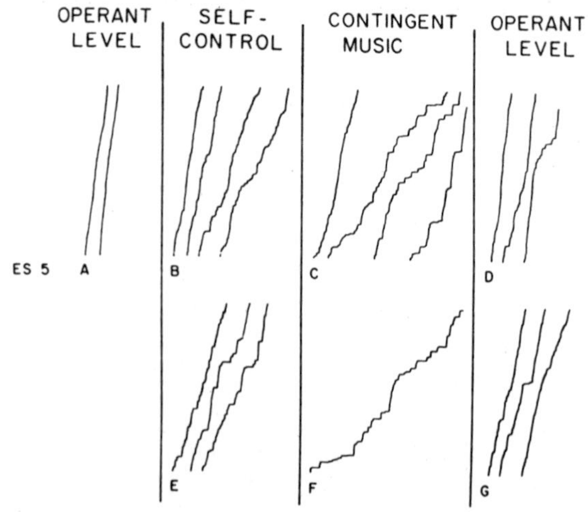

FIG. 3. A continuous cumulative record of the fifth experimental session showing rate changes under sustained self-control compared with the greater reduction under tic-produced interruption of music. The sequence of conditions is indicated by letters.

during various hours of the day and evening to capitalize on limited time, neither fatigue nor hunger affected tic rate or response to experimental conditions.*

Effects of noise. There was a very slight increase in the tic rate during a brief seven-minute period when continuous white noise (60 db) was played ("noise" in Fig. 2). However, when made tic-contingent, noise reduced the tic rate to about 40 tpm ("contingent noise" in Fig. 2). The long tic-free intervals toward the end of the contingent noise period may have been due to dozing which the patient later reported. Because of its apparent soporific effect, noise was not used further.

Effects of music. Continuous music ("music" in Fig. 2) reduced the tic rate about as much as did contingent noise (40 tpm). However, when each tic interrupted the music ("contingent music"), the rate was lowered to 15 to 30 tpm. During every period of contingent music, the effect of the contingency was an additional reduction of 40 to 50 per cent in tic rate. After the first session there was no overlap between the range of rates under continuous music and under tic-contingent interruption of music. The differential magnitude of these effects on this patient thus requires no statistical test.

The fact that contingent music produced a greater reduction in rate of ticing than did continuous music appears to be the result of longer, more frequent tic-free periods when the contingency was in effect. The improbability of fatigue effects is indicated by a comparison of the 4A rate under contingent music obtained at the start of a morning session with the 1D, 2C, and 3E rates under this condition recorded at the end of the three previous sessions.

Effects of self-control. The tic-reducing effect of contingent music is compared with the patient's sustained efforts of self-control in Fig. 3 (fifth session). In response to instructions and a signal light, the patient reduced his tic rate to 50 to 60 per minute. This rate is only slightly higher than that previously obtained with contingent noise and non-contingent music. Under the condition of tic-contingent interruption of music, however, rates were considerably lower, ranging from 20 to 35 per minute.** Again there was no overlap between the range of rates under the three conditions (operant level, self-control, and contingent music). Note the initial rapid tic rate at the beginning of the C period of contingent music. This increase in rate following a period of self-control (B) parallels what clinicians have observed in tiqueurs

* Sessions 2, 4, and 8 were run in the morning and terminated for the patient's lunch; sessions 1 and 3 occurred in the afternoon; sessions 5 and 7 were conducted in the evening.

** This differential effect was reproduced repeatedly in session 6, which is not shown here.

(17). It appears that this effect was strong enough to counteract temporarily the effect of the contingent music (C).

In addition to the differential effects on tic rate of self-control and the music contingency condition, there was also a difference in the patient's general behavior topography. In the B period of self-control, the patient was observed to engage in headholding and general prolonged contraction. In contrast, during the E period of self-control, he engaged in relaxed tapping with finger or foot and occasional singing. This new form of behavior was first observed as the patient accompanied contingent music in the C period.

These differences in behavior topography shown during the B and E periods of self-control may account for the longer tic-free intervals in E than in B. They may also explain the differential response to contingent music in C and F. In other words, it appeared that the patient used two different methods of reducing his tics and that these two methods had different effects on subsequent tic reduction under contingent music. During B, self-control was effected by a generalized rigid contraction which was followed in C by an initial increase in rate despite the availability of contingent music. In contrast, during E self-control was achieved through release methods with the subsequent rapid and marked rate reduction under contingent music (F).

Reliability of the effect of contingent music. The previously described data from six experimental sessions showed that tic-contingent interruption of music reduced the patient's tic rate far more than did non-contingent music, tic-produced white noise, or the patient's efforts at self-control. During those sessions, the patient had approximately six hours' exposure to contingent music. Following a two-month interruption of the experiment, the reliability of the tic-reducing effect of contingent music was subjected to empirical test by a series of replications on the same patient.* The result of alternating operant level control periods (7A, 7C, 7E, and 7G; and 8A, 8C, 8E, and 8G) with periods of tic-produced interruption of music (7B, 7D, and 7F; and 8B, 8D, and 8F) are shown in Fig. 4. The effect of contingent music on tic-free intervals was dramatically and reliably demonstrated by reductions of from 55 to 85 per cent below the operant rate on each of these six replications.

The tic-reducing effect of contingent music was more immediate and prolonged than in earlier sessions. Tic-free intervals were, for the most part, considerably longer and more frequent than previously, and only brief bursts of tics occurred with high local rate. The patient expressed irritation at the end of session 8 because he had wanted to hear the

* Both Claude Bernard, in 1865 (2), and Murray Sidman, in 1961 (14), have pointed out that the most convincing test of reliability of an "effect" is the demonstration of its reproducibility in a series of replications.

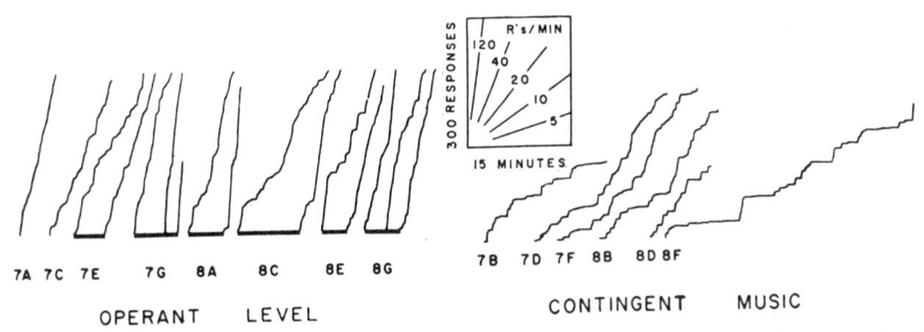

FIG. 4. Records of sessions 7 and 8 demonstrating reproducibility of the marked tic-reducing effect of tic-contingent interruption of music in six replications. Letters designate the sequence of conditions within numbered sessions.

remainder of a jazz concert being played during 8F (the period with lowest tic rate: nine per minute). He commented that he was concentrating on the musical ideas and became annoyed when his brief bursts of tics interrupted it. During most of the 44-minute 8F period of contingent music he was observed to be almost motionless as he listened to the music.

The pattern of tic-free intervals followed by brief intervals of heightened local rate which developed in response to contingent music appeared to generalize to the operant ticing rate as early as session 4. If this was a true generalization, it may have therapeutic implications. On the other hand, it may simply represent a minor shift of unknown nature in the tic rate. Because of possible operandum unreliability (discussed below), the most valid comparisons should be limited to the differential effects of self-control, non-contingent music, and contingent music relative to the operant tic rate.

Intrasession decrease in operant level rate did appear with regularity during the last two sessions (Fig. 4). Operant tic rates 7C, 7E, 8C, and 8E, which were recorded between periods of contingent music, showed somewhat longer tic-free intervals than those recorded at the beginning of these sessions (7A and 8A) or those recorded at the end of these sessions (7G and 8G). The reasons for this decrease are far from clear, but the decrease may have something to do with attention. The patient reported that during these sessions he was anticipating more music and knew he would not hear it if he had many tics.

Discussion

The results of this experiment clearly demonstrate that non-contingent music and tic-contingent white noise reduced the tic rate to a level comparable with that produced by self-control. A far more powerful reduction was produced by tic-contingent interruption of music.

In evaluating the differential control of tic rate shown in these data and the possible extensions of the basic method to other symptoms for either therapeutic or research purposes, the most pertinent consideration is the design of the operandum, the device which permits the symptom to operate a switch (16). Two major requirements of a good operandum are the reliability of its operation and the specificity of the response class which actuates it.* The fragile tape arrangement of our crude operandum does not insure reliable operation for continued general application. It is not stable enough to maintain accurate calibration during repeated use. A more stable operandum might have permanently fixed pickups, preferably embedded in upholstery in different areas of a chair.

Although a chair operandum provided a relatively comfortable situation for the patient, it did restrict his motility more than might be desired. Moreover, it was not specific to tic movements alone. A more tic-specific operandum would be operated solely by tic movements. Improved specificity of tic measurement without restrictions on motility might be obtained by pickups placed at the loci of various tics which would be telemetered by transmitters worn on the patient's belt or in a pocket (8). The patient could then engage in routine daily activities while effects of interest are continuously recorded.

Once the operandum requirements have been refined, therapeutic effects can be more reliably evaluated. The use of tic-contingent interruption of music could be extended in time or otherwise modified. For example, the duration of the tic-free interval necessary to produce music could be progressively lengthened. With remote recording, the long term effects of an appropriate contingency arrangement could be evaluated by furnishing the patient with a portable contingency controller to plug into his home radio or television set for relief of his symptom. The contingencies for music and noise, already demonstrated to be effective, could be combined in a multiple contingency whereby each tic would bring 1.5 seconds of noise and pauses greater than 1.5 seconds would bring music, until the next tic impulse simultaneously interrupted the music and restored the white noise.

The observed behavior changes offered as possible explanations for differential tic rates recorded under self-control could be objectively measured to evaluate the interaction between symptomatic and nonsymptomatic responses. For example, if operanda had been provided for simultaneously recording the patient's finger-tapping and singing, it might have been possible to show an inverse relationship between

* Ferster (4) has discussed in some detail the general requirements of an accurate operandum (manipulandum). This device, which is manipulated by the subject's behavior, also defines the response being conditioned or attenuated. It is the point of contact between the subject and the automatic recording equipment. For these reasons its operating characteristics are of utmost importance.

the rate of vocalizing and finger-drumming and the tic rate. In addition, experiments could be run to determine whether tic movements may be diminished or even eliminated by differentially reinforcing another more circumscribed and more socially acceptable motor response which serves the same discharge function as tics.

A free operant conditioning analogy to the negative practice technique used by Yates (18) could be readily investigated by positively reinforcing the patient for each tic. If this variation of the method is therapeutic, positive reinforcement of the symptom should be followed by reduction in the operant tic rate.

The general aspects of the pickup and continuous recording system described here provide a method for direct and objective behavioral measurement of motor symptom frequency which would be useful in studying the effects of drugs, the influence of attention, and variations in tic rate during diagnostic or therapeutic interviews.

Summary

A method for continuous automatic recording of the rate of multiple tics has been used in a demonstration of differential control of tic rate by free operant conditioning procedures.

The results showed that the multiple tics of a neurological patient, previously refractory to pharmacological and psychological therapies, could be reduced in rate by self-control, by tic-produced white noise, and by continuous music. The most dramatic, rapid, and reliable reduction resulted from tic-produced interruption of music. The power of tic-contingent environmental consequences in controlling this patient's symptom was shown, and suggestions were offered for extending and refining the basic method for more definitive investigations of this and other motor disturbances.

References

1. Azrin, N. H.: Some effects of noise on human behavior. *J. Exp. Anal. Behav., 1*: 183-200, 1958.
2. Bernard, C.: *Introduction to the Study of Experimental Medicine*. Paris, 1865, translated 1927. Dover Publications, New York, 1957.
3. Brady, J. P. and Lind, D. L.: Experimental analysis of hysterical blindness. *A.M.A. Arch. Gen. Psychiat., 4*: 331-339, 1961.
4. Ferster, C. B.: The use of the free operant in the analysis of behavior. *Psychol. Bull., 50*: 263-274, 1953.
5. Ferster, C. B.: The development of performances in autistic children in an automatically controlled environment. *J. Chron. Dis., 13*: 312-345, 1961.
6. Ferster, C. B. and Skinner, B. F.: *Schedules of Reinforcement*. Appleton-Century-Crofts, New York, 1957.

7. Flanagan, B., Goldiamond, I. and Azrin, N. H.: Operant stuttering: The control of stuttering behavior through response-contingent consequences. *J. Exp. Anal. Behav., 1*: 173-177, 1958.
8. Hefferline, R. F.: Learning theory and clinical psychology—an eventual symbiosis? In Bachrach, A. J., ed. *Experimental Foundations of Clinical Psychology*. Basic Books, New York, 1962.
9. Lindsley, O. R.: Operant conditioning methods applied to research in chronic schizophrenia. *Psychiat. Res. Rep. Amer. Psychiat. Ass., 5*: 118-139, 1956.
10. Lindsley, O. R.: Reduction in rate of vocal psychotic symptoms by differential positive reinforcement. *J. Exp. Anal. Behav., 2*: 269, 1959.
11. Lindsley, O. R.: Characteristics of the behavior of chronic psychotics as revealed by free-operant conditioning methods. *Dis. Nerv. Syst. Monogr. Suppl., 21*: 66-78, 1960.
12. Lindsley, O. R.: Direct measurement and functional definition of vocal hallucinatory symptoms in chronic psychosis. Paper presented at Third World Congress of Psychiatry, Montreal, Canada, June, 1961.
13. Shearn, D., Sprague, R. L. and Rosenzweig, S.: A method for the analysis and control of speech rate. *J. Exp. Anal. Behav., 4*: 197-201, 1961.
14. Sidman, M.: *The Tactics of Scientific Research*. Basic Books, New York, 1961.
15. Skinner, B. F.: *The Behavior of Organisms*. Appleton-Century, New York, 1938.
16. Skinner, B. F.: Operandum. *J. Exp. Anal. Behav., 5*: 224, 1962.
17. Wechsler, I. S.: *Clinical Neurology*. Saunders, Philadelphia, 1952.
18. Yates, A. J.: The application of modern learning theory to the treatment of tics. *J. Abnorm. Soc. Psychol., 56*: 175-182, 1958. Reprinted in Eysenck, H. J., ed. *Behaviour Therapy and the Neuroses*. Pergamon Press, New York, 1960.

Ogden R. Lindsley, Ph.D., Director of Behavior Research Laboratory, Metropolitan State Hospital, Waltham, Massachusetts, generously supplied the diagrammatic sketch in Figure 1 and the controlling and recording equipment. His advice and encouragement were invaluable in the conduct of this experiment. This research was supported by Research Training Grant 2M-7084 and Research Grant MY-2778 from the National Institute of Mental Health, U.S. Public Health Service.

SUPPLEMENTARY BIBLIOGRAPHY

The following resource articles are confined to the English language and, in general, focus upon the practical applications of conditioning and associated techniques in the clinical situation. Duplication of papers already referred to in the introductory or reprinted material has been avoided. The many pertinent articles appearing in issues of *Behaviour Research and Therapy* other than volume 1 No. 1 have been excluded from this bibliography.

Alexander, L. Effect of hydroxyphenamate on the conditional psychogalvanic reflex in man. *Dis. nerv. Syst., Suppl. 22,* No. 9, 1961, 17-24.

Alexander, L. A conditional autonomic response (the conditional psychogalvanic reflex) as a parameter of psychiatric diagnosis. *Dis. nerv. Syst.,* 1962, *23,* 597.

Ashem, B. The treatment of a disaster phobia by systematic desensitization. *Behav. Res. Ther.,* 1963, *1,* 81-84.

Astrup, C. *Schizophrenia: conditioned reflex studies.* Springfield, Ill.: Chas. C. Thomas, 1962.

Ayllon, T. Intensive treatment of psychotic behaviour by stimulus satiation and food reinforcement. *Behav. Res. Therap.,* 1963, *1,* 53-61.

Azrin, N. H., Holz, W., Ulrich, R. & Goldiamond, I. The control of the content of behavior through reinforcement. *J. exp. anal. Behav.,* 1961, *4,* 25-30.

Babladelis, G. Personality and verbal conditioning effects. *J. abnorm. soc. Psychol.,* 1961, *62,* 41-43.

Baer, D. M. Laboratory control of thumbsucking by withdrawal and representation of reinforcement. *J. exp. anal. Behav.* 1962, *5,* 525-528.

Bandura, A. Psychotherapy as learning process. *Psychol. Bull.,* 1961, *58,* 143-159.

Barrett, B. H., & Lindsley, O. R. Deficits in acquisition of operant discrimination and differentiation shown by institutionalized retarded children. *Amer. J. ment. Def.,* 1962, *67,* 424-436.

Beier, D. C. Conditioned cardiovascular responses and suggestions for the treatment of cardiac neuroses. *J. exp. Psychol.,* 1940, *26,* 311-321.

Bender, L. & Schilder, P. Unconditioned and conditioned reactions to pain in schizophrenia. *Amer. J. Psychiat.,* 1930, *87,* 365-384.

Bijou, S. W. & Orlando, R. Rapid development of multiple-schedule performances with retarded children. *J. exp. anal. Behav.,* 1961, *4,* 7-16.

Blakemore, C. B., Thorpe, J. G., Barker, J. C., Conway, C. G. & Lavin, N. I. The application of faradic aversion conditioning in a case of transvestism. *Behav. Res. Ther.,* 1963, *1,* 29-34.

Bond, I. K. & Hutchinson, H. C. Application of reciprocal inhibition therapy to exhibitionism. *Canad. med. Ass. J.,* 1960, *83,* 123-128.

Botwinick, J., & Kornetsky, C. Age differences in the acquisition and extinction of the GSR. *J. Geront.,* 1960, *15,* 83-84.

Bridger, W. H. Contributions of conditioning principles to psychiatry. In *Pavlovian conditioning and psychiatry*. Group for the Advancement of Psychiatry, Symposium No. 9, 1964, 181-198.

Brady, J. P., Levitt, E. E., & Baydan, N. An operant-reinforcement paradigm in the study of drug effects. *Dis. nerv. Syst.*, 1962, *23*, 1-6.

Brady, J. P., Pappas, N., Tausig, T. N. & Thornton, D. R. MMPI correlates of operant behavior. *J. clin. Psychol.*, 1962, *18*, 67-70.

Bullock, D. H. Some aspects of human operant behavior. *Psychol. Rec.*, 1960, *10*, 241-258.

Bullock, D. H. & Brunt, M. Y., Jr. The testability of psychiatric patients in an operant conditioning situation. *Psychol. Rec.*, 1959, *9*, 165-170.

Buss, A. H., & Durkee, A. Conditioning of hostile verbalizations in a situation resembling a clinical interview. *J. consult. Psychol.*, 1958, *6*, 415-418.

Chaiklin, J. B., Ventry, I. M., & Barrett, L. S. Reliability of conditioned GSR pure-tone audiometry with adult males. *J. speech hear. Res.*, 1961, *4*, 269-280.

Clark, D. F. The treatment of menosymptomatic phobia by systematic desensitization. *Behav. Res. Ther.*, 1963, *1*, 63-68.

Clark, D. F. Fetishism treated by negative conditioning. *Brit. J. Psychiat.*, 1963, *109*, 404-407.

Cohen, E. & Cohen, B. D. Verbal reinforcement in schizophrenia. *J. abnorm. soc. Psychol.*, 1960, *60*, 443-446.

Cohen, L. H., Hilgard, E. R. & Wendt, G. R. Sensitivity to light in a case of hysterical blindness studied by reinforcement-inhibition and conditioning methods. *Yale J. Biol. Med.*, 1933, *6*, 61-67.

Cooper, A. J. A case of fetishism and impotence treated by behaviour therapy. *Brit. J. Psychiat.*, 1963, *109*, 649-652.

Corn-Becker, F., Welch, L., & Fisichelli, V. Conditioning factors underlying hypnosis. *J. abnorm. soc. Psychol.*, 1949, *44*, 212-222.

Cowan, E. A., & Foulke, M. Variation in susceptibility to the conditioning of inhibition as an index of constitutional type. *Child Developm.*, 1934, *5*, 201-236.

Cowden, R., & Ford, L. Systematic desensitization with phobic schizophrenics. *Amer. J. Psychiat.*, 1962, *119*, 241-245.

Crosby, N. D. Essential enuresis: successful treatment based on physiological concepts. *Med. J. Austral.*, 1950, *2*, 533-543.

Crowell, D. H., Peterson, J. & Safely, M. A. An apparatus for infant conditioning research. *Child Developm.*, 1960, *31*, 47-51.

DeMyer, M. K., & Ferster, C. B. Teaching new social behavior to schizophrenic children. *J. Amer. acad. Child Psychiat.*, 1962, *1*, 443-461.

Dinoff, M., Horner, R. F., Kurpiewski, B. S., Richard, H. C., & Timmons, E. O. Conditioning verbal behavior of a psychiatric population in a group therapy-like situation. *J. clin. Psychol.*, 1960, *16*, 371-372.

Dinoff, M., Horner, R. F., Kurpiewski, B. S., & Timmons, E. O. Conditioning verbal behavior of schizophrenics in a group therapy-like situation. *J. clin. Psychol.*, 1960, *16*, 367-370.

Doll, E. A., & Aldrich, C. G. Simple conditioning as a method of studying sensory discrimination among idiots. *J. gen. Psychol.*, 1932, *7*, 104-142.

Ellson, D. G. Experimental extinction of an hallucination produced by sensory conditioning. *J. exp. Psychol.*, 1941, *28*, 350-361.

Eriksen, C. W., & Kuethe, J. L. Avoidance conditioning of verbal behavior without awareness: a paradigm of repression. *J. abnorm. soc. Psychol.*, 1956, *55*, 203-209.

Ferster, C. B., & deMyer, M. K. Increased performance of an autistic child with prochlorperazine administration. *J. exp. anal. Behav.*, 1961, *4*, 84.

Ferster, C. B., Levitt, E. E., Zimmerman, J. & Brady, J. P. The measurement of hypnotic effects by operant-reinforcement techniques. *Psychol. Rec.*, 1961, *11*, 427-429.

Field, J. G., & Brengelmann, J. C. Eyelid conditioning and three personality parameters. *J. abnorm. soc. Psychol.*, 1961, *63*, 517-523.

Flanagan, B., Goldiamond, I., & Azrin, N. H. Operant stuttering: the control of stuttering behavior through response-contingent consequences. *J. exp. anal. Behav.*, 1958, *1*, 173-177.

Flanagan, B., Goldiamond, I., & Azrin, N. H. Instatement of stuttering in normally fluent individuals through operant procedures. *Science*, 1959, *130*, 979-981.

Fleck, S. The cardiac component of orienting behavior: response to stimuli of varying intensity. *Amer. J. gen. Psychol.*, 1953, *48*, 163-168.

Fleck, S. Vigilance (orienting behavior) conditional reactions and adjustment patterns in schizophrenic and compulsive patients. *Ann. N.Y. Acad. Sci.*, 1953.

Franks, C. M. Recidivism, psychopathy and delinquency. *Brit. J. Delinq.*, 1956, *6*, 192-201.

Franks, C. M. Conditioning and personality: a study of normal and neurotic subjects. *J. abnorm. soc. Psychol.*, 1956, *52*, 143-150.

Franks, C. M. Alcohol, alcoholism and conditioning: a review of the literature and some theoretical considerations. *J. ment. Sci.*, 1958, *104*, 14-33.

Franks, C. M., & Leigh, D. The conditioned eyeblink response in asthmatic and non-asthmatic subjects. *J. psychosom. Res.*, 1959, *4*, 88-98.

Franks, C. M., & Trouton, D. Effects of amobarbital sodium and dexamphetamine sulfate on the conditioning of the eyeblink response. *J. comp. physiol. Psychol.*, 1958, *51*, 220-222.

Franks, Violet & Franks, C. M. Conditionability in defectives and in normals as related to intelligence and organic deficit: the application of a learning theory model to a study of the learning process in the mental defective. In B. W. Richards (Ed.) *Proc. Lond. Conf. Sci. Stud. Ment. Def.*, Dagenham, England: May & Baker, 1960, pp. 577-583.

Fuller, P. R. Operant conditioning of a vegetative human organism. *Amer. J. Psychol.*, 1949, *62*, 587-590.

Galloway, T. F., & Butler, A. Conditioned eyelid response to tone as an objective test of hearing. *J. speech hear. Dis.*, 1956, *21*, 47-55.

Gantt, W. H. Principles of nervous breakdown—schizokinesis and autokinesis. *Ann. N.Y. Acad. Sci.*, 1953, *56*, 143-163.

Gantt, W. H. Objective methods in psychiatric diagnosis. *Dis. nerv. Syst.*, 1962, *23*, 596-597.

Gardner, G. E. The conditioned reflex of Pavlov: conditioned behavior. *New Engl. J. Med.*, 1941, *225*, 775-777.

Gardner, L. P. Responses of idiots and imbeciles in a conditioning experiment. *Amer. J. ment. Def.*, 1944-45, *49*, 459-462.

Gesell, A. The conditioned reflex and the psychiatry of infancy. *Amer. J. Orthopsychiat.*, 1938, *8*, 19-30.

Gillison, T. H., & Skinner, J. L. Treatment of nocturnal enuresis by the electric alarm. *Brit. med. J.*, 1958, *2*, 1268-1272.

Gladfelter, J. H., & Hall, J. A. The relationship of hypnotic phenomena to conditioning. *Texas Rep. Biol. Med.*, 1962, *20*, 53-60.

Gliedman, L. H., Gantt, W. H., & Teitelbaum, H. A. Some implications of conditional reflex studies for placebo research. *Amer. J. Psychiat.*, 1957, *113*, 1103-1107.

Golin, S. Incubation effect: role of awareness in an immediate versus delayed test of conditioned emotionality. *J. abnorm. soc. Psychol.*, 1961, *63*, 534-539.

Granda, A. M., & Hammack, J. T. Operant behavior during sleep. *Science*, 1961, *133*, 1485-1486.

Grings, W. W., Lockhart, R. A., & Dameron, L. E. Conditioning autonomic responses of mentally subnormal individuals. *Psychol. Monogr.*, 1962, *76*, No. 39.

Grings, W. W., Lowell, E. L., & Rushford, G. M. Role of conditioning in GSR audiometry with children. *J. speech hear. Dis.*, 1959, *24*, 380-390.

Halberstam, J. L. Some personality correlates of conditioning, generalization and extinction. *Psychosom. Med.*, 1961, *23*, 67-76.

Headrick, M. W. Operant conditioning in mental deficiency. *Amer. J. ment. Def.*, 1963, *67*, 924-929.

Hefferline, R. F., & Perera, T. B. Proprioceptive discrimination of a covert operant without its observation by the subject. *Science*, 1963, *139*, 834-835.

Higgins, H. L. The conditioned reflex of Pavlov: practical clinical applications, especially to children. *New Engl. J. Med.*, 1941, *225*, 772-775.

Holmes, F. B. An experimental investigation of a method of overcoming children's fears. *Child Developm.* 1936, *7*, 6-30.

Holz, W. C., Azrin, N. H., & Ayllon, T. Elimination of behavior of mental patients by response-produced extinction. *J. exp. anal. Behav.*, 1963, *6*, 407-414.

Hutchinson, R. R., & Azrin, N. H. Conditioning of mental hospital patients to fixed-ratio schedules of reinforcement. *J. exp. anal. Behav.*, 1961, *4*, 87-95.

Isaacs, W., Thomas, J., & Goldiamond, I. Application of operant conditioning to reinstate verbal behavior in psychotics. *J. speech hear. Dis.*, 1960, *25*, 8-12.

Ischlondsky, N. The role of the cortex in consciousness as learned from conditioned-reflex studies. *J. nerv. ment. Dis.*, 1952, *116*, 440-453.

Ivanov-Smolensky, A. G. On the methods of examining the conditioned food reflexes in children and in mental disorders. *Brain*, 1927, *50*, 138-141.

Ivanov-Smolensky, A. G. Neurotic behavior and teaching of conditional reflexes. *Amer. J. Psychiat.*, 1927, *84*, 483-488.

Ivanov-Smolensky, A. G. The pathology of conditioned reflexes and the so-called psychogenic depression. *J. nerv. ment. Dis.*, 1928, *67*, 346-350.

Jersild, A. T., & Holmes, F. B. Methods of overcoming children's fears. *J. Psychol.*, 1935, *1*, 75-103.

Jones, H. G. Specific conditioning treatment of enuresis nocturna. *Cerebral Palsy Bull.*, 1961, *3*, 227-236.

Kant, F. Further modifications in the technique of conditioned-reflex treatment of alcohol addiction. *Quart. J. Stud. Alcohol,* 1944, *5,* 229-232.

Kant, F. The conditioned reflex treatment in the light of our knowledge of alcohol addiction. *Quart. J. Stud. Alcohol,* 1944, *5,* 371-377.

Kempf, E. J. Neuroses as conditioned, conflicting, holistic, attitudal, acquisitive avoidant reactions. *Ann. N.Y. Acad. Sci.,* 1953, *56,* 307-329.

King, G. F., Armitage, S. G., & Tilton, J. R. A therapeutic approach to schizophrenics of extreme pathology. An operant-interpersonal method. *J. abnorm. soc. Psychol.,* 1960, *61,* 276-286.

King, G. F., Merrell, D. W., Lovinger, E., & Denny, M. R. Operant motor behavior in acute schizophrenics. *J. Personal.,* 1957, *25,* 317-326.

Kopeloff, N., Upton, M. F., Raney, M. E., & Kopeloff, L. M. Typhoid agglutinins as influenced by the conditioned reflex in man. *Proc. Soc. exper. Biol. Med.,* 1932, *30,* 11-12.

Krasnogorski, N. I. The conditioned reflex and children's neuroses. *Amer. J. Dis. Child.,* 1925, *30,* 753-768.

Krasnogorski, N. I. Conditioned reflexes in the psychopathology of childhood. *Amer. J. Dis. Child.,* 1933, *45,* 335-370.

Krasnogorski, N. I. Physiology of cerebral activity in children as a new subject of pediatric investigation. *Amer. J. Dis. Child.,* 1933, *46,* 473-494.

Lacey, J. I., & Smith, R. L. Conditioning and generalization of unconscious anxiety. *Science,* 1954, *120,* 1045-1052.

Lacey, J. I., Smith, R. L., & Green, A. Use of conditioned autonomic responses in the study of anxiety. *Psychosom. Med.,* 1955, *17,* 208-217.

Lane, H., & Curran, C. Gradients of auditory generalization for blind, retarded children. *J. exp. anal. Behav.,* 1963, *6,* 585-588.

Lang, P. J., & Lazovik, A. D. Experimental desensitization of a phobia. *J. abnorm. soc. Psychol.,* 1963, *66,* 519-525.

Lavin, N. I., Thorpe, J. G., Barker, J. C., Blakemore, C. B., & Conway, C. G. Behavior therapy in a case of transvestism. *J. nerv. ment. Dis.,* 1961, *133,* 346-353.

Lazarus, A. A. Group therapy of phobic disorders by systematic desensitization. *J. abnorm. soc. Psychol.,* 1961, *63,* 504-510.

Lazarus, A. A. The treatment of chronic frigidity by systematic desentization. *J. nerv. ment. Dis.,* 1963, *136,* 272-278.

Le Cron, L. M. The loss during hypnotic age regression of an established conditioned reflex. *Psychiat. Quart.,* 1952, *26,* 657-662.

Lemere, F., Voegtlin, W. L., Broz, W. R., & O'Hallaren, P. Conditioned reflex treatment of chronic alcoholism, 5. Type of patient suitable for this treatment. *Northw. Med.,* 1942, *4,* 88-89.

Lemere, F., Voegtlin, W. L., Broz, W. R., O'Hallaren, P., & Tupper, W. E. Conditioned reflex treatment of chronic alcoholism, 7. Technique. *Dis. nerv. System,* 1942, *3,* 243-247.

Leuba, C. Conditioning during hypnosis. *J. clin. exp. Hypnosis,* 1955, *3,* 256-259.

Liddell, H. S. Emotional hazards in animals and man. Springfield, Ill.: Chas. C. Thomas, 1956.

Linde, T. Techniques for establishing motivation through operant conditioning. *Amer. J. ment. Defic.,* 1962, *67,* 437-440.

Lindsley, O. R. Operant behavior during sleep: a measure of depth of sleep. *Science,* 1957, *126,* 1290-1291.

Lindsley, O. R. Direct measurement and functional definition of vocal hallucinatory symptoms. *J. nerv. ment. Dis.,* 1963, *136,* 203-207.

Lindsley, O. R., Hobika, J. H., & Etsten, B. E. Operant behavior during anesthesia recovery: a continuous and objective method. *Anesthesiol.,* 1961, *22,* 937-946.

Loewendahl, E. Significance of neuronal developmental and conditioned patterns in control of functions of the foot. *Internat. Rec. Med.,* 1957, *170,* 439-441.

McCranie, E. J., & Crasilneck, H. B. The conditioned reflex in hypnotic age regression. *J. clin. exp. Psychopath.,* 1955, *16,* 120-123.

McGill, V. J., & Welch, L. Hysteria as a conditioning process. *Amer. J. Psychother.,* 1947, *1,* 253-278.

Malleson, N. Panic and phobia. A possible method of treatment. *Lancet,* 1959, *I,* 225-227.

Malmo, R. B., Davis, J. F., & Barza, S. Total hysterical deafness: an experimental case study. *J. Personal.,* 1952, *21,* 188-204.

Martin, B., & Kubly, D. Results of treatment of enuresis by a conditioned response method. *J. consult. Psychol.,* 1955, *19,* 71-73.

Mertens, G. C., & Fuller, G. B. Conditioning of molar behavior in "regressed" psychotics: An objective measure of personal habit training with "regressed" psychotics. *J. Clin. Psychol.,* 1963, *19,* 333-357.

Metzner, R. Learning theory and the therapy of the neuroses. *Brit. J. Psychol., Monogr. Suppl.,* 1961, No. 33.

Meyer, V. The treatment of two phobic patients on the basis of learning principles. *J. abnorm. soc. Psychol.,* 1957, *55,* 261-266.

Meyer, V., & Gelder, M. G. Behavior therapy and phobic disorders. *J. ment. Sci.,* 1963, *109,* 19-28.

Michael, J., & Meyerson, L. A behavioral approach to counseling and guidance. *Harvard educ. Rev.,* 1962, *32,* 382-402.

Mitchell, L. E., & Zax, M. The effects of chlorpromazine on GSR conditioning. *J. abnorm. soc. Psychol.,* 1959, *59,* 246-249.

Montagu, M. F. A. Conditioning and reconditioning in the psychotherapeutic situation. *Amer. J. Psychol.,* 1945, *58,* 391-392.

Moore, W. E. A conditioned reflex study of stuttering. *J. speech Dis.,* 1938, *3,* 163-183.

Moos, R. H. The retention and generalization of operant conditioning effects in an interview situation. *J. abnorm. soc. Psychol.,* 1963, *66,* 52-58.

Motokawa, K., & Huzimori, B. Electroencephalograms of man in the generalization and differentiation of conditioned reflexes. *Tohoku J. exp. Med.,* 1949, *50,* 225-234.

Oakes, W. F., & Droge, A. E. Operant conditioning of response to social introversion scale items on the MMPI. *Psychol. Rep.,* 1960, *6,* 223-225.

O'Connor, N., & Rawnsley, K. Two types of conditioning in psychotics and normals. *J. abnorm. soc. Psychol.,* 1959, *58,* 157-161.

Orlando, R. The functional role of discriminative stimuli in free operant performance of developmentally retarded children. *Psychol. Rec.,* 1961, *11,* 153-161.

Palermo, D. S. Thumbsucking, a learned response. *Pediatrics,* 1936, *17,* 392-399.

Papousek, H. Conditioned head rotation reflexes in infants in the first months of life. *Acta Paediatr.,* 1961, *50,* 565-576.

Perez-Cruet, J. Conditioning of extrasystoles in humans with respiratory maneuvers as unconditional stimulus. *Science,* 1962, *137,* 1060-1061.

Peters, H. N. Learning as a treatment method in chronic schizophrenia. *Amer. J. occup. Ther.,* 1955, *9,* 185-201.

Peters, H. N., & Murphree, O. D. The conditioned reflex in the chronic schizophrenic. *J. clin. Psychol.,* 1954, *10,* 126-130.

Pfaffmann, C., & Schlosberg, H. The conditioning knee jerk in psychotic and normal individuals. *J. Psychol.,* 1936, *1,* 201-206.

Rachman, S. The treatment of anxiety and phobic reactions by systematic desensitization psychotherapy. *J. abnorm. soc. Psychol.,* 1959, *58,* 259-263.

Rachman, S. Introduction to behaviour therapy. *Behav. Res. Ther.,* 1963, *1,* 3-15.

Rachman, S., & Costello, C. G. The aetiology and treatment of children's phobias: a review. *Amer. J. Psychiat.,* 1961, *118,* 97-105.

Rafi, A. A. Learning theory and the treatment of tics. *J. Psychosom. Res.,* 1962, *6,* 71-76.

Rahmani, L. Considerations on Pavlovian theory in psychopathology. *J. nerv. ment. Dis.,* 1963, *137,* 548-551.

Razran, G. Conditioned responses in children. *Arch. Psychol.,* 1933, *148,* 3-121.

Razran, G. Conditioning away social bias by the luncheon technique. *Psychol. Bull.,* 1938, *35,* 693.

Razran, G. The place of the conditioned reflex in psychology and psychiatry. In *Pavlovian conditioning and psychiatry.* Group for the Advancement of Psychiatry, Symposium No. 9, 1964, 161-180.

Reese, W. G. Certain aspects of conditioning in the human. Comparative conditioned neuroses. *Ann. N.Y. Acad. Sci.,* 1953, *56,* 330-341.

Rheingold, H. L., Stanley, W. C., & Cooley, J. A. Method for studying exploratory behavior in infants. *Science,* 1962, *136,* 1054-1055.

Rickard, H. C., Dignam, P. J., & Horner, R. F. Verbal manipulation in a psychotherapeutic relationship. *J. clin. Psychol.,* 1960, *16,* 364-367.

Robinson, N. M., & Robinson, H. B. A method for the study of instrumental avoidance conditioning with young children. *J. comp. physiol. Psychol.,* 1961, *54,* 20-23.

Rogers, J. M. Operant conditioning in a quasi-therapy setting. *J. abnorm. soc. Psychol.,* 1960, *60,* 247-252.

Rudolf, G. de M. Deconditioning and time-therapy. *J. ment. Sci.,* 1961, *107,* 1097-1101.

Salter, A. *A conditioned reflex therapy: the direct approach to the reconstruction of personality.* New York: Farrar, Straus, 1949; also 2nd ed. Putnam (Capricorn, paper back), 1961.

Salzinger, K., & Pisoni, S. Reinforcement of affect responses of schizophrenics during the clinical interview. *J. abnorm. soc. Psychol.,* 1956, *57,* 84-90.

Salzinger, K., & Pisoni, S. Some parameters of the conditioning of verbal affect responses in schizophrenic subjects. *J. abnorm. soc. Psychol.,* 1961, *63,* 511-516.

Sanderson, R. E., Campbell, D., & Laverty, S. G. Traumatically conditioned responses acquired during respiratory paralysis. *Nature,* 1962, *196,* 1235-1236.

Saul, L. J., Rome, H., & Louser, E. Desensitization of combat fatigue patients. *Amer. J. Psychiat.,* 1946, *102,* 476-478.

Schilder, P. Conditioned reflexes. *Arch. Neurol. Psychiat.,* 1929, *22,* 425-443.

Schneider, R. A., & Costiloe, J. P. Effect of centrally active drugs on conditioning in man: the inhibiting and facilitating effects of chlorpromazine, amobarbital and methylphenidylacetate on the conditioned galvanic skin response. *Amer. J. med. Sci.,* 1957, *233,* 418-423.

Schutz, R. E., Staats, A. W., & Staats, C. K. Conditionability of responses to occupational scale items of the Strong Vocational Interest Blank for men. *Psychol. Rep.,* 1962, *10,* 447-450.

Schwitzgebel, R. A new approach to understanding delinquency. *Fed. Probat.,* 1960, *5,* 31-35.

Sears, R. R., & Cohen, L. H. Hysterical anaesthesia, analgesia and astereognosis. *Arch. Neur. Psychiat.,* 1933, *29,* 260-271.

Seham, M. The "conditioned reflex" in relation to functional disorders in children. *Amer. J. Dis. Child.,* 1932, *43,* 163-186.

Sheehan, J. G., & Voas, R. B. Stuttering as conflict: 1. Comparison of therapy techniques involving approach and avoidance. *J. speech hear. Dis.,* 1957, *22,* 714-723.

Simmons, M. W., & Lipsitt, L. P. An operant discrimination apparatus for infants. *J. exp. anal. Behav.,* 1961, *4,* 233-235.

Simonart, P. C. Allergy and conditioning. *A.M.A. Arch. Derm.,* 1959, *79,* 700-704.

Singer, R. D. Verbal conditioning and generalization of prodemocratic responses. *J. abnorm. soc. Psychol.,* 1961, *63,* 43-46.

Slechta, J., Gwynn, W., & Peoples, C. Verbal conditioning of schizophrenics and normals in a situation resembling psychotherapy. *J. consult. Psychol.,* 1963, *27,* 223-227.

Smith, J. W. Antibodies and conditioned reflexes. *Stanford Med. Bull.,* 1951, *9,* 171-174.

Southwell, E. A. Conditioning of hostile and neutral verbs in neurotics and normals. *J. consult. Psychol.,* 1962, *26,* 257-262.

Sparke, L. *Self-hypnosis: a conditioned response technique.* New York: Grune & Stratton, 1962.

Spelt, David K. The conditioning of the human fetus in utero. *J. exp. Psychol.,* 1948, *38,* 338-346.

Spence, W. K. *Behavior theory and conditioning.* New Haven: Yale Univ. Press, 1956.

Staats, A. W., & Staats, C. K. Attitudes established by classical conditioning. *J. abnorm. soc. Psychol.,* 1958, *57,* 37-40.

Stagner, R., & Britton, R. H. The conditioning technique applied to a public opinion problem. *J. soc. Psychol.,* 1949, *29,* 103-111.

Stevens, J. R. Endogenous conditioning to abnormal cerebral electrical transients in man. *Science,* 1962, *137,* 974-976.

Stevens, J. R., & Stevens, C. M. Cyclic conditioning of epileptic discharges. *EEG clin. Neurophysiol.,* 1960, *12,* 705-714.

Stewart, M. A., Winokur, G., Stern, J. A., Guze, S. B., Pfeiffer, E., & Hornung, F. Adaptation and conditioning of the galvanic skin responses in psychiatric patients. *J. ment. Sci.* 1959, *105*, 1102-1111.

Sutherland, G. F., & Katz, R. A. Apparatus for study of salivary conditional reflex in man. *J. appl. Physiol.*, 1961, *16*, 740-741.

Taffel, C. Anxiety and the conditioning of verbal behavior. *J. abnorm. soc. Psychol.*, 1955, *51*, 496-501.

Taylor, J. A., & Spence, K. W. Conditioning level in the behavior disorders. *J. abnorm. soc. Psychol.*, 1954, *40*, 497-502.

Thompson, G. N., & Bielinski, B. Improvement in psychosis following conditioned reflex treatment in alcoholism. *J. nerv. ment. Dis.*, 1953, *117*, 537-543.

Turnbull, J. W. Asthma conceived as a learned response. *J. Psychosom. Res.*, 1962, *6*, 59-70.

Uhr, L., Clay, M., Platz, A., Miller, J. G., & Kelley, E. L. Effects of meprobamate and prochlorperasine on positive and negative conditioning. *J. abnorm. soc. Psychol.*, 1961, *63*, 546-551.

Ullmann, L. P., Krasner, L., & Collins, B. J. Modification of behavior through verbal conditioning: effects in group therapy. *J. abnorm. soc. Psychol.*, 1961, *62*, 128-132.

Visser, S. L. Correlations between the contingent alpha blocking, EEG characteristics and clinical diagnosis. *Electroenceph. clin. Neurophysiol.*, 1961, *13*, 438-446.

Vogel, M. D. GSR conditioning and personality factors in alcoholics and normals. *J. abnorm. soc. Psychol.*, 1961, *63*, 417-421.

Wallerstein, R. S. *Hospital treatment of alcoholism.* New York: Basic Books, 1957.

Walter, W. G. Conditioning theories and their therapeutic applications. *Proc. Royal Soc. Med.*, 1960, *53*, 495-503.

Weiner, H. Response cost and the aversive control of human operant behavior. *J. exp. anal. Behav.*, 1963, *6*, 415-421.

Weiss, R. L., Krasner, L., & Ullmann, L. Responsivity of psychiatric patients to verbal conditioning: "success" and "failure" conditions and pattern of reinforced trials. *Psychol. Rep.*, 1963, *12*, 423-426.

Wells, C. E., & Wolff, H. G. Formation of temporary cerebral connections in normal and brain-damaged subjects. *Neurology*, 1960, *10*, 335-340.

Wells, C. E., & Wolff, H. G. Electrographic evidence of impaired brain function in chronically anxious patients. *Science*, 1960, *131*, 1671-1672.

Wendt, G. R. Two and one-half year retention of a conditioned response. *J. gen. Psychol.*, 1937, *17*, 178-180.

Wieland, W. F., Stein, M., & Hamilton, C. H. Intensity of the unconditional stimulus as a factor in conditioning out of awareness. *Psychosom. Med.*, 1963, *25*, 124-132.

Williams, C. D. The elimination of tantrum behavior by extinction procedures. *J. abnorm. soc. Psychol.*, 1959, *59*, 269.

Winokur, G., Guze, S., Stewart, M., Pfeiffer, E., Stern, J., & Hornung, F. Association of conditionability with degree of reactivity in psychiatric patients. *Science*, 1959, *129*, 1423-1424.

Wolf, S. Effects of suggestion and conditioning on the action of chemical agents in human subjects—the pharmacology of placebos. *J. clin. Invest.*, 1950, *29*, 100-109.

Wolpe, J. Isolation of a conditioning procedure as the crucial psychotherapeutic factor: a case study. *J. nerv. ment. Dis.*, 1962, *134*, 316-329.

Wolpe, J. The resolution of neurotic suffering by behavioristic methods: an evaluation. *Amer. J. Psychotherap.*, 1964, *18*, 23-32.

Wolpe, J., Salter, A., & Reyna, L. J. *Conditioning therapies: the challenge in psychotherapy*. New York: Holt, Rinehart & Winston, 1964.

Zedek, M. E. The conditioning of verbal behavior with negative cultural connotations. *J. Pers.*, 1959, *27*, 477-486.

INDEX